TABLE OF CONTENTS

ACTIVITIES

APPENDICES

INDICES

D1567066

ACKNOWLEDGMENTS

CONTENT EXPERTS

Alicia Benavidez, Zuni Public Schools, NM

Kirsten Brazier, Crawfordville Elementary School, FL

Andrew Burnett, U.S. Fish and Wildlife Service (Retired), DC

Jill Carter, Science and Environmental Education Consultant, IL

Alan Comnes, Energy GPS, OR

Leslie Comnes, Writing for Education, OR

Aprille Cook, Westervelt Company, AL

Kay Antunez de Mayolo, California Department of Forestry and Fire Protection (Retired), CA

Ann Duff, WestRock, FL

Debbie Fluegel, Trees Forever, IL

Karen Johnson Folsom, Hillsborough County Public Schools, FL

Mary Ford, National Geographic, DC

Gilberto Garcia, Christopher Dena Elementary School, CA

Running Grass, U.S. Environmental Protection Agency, Region 10

Joe Hoffman, Mid-State Technical College, WI

Jennifer Lee, Howard University, DC

Tehama Lopez-Bunyasi, George Mason University, VA

Pat Otto, Pacific Education Institute, Consultant (Retired), WA

Ladan Rahnema, Howard University, DC

Samantha Borders Shoemaker, George Mason University, VA

Susan Snyder, Ogden Nature Center, UT

Anne Umali, North American Association for Environmental Education, DC

Robin Will, US Fish and Wildlife Service (Retired), FL

PRACTITIONER REVIEWERS

Maria Barr, Savanna Oaks Middle School, WI

Donna Barton, Argyle Elementary School, FL

Heidi Bjerke, Jefferson Middle School, IL

Clarissa Brown, Warrensburg High School, MO

Lisa Brown, Sam Houston State University, TX

David Bydlowski, AEROKATS and ROVER Education Network & The Global Program, MI

Susan Hawke, Middleton Middle School, ID

Chris Hwande, Captain Elementary School, MO

Michael Jabot, The State University of New York at Fredonia, NY

Tracy McCord, Lyon Academy at Blow, MO

Kelly White, New Mexico Museum of Natural History Foundation, NM

PILOT TESTERS

Laura Bland, Michigan State Parks, MI

Wendy Boles, Olympic Middle School, WA

Kelly Aileen Brown, Mountain View Elementary School, ID

Maia Chaney, Aldo Leopold Charter School, NM

Jason Cyr, Waterville Junior High School, ME

Gail DeRobbio, Stone Hill Elementary School, RI

JoAnna Dietz, Larkspur Elementary School, CO

Jennifer Douglass, Euchee Creek Elementary School, GA

Tracey Dranttel, Wake County Public Schools, NC

Trudi Driscoll, Sacred Heart School, CA

Jody Durand, School of Engineering and Arts, MN

Jennifer Elsworth, Metroparks Toledo, OH

Melanie Falcon, Smoky Valley Middle School, KS

Beth Felder, Calhoun Academy, SC

Kerry Gallimore, Hickman County Schools, KY

Gilberto Garcia, Christopher Dena Elementary School, CA

Katie Green, YMCA, NJ

Dana Hansen, Payne Junior High School, AZ

Deborah Herrera, McKinley Elementary School, CA

Molly Hoopes, Mount Washington Elementary School, MD

Jay Horn, Watersmeet Township School, MI

Leanne Keller, Laconia Middle School, NH

Mandy Kern, Kansas Wetlands Education Center, KS

Valerie Lassiter, St. Charles Borromeo Catholic School, OK

Megan Lee, Lowry Elementary School, CO

Jamie Mastrocola, Magee Elementary School, WI

Amber Mattingley, Sacred Heart Middle School, MN

Robin McLean, Northern Burlington County Regional, NJ

Jessica Metz, New Kituwah Academy, NC

Rebecca Musso, T. Benton Gayle Middle School, VA

Tony Napoletano, Central Elementary School, MT

Jennifer Sauer, South Doyle Middle School, TN

Jackie Scott, Horace Mann Magnet Middle School, AR

Patricia Shulenburg, Save The River, NY

Ann Smart, Cabrini High School, LA

Heidi Stream, U.S. Fish and Wildlife Santa Ana National Wildlife Refuge, WV

Erica Taylor-Reynolds, Johnson County Conservation District, KY

Krystle Teague, Sylvan Hills Middle School, AR

Kate Wedge, Sibley-Ocheyedan Middle School, IA

Kristina Woods, Lawrence School, MA

NEXT GENERATION SCIENCE STANDARDS

Vivian Bowles, Kentucky Association for Environmental Education, KY

Melinda Wilder, Professor Emeritus, Eastern Kentucky University, KY

Brittany Wray, Kentucky Association for Environmental Education, KY

In addition, PLT State Coordinators, Education Operating Committee members, and SFI staff contributed to the development of this guide. We're grateful to all the educators, curriculum specialists, technical experts, resource professionals, and partners who help support, develop, and deliver high-quality environmental education.

PROJECT LEARNING TREE
An initiative of SFI

INTRODUCTION

ABOUT PROJECT LEARNING TREE

Project Learning Tree® (PLT) is an award-winning environmental education initiative designed for teachers and other educators, parents, and community leaders working with youth from preschool through grade 12. PLT advances environmental literacy, stewardship, and career pathways, using trees and forests as windows on the world.

PLT provides educators with high-quality professional development, hands-on activities, and multi-disciplinary supplemental curriculum that can be easily integrated into lesson plans for all grades and subject areas to help teach youth about trees, forests, and the environment. PLT helps develop students' awareness, knowledge, and appreciation of the environment; builds their skills and ability to make informed decisions; and encourages them to take personal responsibility for sustaining the environment and our quality of life that depends on it. For more about PLT's offerings, visit us online at plt.org.

The Sustainable Forestry Initiative® (SFI) advances sustainability through forest-focused collaborations. PLT is an initiative of SFI. Through PLT and other initiatives, SFI supports getting youth outdoors and into nature in ways that inspire them to become environmental stewards and future conservation leaders, and that introduce them to green careers. Learn more at forests.org.

DEFINING ENVIRONMENTAL EDUCATION

Environmental education is a process that increases the learner's awareness and knowledge about the environment and related issues. It helps to develop the necessary skills and expertise to address these issues and fosters attitudes, motivations, and commitments to make informed decisions and take responsible action.

Environmental education does not advocate a particular viewpoint or course of action. Instead, it enhances critical thinking, problem solving, and effective decision-making skills and teaches individuals to weigh various aspects of an environmental issue to make informed and responsible decisions.

PLT's supplementary curriculum materials are designed to help students learn *how* to think, not *what* to think. They provide educators with engaging lessons that are proven to increase students' environmental literacy. The activities encompass the economical, ecological, and social aspects of environmental issues.

The activities also comply with guidelines set by the North American Association for Environmental Education (NAAEE) for high-quality environmental education materials, by showing these six key characteristics:

- Fairness and accuracy
- Depth
- Emphasis on skills building
- Action orientation
- Instructional soundness
- Usability

THE PLT APPROACH

PLT's supplementary curriculum materials provide educators with engaging, hands-on lessons that are proven to increase students' environmental literacy.

OUR CONCEPTUAL FRAMEWORK

A primary job of educators is to facilitate students' active participation in the learning process. Teaching for conceptual understanding often means covering less breadth and more depth. One way to make "less" go farther is to use themes to connect concepts that transcend traditional subject areas.

PLT's Conceptual Framework serves as a foundation for all of PLT's curriculum materials and is arranged around five major themes:

- Patterns
- Interrelationships
- Systems
- Structure and Scale
- Stability and Change

Each theme also encompasses topics of Environment, Economy, and Society, the three elements that provide a "triple bottom line" approach to achieving sustainability.

PLT's Conceptual Framework may be found in Appendix G.

FOREST LITERACY FRAMEWORK

To translate the complex language of forests, trees, forest practices, and sustainable forest management into concepts that are appropriate for K–12 learners, PLT has developed the *Forest Literacy Framework*. This document presents a learning pathway for educating K–12 students about forests, with the goal of a forest-literate future.

PLT's *Forest Literacy Framework* promotes education that empowers learners to apply critical thinking and innovation to make decisions about forests and forest resources, understand the role forests play in addressing local and global environmental challenges, and grow up to be stewards of the forest.

It has applications for K–12 youth, teachers, and nonformal educators across the United States and Canada. It also incorporates diverse voices and perspectives, which enhance our collective ability to understand the forest and each other.

The *Forest Literacy Framework* offers 100 forest concepts organized into four themes, each with topics and concepts that address its central question:

Theme 1: What is a forest?
Theme 2: Why do forests matter?
Theme 3: How do we sustain our forests?
Theme 4: What is our responsibility to forests?

Explore the *Forest Literacy Framework* at plt.org/forestliteracy. Also see Appendix H: Units of Instruction for suggested connections to activities in this guide.

EVERY STUDENT LEARNS OUTSIDE

Today's children are increasingly disconnected from the natural world. Not only is this disconnect unhealthy, it weakens children's ability to learn. Research indicates that exposing children to the outdoors improves emotional and physical well-being, enhances learning, promotes positive social behavior, and increases children's tendencies to care about and conserve their environment.

PLT activities provide enjoyable and educational opportunities to help children connect with nature. Taking students outdoors to make observations or collect data is the core of many lessons. All activities offer ways to "Take It Outside!," making outdoor experiences part of everyday learning. In addition, many suggest service-learning opportunities that take students into the community. See Appendix B: Tips for Teaching Outdoors.

HANDS-ON LEARNING AND TEACHING

PLT activities are hands-on and investigation-based, making learning fun while also building skills, stimulating knowledge gains, and actively engaging students.

The activities are based largely on constructivist learning theory, which recognizes that new understanding is constructed by combining previous knowledge with new discoveries. PLT's hands-on activities afford students the opportunity to learn through real experiences, rather than just reading or hearing about them. PLT activities:

- Actively engage students in real-world observations and questions.
- Invite students to design and carry out their own investigations.
- Allow students to practice disciplinary skills.
- Encourage critical thinking and problem solving.
- Promote student-centered learning.
- Help bring learning to life.

HIGH-QUALITY CURRICULUM

From its beginnings in 1976, PLT has exemplified high-quality environmental education.

THE WORK OF MANY HANDS

PLT has drawn together thousands of committed educators, curriculum specialists, and technical experts around a single goal: to produce the highest quality environmental education materials possible. PLT's core curriculum materials are reviewed and updated periodically to meet the changing needs of educators and students—and to stay abreast of new developments in science, technology, and education.

We're grateful to the many educators, resource professionals, and program partners who contributed to this guide. Its strengths are the product of their energy and expertise. We'd also like to acknowledge the professionals who contributed to earlier editions, which serve as the foundation for PLT's environmental education work.

Finally, we'd like to thank all PLT State Coordinators and Facilitators for their boundless spirit and enthusiasm for PLT. It is through their work that PLT reaches 15,000 educators and 3 million students every year. Where we have made a difference, they deserve a large measure of the credit.

CURRICULUM DEVELOPMENT PROCESS

To ensure the effectiveness of its materials, PLT uses an extensive, multi-layered curriculum development process. As an initiative of SFI, PLT has direct access to natural resource professionals and conservation experts that further strengthen and ensure the validity of all content presented. Hallmarks of this process include:

- **Activity Development.** Each activity is developed through extensive research and review by a large group of educators and subject experts, including classroom teachers, curriculum specialists, nonformal educators, natural resource managers, and university faculty.

- **Teacher Tested and Evaluated.** New PLT activities are field tested by educators working with students, then revised based on their feedback.

- **Continuous Improvement.** PLT materials are continually evaluated and updated, allowing PLT to keep pace with the changing needs of educators.

- **Independent Evaluation.** PLT activities undergo formal evaluation by independent consultants to ensure their instructional effectiveness.

PLT CURRICULUM DESIGN AND DEVELOPMENT

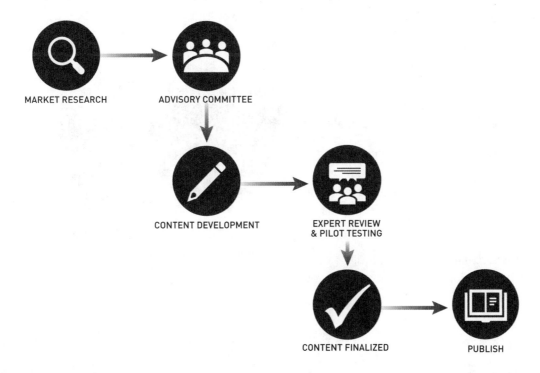

MARKET RESEARCH

ADVISORY COMMITTEE

CONTENT DEVELOPMENT

EXPERT REVIEW & PILOT TESTING

CONTENT FINALIZED

PUBLISH

EQUITY AND INCLUSION

PLT strives to reach every student, regardless of their social or economic identity, and connect them to nature. We are committed to equity and inclusion, both within our organization and in the programs we offer, and to uncovering our own unconscious biases.

We are working to build an inclusive movement toward forest and environmental literacy to promote ecological integrity, economic prosperity, and social equity. Thus, PLT is dedicated to ensuring that our education materials contribute to authentic and meaningful learning environments that represent diverse voices.

Content in this guide was reviewed by experts in equity, inclusion, racial bias, and Indigenous perspectives, with an additional independent evaluation and pilot testing of the new activity Environmental Justice for All. As it is critical to engage youth in conversations about equity, PLT has sought to ensure that activities align with best practices and represent a wide range of individuals, including those who have been disproportionally exposed to environmental injustices. Each activity in this guide has received thorough internal and external review, with a special effort to eliminate bias and create new opportunities for diverse representation through varying case studies, experiences, and methods of instruction. PLT's curriculum has also been developed through a critical lens of justice and inclusion.

Our model of delivery through regional partners ensures that instruction and content strategies can be modified to meet the needs of all learners. PLT's flexible and hands-on instructional resources enable adaptation to diverse and localized contexts for the educators who deliver our materials.

PLT activities include differentiated instruction to help educators reach students who have varying individual strengths, needs, and talents; different academic preparation and prior experiences; and a wide range of English-language proficiency.

We acknowledge that we have much to learn and will continue to dialogue with educators on how to make PLT even more accessible and empowering.

USING THIS GUIDE

PLT activities are designed to be easy to use. Each activity contains all the information needed to teach the core lesson, including background information, preparation instructions, materials and time requirements, step-by-step instructions, student pages, assessment suggestions, and suggestions for extending the lesson.

GRADE-LEVEL ORGANIZATION

To make it easier to use, this resource is organized into three distinct grade bands: Grades K–2, Grades 3–5, and Grades 6–8. This grade-level designation aligns with national academic standards, such as the Next Generation Science Standards.

These grade-level sections are also denoted by color: red for Grades K–2 activities, green for Grades 3–5 activities, and blue for Grades 6–8 activities.

While PLT has assigned specific activities to specific grade bands, many activities also offer a Variation to meet the needs of an expanded grade level. These Variations are noted on the first page of each activity, the section dividers, and the At-a-Glance Index.

Within each section, the activities are arranged alphabetically. Educators may use the activities individually or combine them in an order that best suits their instructional goals. For suggestions for combining activities using storylines, see Appendix H: Units of Instruction.

GRADE SPECIFIC E-UNITS

- Grades K-2: Treemendous Science!
- Grades 3-5: Energy in Ecosystems
- Grades 6-8: Carbon & Climate

Visit plt.org/eunits for more!

KEY FEATURES AND ICONS

The following icons are designed to help you identify PLT activities that meet your instructional needs. They are located at the top of the sidebar, just below the activity titles. For more details, see Icons in the At-a-Glance Index.

 Outdoors—Indicates that the activity requires an outdoor setting to meet learning outcomes. For more information about outdoor learning, see Appendix B.

 Urban—Indicates that the activity is an excellent way to explore urban environments. For more information about using PLT in urban settings, see Appendix C.

 Nonformal—Indicates that the activity works well in nonformal education settings, such as in nature centers or with afterschool groups, although these activities are also suitable for formal classroom settings. For more information about using PLT in nonformal education, see Appendix D.

 STEM—Indicates that the activity is a STEM exemplar, combining the four elements of STEM—Science, Technology, Engineering, and Math—while engaging students in problem-solving. Note that every activity in this guide incorporates at least some elements of STEM and lists relevant STEM skills. For more information about PLT and STEM, see Appendix E.

 Long-term—Indicates that the activity requires more than two 50-minute periods of instruction.

The following activity features will help you adapt the activities for your particular group and setting. They are located within each activity and signified by the following design elements:

 Take It Outside!—Describes how to extend student learning into the outdoors. See Appendix B: Tips for Teaching Outdoors.

 Differentiated Instruction—Indicates the use of specific differentiated instruction strategies. See Appendix F: Differentiated Instruction for definitions of these strategies.

- Cooperative Learning
- Literacy Skills
- Hands-on Learning
- Higher-order Thinking
- Multiple Solution Pathways
- Nonlinguistic Representations
- Personal Connections
- Student Voice

 Did You Know? Forest Fact—Presents interesting insights into forests as global solutions for environmental, economic, and social sustainability.

 **Career Corner**—Introduces youth to related green careers. For more information, see Appendix J: Exploring Forest Careers.

Safety!—Indicates safety issues to consider when planning and conducting the activity.

ACTIVITY COMPONENTS

Title

The "attention grabber" that relates to the activity's content.

Overview

A brief summary of the activity.

Subjects

The school subjects incorporated in the activity, such as science, English language arts, math, or social studies.

PLT Concepts

The concepts from PLT's Conceptual Framework that the activity addresses. Refer to Appendix G: Conceptual Framework.

STEM Skills

The STEM skills that students use in the activity.

Materials

The materials needed to do the activity, in addition to the provided student pages.

Time Considerations

Recommended time allotment for each part of the core activity, including preparation. Times are based on 50-minute class periods.

Grade Level and Variation

A colored flag designates the targeted grade level and available variations. Variations recommend alternate procedures for doing the activity with different grade level or audiences (included with some but not all activities).
For more details, see the At-a-Glance Index.

GRADES 3–5
VARIATION 6–8

This fun and active modeling simulation reviews the conditions that trees need to live and grow, while also demonstrating that trees must compete to meet their needs.

EVERY TREE FOR ITSEL

SUBJECTS
Science, English Language Arts, Math

PLT CONCEPTS
1.3, 2.1, 2.2

STEM SKILLS
Collaboration, Investigation, Organization

DIFFERENTIATED INSTRUCTION
Hands-on Learning, Higher-order Thinking, Student Voice

MATERIALS
Tree trunk or branch cross-section, 8" x 10" (20 cm x 25 cm) pieces of paper or white paper plates, markers or crayons, and 4–6 different colors of math cubes, poker chips, or construction paper.

TIME CONSIDERATIONS
Preparation: 15 minutes
Activity: 50 minutes

OBJECTIVES
Students will
- Model how trees compete to meet their essential needs.
- Describe how varying amounts of light, water, and nutrients affect tr growth.

BACKGROUND
What do trees need so they can grow? Some of their needs are the same as th of people and other animals. For example, trees need air, water, and food. Bu while people and animals eat their food, trees get food in a different way. Tree produce their own "food" by using the **chlorophyll** in their leaves to capture e from the sun in a process called **photosynthesis**, which uses carbon dioxide fro the air and water from rainfall. Just as people and animals need vitamins for growth, trees also need mineral nutrients, such as nitrogen and phosphorus, they get from the soil.

If trees don't get enough sunlight, air, water, or nutrients, they may grow slow even die. You can see how well a tree grew in different years of its life by look at growth rings in a cross-section of its trunk. In general, wide rings indicate good conditions for growth (plenty of resources), while narrow rings often indi less favorable growth conditions (drought, insect damage, lack of nutrients, o competition with other plants).

Forest managers use a variety of strategies to ensure that trees get what they to thrive. A process called **thinning** selectively removes some of the trees, allo more water, sunlight, and nutrients for the trees that remain. Controlling the underbrush and other vegetation also reduces competition for limited resourc Since different tree species need different conditions to thrive, forest manage make decisions based on the types of trees that are growing and regenerating.

While trees may compete for limited resources, they sometimes also share resources or "cooperate" through underground fungi networks. In a forest ecosystem, for example, fir trees and birch trees might exchange nutrients thr a network of fungi that live among their roots.

110 PROJECT LEARNING TREE © SUSTAINABLE FORESTRY INITIATIVE

Objectives

The learning objectives targeted in the activity.

Background

Relevant information to help plan for engaging learners in the activity. **Bold words are included in the Glossary** at plt.org/glossary.

PROJECT LEARNING TREE
An initiative of SFI

cademic Standards

onnections to science, English language arts, math, and social
tudies curriculum standards, including practices or skills, and
oncepts or content. Refer to Appendix A, Teaching to Standards.

ssessment

low to assess students' understanding of the concepts covered in
he activity and how students can apply their new knowledge.

nrichment

Vays to enrich or extend the learning experience of the activity.

FOREST FACT

did you know

Did you know that the closer trees get to the equator, the faster they grow? In fact, growth rings in tropical areas are often associated with wet and dry seasons, instead of with the four annual seasons that we recognize. This means that some tropical trees show multiple growth rings in one year!

TING READY

ain one or more cross-sections of a tree trunk or branch. These are often
ilable from tree-trimming services or forest product companies. To help
vent the spread of invasive species, make sure to source local samples. If
are unable to obtain a cross-section, draw one where the whole group can
it. See the activity Tree Cookies for a sample drawing.

her 4–6 different colors of math cubes or poker chips—such as blue,
ow, white, green, black, and red—with enough of each color so that each
ent can have two cubes or chips. Keep the colors separate to start. As an
rnative, cut 3" x 3" (7.6 cm x 7.6 cm) squares out of different colors of
struction paper.

ke copies of the Tree Needs student page.

ional: Laminate growth ring drawings (from Step 3) to use in Steps 4–10.

NG THE ACTIVITY

Ask students what they think trees need in order to grow. (They might mention
water, sunlight, air, or nutrients. You may want to point out that most of a tree's
mass is made of carbon, which comes from the air.) Ask: What do you think
would happen if a tree doesn't get all the things it needs? How might we find out?

Suggest that students construct a model to help them understand how and why
a tree might not get all its needs met. Propose the following model that students
can adapt, using their own ideas. For this model, students will personify trees in an
active simulation.

HANDS-ON LEARNING To start, show students the tree trunk or branch cross-
section (or drawing), pointing out the growth rings. Explain that the number
of rings indicates the age of the tree trunk or branch at the time it was cut. Invite
students to imagine that they are trees, and to draw a cross-section representing
their age in growth rings on a piece of paper or a paper plate.

Have students spread out about 3 feet (90 cm) apart and stand (or sit in chairs) on
their cross-section paper or paper plate. Explain that their goal as trees is to meet
as many of their needs as they can.

EVERY TREE FOR ITSELF **111**

Getting Ready

How to prepare to lead the activity.

Doing the Activity

Step-by-step procedures for leading the activity.

Student Pages

Copyright-free student pages to enhance learning
in the activity. Note that most, but not all, activities
include one or more student pages.

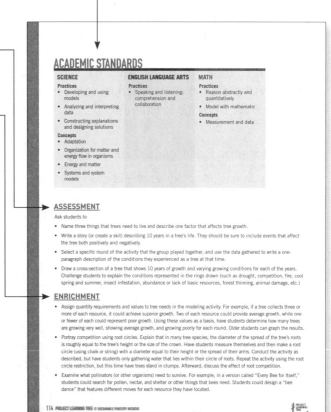

ACADEMIC STANDARDS

SCIENCE	ENGLISH LANGUAGE ARTS	MATH
Practices	**Practices**	**Practices**
• Developing and using models	• Speaking and listening; comprehension and collaboration	• Reason abstractly and quantitatively
• Analyzing and interpreting data		• Model with mathematic
• Constructing explanations and designing solutions		**Concepts**
Concepts		• Measurement and data
• Adaptation		
• Organization for matter and energy flow in organisms		
• Energy and matter		
• Systems and system models		

ASSESSMENT

Ask students to

• Name three things that trees need to live and describe one factor that affects tree growth.

• Write a story (or create a skit) describing 10 years in a tree's life. They should be sure to include events that affect the tree both positively and negatively.

• Select a specific round of the activity that the group played together, and use the data gathered to write a one-paragraph description of the conditions they experienced as a tree at that time.

• Draw a cross-section of a tree that shows 10 years of growth and varying growing conditions for each of the years. Challenge students to explain the conditions represented in the rings drawn (such as drought, competition, fire, cool spring and summer, insect infestation, abundance or lack of basic resources, forest thinning, animal damage, etc.)

ENRICHMENT

• Assign quantity requirements and values to tree needs in the modeling activity. For example, if a tree collects three or more of each resource, it could achieve superior growth. Two of each resource could provide average growth, while one or fewer of each resource could represent poor growth. Using these values as a basis, have students determine how many trees are growing very well, showing average growth, and growing poorly for each round. Older students can graph the results.

• Portray competition using root circles. Explain that in many tree species, the diameter of the spread of the tree's roots is roughly equal to the tree's height or the size of the crown. Have students measure themselves and then make a root circle (using chalk or string) with a diameter equal to their height or the spread of their arms. Conduct the activity as described, but have students only gathering water that lies within their circle of roots. Repeat the activity using the root circle restriction, but this time have trees stand in clumps. Afterward, discuss the effect of root competition.

• Examine what pollinators (or other organisms) need to survive. For example, in a version called "Every Bee for Itself," students could search for pollen, nectar, and shelter or other things that bees need. Students could design a "bee dance" that features different moves for each resource they have located.

114 PROJECT LEARNING TREE © SUSTAINABLE FORESTRY INITIATIVE

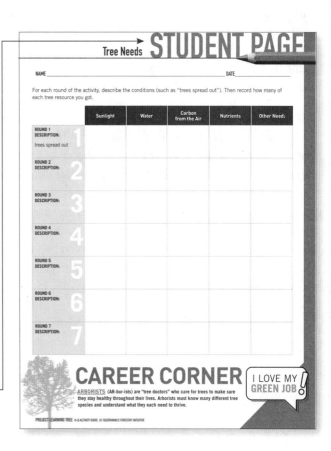

Tree Needs ## STUDENT PAGE

NAME _____ DATE _____

For each round of the activity, describe the conditions (such as "trees spread out"). Then record how many of each tree resource you got.

	Sunlight	Water	Carbon from the Air	Nutrients	Other Need:
ROUND 1 DESCRIPTION: 1 trees spread out					
ROUND 2 DESCRIPTION: 2					
ROUND 3 DESCRIPTION: 3					
ROUND 4 DESCRIPTION: 4					
ROUND 5 DESCRIPTION: 5					
ROUND 6 DESCRIPTION: 6					
ROUND 7 DESCRIPTION: 7					

CAREER CORNER I LOVE MY GREEN JOB!

ARBORISTS (AR-bur-ists) are "tree doctors" who care for trees to make sure they stay healthy throughout their lives. Arborists must know many different tree species and understand what they each need to thrive.

PROJECT LEARNING TREE K-8 ACTIVITY GUIDE © SUSTAINABLE FORESTRY INITIATIVE

ACADEMIC STANDARDS CONNECTIONS

Classroom educators and nonformal educators alike need to ensure that instruction helps diverse learners meet rigorous academic benchmarks. To further support educators, each PLT activity displays explicit connections to practices and concepts mandated by the following national academic standards:

- Next Generation Science Standards (NGSS)
- Common Core State Standards—English Language Arts (CCSS.ELA)
- Common Core State Standards—Mathematics (CCSS. MATH)
- College, Career, and Civic Life Framework for Social Studies (C3)

Although each PLT activity can be used as a stand-alone lesson, linking activities helps students connect concepts and provides more depth to the learning experience. See Appendix H: Units of Instruction, for suggested storylines that provide an in-depth learning progression.

For more details, see Appendix A: Teaching to Standards.

STEM SKILLS

PLT activities support STEM education by presenting real-world opportunities to apply science, technology, engineering, and math in problem-solving. Each activity identifies STEM skills that students practice through direct experience. For more details, see Appendix E: STEM Skills.

A LOOK AT ASSESSMENT

PLT provides authentic assessment opportunities for each activity. The activities suggest effective strategies for students to apply and demonstrate what they learned from the activity, rather than simply state what they learned. Where appropriate, some suggestions focus on applying what has been learned to local environments and situations, strengthening opportunities for outdoor exploration and place-based learning. For support in quantifying assessments, see Appendix M: Assessment Rubric.

ONLINE SUPPORT MATERIALS

Visit plt.org/myk8guide for support materials and additional resources to enhance the activities:

- **Glossary**
  Terms and definitions relevant to the activities in this guide. See Appendix I: Using the Glossary, for suggestions for using the Glossary with your students.

- **Student Pages**
  Download printable student pages and other supporting activity-specific resources.

- **Reading Connections**
  Grade level–appropriate fiction and nonfiction books relevant to the activity.

- **Resources**
  Webpages, videos, and reference materials to support teaching and learning about the activity topic.

- **Standards Alignment**
  Correlations between PLT activity content and national, state, and nonformal programmatic benchmarks. National standards include Common Core and the Next Generation Science Standards, while nonformal programs include 4-H, Boy Scouts of America, Girl Scouts of the USA, and more.

PLT'S STRENGTH LIES IN OUR NETWORK

Our 50-state and international network provides educators with hands-on professional development, state-specific supplements that address local academic standards and environmental issues, and customized assistance for adopting environmental education. The link below provides contact information for the PLT coordinator in your state.

Please consider this a personal invitation to reach out and get involved today!

CONTACT YOUR PLT STATE COORDINATOR FOR:

- Local resources and assistance
- Ideas for incorporating environmental education and outdoor learning into your program
- Connections to mentor teachers, community members, and natural resource professionals
- Information about in-person professional development events near you
- Becoming a PLT professional development facilitator

EXPERIENCE PLT'S PROFESSIONAL DEVELOPMENT TO:

- Gain new teaching skills, deepen your content knowledge, and become comfortable teaching outdoors
- Receive instructional materials tailored to your state's standards
- Experience PLT activities, develop an action plan, and get lesson planning tips specific to your setting
- Get access to a network of professionals and support
- Earn continuing education credits

GET CONNECTED TODAY

https://www.plt.org/yourstate

ACTIVITY	K-2	3-5
A Tree's Life	O	⇅
Adopt A Tree	O	⇅
Backyard Safari	O	⇅
Birds and Bugs	O	⇅
Bursting Buds	O	⇅
Did You Notice?	O	⇅
Have Seeds, Will Travel	O	⇅
Here We Grow Again	O	⇅
Make Your Own Paper	O	⇅
Peppermint Beetle	O	⇅
The Closer You Look	O	
Trees as Habitats	O	
We All Need Trees	O	⇅

O = Core Activity   ⇅ = Grade-Level Variation

For more details, see Grade Level in the At-a-Glance Index.

GRADES
K-2
ACTIVITIES

explore your environment

Students discover that trees have life stages that are similar to those of other living things. They discuss a tree's role in the ecosystem at each stage of its life.

A TREE'S LIFE

SUBJECTS
Science, English Language Arts, Visual Arts, Performing Arts

PLT CONCEPTS
5.1, 5.3

STEM SKILLS
Collaboration, Communication, Creativity, Technology Use

DIFFERENTIATED INSTRUCTION
Cooperative Learning, Nonlinguistic Representations, Personal Connections

MATERIALS
Digital devices that students can use to take pictures, internet access. Optional: Picture books

TIME CONSIDERATIONS
Preparation: 20 minutes

Activity: Two 40-minute periods

OBJECTIVES

Students will

- Model the life stages of a tree.
- Observe and compare trees at different stages of life.
- Make a diagram to show their understanding of a tree's life stages and how they are similar to human life stages.

BACKGROUND

Trees, like all living things, have life stages that include starting their lives, growing, experiencing injury and disease, aging, and dying. As trees go from birth to death, their physical forms change, as well as their role in the forest ecosystem. You can learn about the changes a tree has experienced in environmental conditions during its life by looking at the growth rings in a cross-section of the tree (see the activity Tree Cookies for Grades 3-5). You can learn even more by observing the tree from its beginnings and as it grows throughout its life. See the *Life Stages of a Tree* diagram.

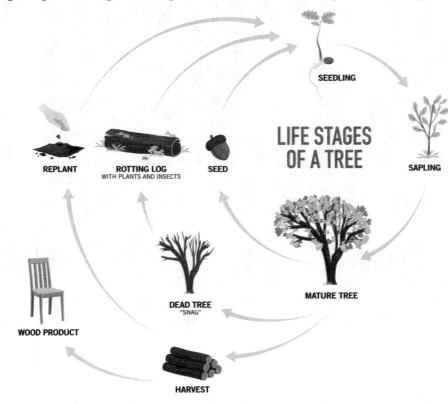

LIFE STAGES OF A TREE

SEEDLING · SAPLING · MATURE TREE · DEAD TREE "SNAG" · HARVEST · WOOD PRODUCT · REPLANT · ROTTING LOG WITH PLANTS AND INSECTS · SEED

Most trees undergo a life cycle that starts with a seed.

FOREST FACT

A row of young trees may sprout from seed atop a rotting log on the forest floor known as a nurse log.

A tree's **life cycle** begins with a **seed**. With favorable soil, climate, and nutrient conditions, a seed germinates and begins to grow. This tiny tree is called a **seedling**.

As the tree grows, its trunk begins to thicken, and it begins to develop branches. A **sapling** is a young tree that is less than 4 inches (10 cm) in **diameter at breast height (DBH)**—less than 4 inches thick when measured at a point about 4.5 feet off the ground—and more than about 4 feet (1.5 m) tall. In the forest, young saplings must compete with other trees and plants for sunlight, nutrients, water, and space. In dense forests, many young trees must wait for years for older trees to fall and leave openings in the **canopy** (the treetop) into which they can grow.

Trees continue to grow throughout their lives. A mature tree is usually more than 4 inches in DBH. The length of time it takes a tree to reach maturity depends on the species of tree. Mature trees have many different roles in the forest, depending on their age and size. Their leaves, bark, seeds, flowers, fruit, and roots provide food for many kinds of animals. Trees also provide roosts, shade, and shelter to many living things. For example, holes in older trees and around their roots provide shelters for nests and dens.

Trees produce many more seeds than survive. Most seeds are destroyed by fungi or other decomposers or eaten by birds or mammals, leaving only a small number of seeds to germinate and grow into seedlings.

Like all living things, trees are subject to disease and injury. Physical damage may not kill a tree, but may provide holes and openings in which animals and insects can live and feed. Eventually, trees weakened by injury and disease will die, fall, and be decomposed. When they die, trees return their nutrients and other elements back to the soil to be recycled through the forest ecosystem.

GETTING READY

- Scout out a place to take students where there are trees or shrubs representing a variety of life stages. It could be a neighborhood, local park, or forest site with plants of various ages. As an alternative, collect pictures of trees at different stages from Arbor Day Foundation's "Tree Life Stages" website at arborday.org, or use picture books or videos. (See plt.org/myk8guide for suggested resources.)

- Obtain one digital device for each group of three students so they can take pictures.

- Make a copy of the Tree & Me student page for each student.

- For the Variation, gather resources that students can use to research trees, including illustrated books on trees, tree identification keys, and field guides, as well as easy links to appropriate websites. Using these resources, compile a list of several tree species for students to research. Make a copy of the Life of a Tree student page for each student.

DOING THE ACTIVITY

1 ➡ **PERSONAL CONNECTIONS** Ask students to think about how people change throughout their life. What are some ways that people change as they get older? Have students name the stages of life that people go through. Make sure they include the stages baby, child, teenager, young adult, and so forth. Write these stages where everyone can see them so they can be used again later.

2 Ask students whether trees are alive and how they know. (They grow.) Do trees have different life stages, too? How do trees start their lives? (From a seed.) Do they die? (Yes, but they can live a long time.)

3 ➡ **NONLINGUISTIC REPRESENTATIONS** Have students spread out so that they can reach out their arms without touching their neighbors. Read aloud the following story and invite students to act out being a seed that grows into a tree.

READ	ACTION
Imagine that you are a tree seed that has fallen from a tree. Lie down on the soil and curl up tightly into a ball.	Children lie down and curl into balls.
You start to grow, and you get bigger and bigger.	Children extend their feet and legs from their curled position.
Wiggle your toes as your roots creep downward deep into the soil.	Children wiggle their toes.
You start to grow a stem and branches. Get on your knees and slowly raise up your arms like branches. You are now a seedling.	Children get on their knees and slowly raise up their arms.
Wave your hands as you grow leaves on all of your branches.	Children wave their hands to imitate leaves.
You are taller and your trunk is thicker. You are now a sapling. Stretch your body, reaching for the sunlight.	Children stand up, reaching their arms high and puffing out their chests.
You are growing taller and stronger. The wind gently blows your leaves and branches.	Children sway back and forth in the wind
Ahhhh! You are now all grown up into a mature tree.	Children say "Ahhhh!"
You begin to make seeds, so many, many seeds! Wiggle your fingers to show your seeds.	Children wiggle their fingers.
Flick your hands to spread those seeds. Bye, bye seeds – have a nice life!	Children flick their hands.
You are a home to lots of wildlife. Birds and squirrels nest in your branches.	Children crook one of their arms to make a spot for nesting.
As you get older, you are attacked by insects and fungi.	Children scratch all over.
You are starting to get weaker. You get hit by lightning and lose a branch.	Children make a loud noise (kchhhh!) and let one arm fall to their sides.
Woodpeckers peck into your dead wood and make holes.	Children make a hammering noise (knock, knock, knock).
After a long while, you fall down in a storm.	Children make a creaking sound and fall down.
After you are dead, you become a home to many small animals and plants.	Children run their fingers from one hand down the other arm.

4 Point out that the story describes the life of a tree. Ask students what stages of life they acted out. Then, ask students what they have noticed about the trees in their area. Are all trees the same size and shape? Are they the same age? Do trees go through life stages similar to people? Explain that they will be doing an investigation to help answer these questions.

5 **COOPERATIVE LEARNING** Take students to the site you identified in Getting Ready. Ask the students to look for trees at different life stages. Divide them into groups of three students each, give each group a digital device, and have them take pictures of the stages. You can assign each group a different stage or allow each group to take pictures of all stages. Stages may include:

TAKE IT OUTSIDE

Conduct the read-aloud story outside. As they do the actions, students can mimic a tree they see nearby.

- Tree seed (acorn, maple samara, etc.)
- Seedling
- Sapling
- Adult
- Injured or unhealthy tree (showing signs of injury, disease, or stress)
- Elderly tree
- Dead tree (when standing, a dead tree is known as a snag)
- Rotting log or dead branches (with plants and insects on them)

If going outside is not possible, have groups use picture books or videos to find the different stages of a tree's life. Students can take pictures from these resources.

6 **NONLINGUISTIC REPRESENTATIONS** Using the pictures students took either outside or from resources, review the different stages of a tree's life. Then have students draw each stage on their Tree & Me student page.

7 **PERSONAL CONNECTIONS** Go back to the list of human life stages from Step 1. Ask students which tree life stage is similar to each human life stage. Direct them to record that information on the student page. Discuss how the life stages of trees are similar to those of humans.

8 Revisit the questions from Step 4. As students answer each question again, you can refer them to the information on their student page.

VARIATION: GRADES 3–5

1 **COOPERATIVE LEARNING** Have students work individually or in teams to research and draw a diagram of the life stages of a tree. Give each student a copy of the Life of a Tree student page, and provide art or drawing materials or access to a presentation app. Tell students to find information from the resource materials or the internet, using the student page to organize their findings.

2 **NONLINGUISTIC REPRESENTATIONS** Tell students to include at least four stages of life (like seed, sprout, sapling, and so on) in their diagrams. They can represent the life cycle using a circle on the page, with illustrations and a label for each stage or life event that occur throughout the tree's life.

3 Have students share their diagrams with the entire group. Create a "History of the Forest" exhibit by posting all the diagrams.

ACADEMIC STANDARDS

SCIENCE

Practices
- Developing and using models
- Obtaining, evaluating, and communicating information

Concepts
- Growth and development of organisms
- Patterns

ENGLISH LANGUAGE ARTS

Practices
- Speaking and listening: comprehension and collaboration
- Language: vocabulary acquisition and use

ASSESSMENT

Ask students to

- Place pictures of a tree's life stages in the correct sequence.
- Use the information on the student page to write or tell a story about the tree's life.

ENRICHMENT

- Invite students to write or draw an imaginative story about the life of their tree. They could write it as a fable in which the trees, plants, and animals can talk. Challenge them to include at least three stages in the tree's life, such as sprouting from a seed or dying and decomposing into the soil.

- Ask students to think of things or events that might alter a tree's life (such as animals eating the tree's seeds, fire or storms damaging the tree, disease from insects or fungi attacking the tree, or an elk rubbing the bark off the tree with their antlers). Challenge them to draw another diagram that includes one or more of these events, showing how the event alters the tree's life. Point out that an event that affects the tree (like fire damage) is likely to clear the way for another event (like birds nesting in a hole).

STUDENT PAGE

NAME _____ DATE_____

Draw each stage of a tree's life in the boxes below. Then write the similar human life stage.

1

Tree Life Stage

Human Life Stage:

_____

2

Tree Life Stage

Human Life Stage:

_____

3

Tree Life Stage

Human Life Stage:

_____

4

Tree Life Stage

Human Life Stage:

_____

5

Tree Life Stage

Human Life Stage:

_____

6

Tree Life Stage

Human Life Stage:

_____

CAREER CORNER

I LOVE MY GREEN JOB!

LOGGERS harvest mature trees for wood and other products that people use. This makes room for young trees to grow and helps the forest stay healthy.

NAME _____ DATE_____

Fill in the information about your tree.

Common name of tree:_____

Where it grows:_____

LIFE STAGE 1: _____

What is the tree's role (job) at this stage?_____

Things tree needs to survive at this stage:_____

Things that need the tree at this stage to survive:_____

Things that might move the tree to the next stage:_____

LIFE STAGE 2: _____

What is the tree's role (job) at this stage?_____

Things tree needs to survive at this stage:_____

Things that need the tree at this stage to survive:_____

Things that might move the tree to the next stage:_____

LIFE STAGE 3: _____

What is the tree's role (job) at this stage?_____

Things tree needs to survive at this stage:_____

Things that need the tree at this stage to survive:_____

Things that might move the tree to the next stage:_____

LIFE STAGE 4: _____

What is the tree's role (job) at this stage?_____

Things tree needs to survive at this stage:_____

Things that need the tree at this stage to survive:_____

Things that might move the tree to the next stage:_____

I LOVE MY GREEN JOB!

CAREER CORNER

PLANT ECOLOGISTS (ee-CALL-uh-jists) study the relationships between plants and the environment. They may observe a plant's life cycle within a specific ecosystem and recommend strategies for ensuring the plant's health.

Students select individual trees to observe over time, deepening their awareness of tree changes and developing a greater appreciation for their local environment.

ADOPT A TREE

SUBJECTS
Science, English Language Arts, Math, Social Studies, Visual Arts

PLT CONCEPTS
2.1, 5.3

STEM SKILLS
Creativity, Data Analysis, Nature-based Design

DIFFERENTIATED INSTRUCTION
Hands-on Learning, Literacy Skills, Nonlinguistic Representations, Personal Connections, Student Voice

MATERIALS
Notebooks or journal-making materials, pencils, crayons or markers. Optional: Different colored yarn, tree field guide, binoculars, magnifying glasses, rulers or measuring tapes, camera

TIME CONSIDERATIONS
Preparation: 15 minutes

Activity: 30 minutes, with optional ongoing visits and projects throughout the year

OBJECTIVES

Students will

- Choose a tree, observe it, and describe it using their observations.
- Organize data they collect.
- Identify relationships between a tree and other organisms.

BACKGROUND

See Background sections for the activities Tree Factory (in Grades 3-5) and Plant a Tree (in Grades 6-8). This activity can be paired with many of the other activities in this guide. See the *More PLT for Your Tree* box for suggestions.

GETTING READY

- Find an area with several trees on or near your site that students can observe over time.

 SAFETY CHECK! Examine the site for any hazards, such as deep holes, sharp objects, or poisonous plants.

- Make a copy of the My Tree Journal student page for each student.
- Gather notebooks or materials for students to make their own tree journals. To make a journal, each student can fold a sheet of construction paper in half, insert blank pages, and staple the book along the folded edge. They can draw or paste a photo of their adopted trees on the cover. Insert copies of the student pages into the journals.

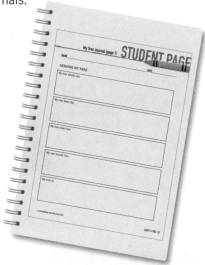

1 **HANDS-ON LEARNING** Take the group with their journals outside to an area that has several trees. Give students a few minutes to use their senses of sight, hearing, smell, and touch to get acquainted with the area. Choose an individual tree for the whole group to observe.

2 **LITERACY SKILLS** Ask volunteers to describe the tree, using first their sense of sight and then their other senses. Invite them to draw or write their responses on the My Tree Journal student page. Summarize each student's description by making comparative statements. Ask individuals to complete this sentence and record it on the student page: "My tree is _____." If their language skills are limited, students can draw pictures instead.

3 Encourage students to complete the student page questions about leaves, either as a group or individually. Invite them to share their leaf drawings or a leaf from their tree with the group.

4 Ask students whether they think the tree is alive or not—and how they know. Depending on your group, pose additional questions for discussion, such as: How are all the trees here alike? How are they different? Are they all alive? What else is alive here? What things do these trees give to humans? How do these trees help the environment?

5 You may choose to give each student a copy of the Adopt a Tree Certificate student page to complete.

6 **NONLINGUISTIC REPRESENTATIONS** Have students revisit the tree over short and long intervals to make continued observations over time. Conduct a variety of journaling activities, such as taking photos of students with their trees; creating drawings, poems, or stories about students' trees; or collecting pressed leaves, rubbings, flowers, or twigs from the trees.

VARIATION: GRADES 3–5

1 **PERSONAL CONNECTIONS** Explain that each person will choose his or her very own special tree to adopt. Students will observe their trees throughout the year, or as much as possible. Take students outside, let each one choose a tree, and have them explain their choices. Students might tie a colored piece of yarn around their tree to identify it. If your site does not have enough trees for each student to adopt a different one, you might have teams adopt trees. Students might also choose trees in their yard or in the neighborhood that they could visit before or after school.

SAFETY CHECK! If students will visit trees outside the group-assigned area, be sure to review safety rules and parental permissions. For trees away from their homes, they should make sure their visit is okay with the site owner and always have a parent or partner present when visiting the tree.

PROJECT LEARNING TREE
An initiative of SFI

FOREST FACT

Attention Deficit Disorder (ADD) symptoms in children can be greatly reduced when children are exposed to forests and other places with high tree densities.

2 Give each student a small journal and tell them to use their journals to record observations and answer questions about their trees. (You can also have them make and decorate their own journals. See Getting Ready.)

3 **HANDS-ON LEARNING** Give students a copy of the Tree Explorations student page and have them conduct one or more of the activities, either with the group or as homework. Suggest that they use their journals to record their written and drawn observations. Students may also develop their own questions or activities. After the initial visit to the tree, you might give students the Adopt a Tree Certificate student page to fill out.

4 **STUDENT VOICE** Have students visit their trees on a regular basis throughout the year and in a variety of weather conditions, noting any changes. At each visit, have students write a few sentences or make sketches in their journals to document changes (such as broken branches or new leaves), animal or human activity on or near the tree (such as a nest or carved initials), and other observations. Ask additional questions with each new season, such as: What color do the leaves turn in the fall? When does the tree bloom in the spring? Have students guess the causes of these changes and predict future changes.

MORE PLT FOR YOUR TREE

Use the following activities to further explore your adopted tree.

- Bursting Buds: Examine your adopted tree's leaf buds.
- Field, Forest, and Stream: Study the environmental factors under your adopted tree and compare them with factors in another area.
- Have Seeds, Will Travel: Study how seeds from your adopted tree and other trees disperse.
- Here We Grow Again: Do an experiment using your adopted tree to learn how it manufactures its own food.
- Nature's Skyscrapers: Measure your adopted tree's height and circumference and compare it with a giant sequoia.
- Plant a Tree: Plant a new tree to adopt.
- Poet-Tree: Write poems about your adopted tree.
- Signs of Fall: Do an experiment using your adopted tree's leaves to learn how the leaves of deciduous trees change color.
- The Closer You Look: Use your adopted tree to make careful observations of trees and their parts.
- Trees as Habitats: Learn what plants and animals depend on your adopted tree.
- Trees in Trouble: Examine the health of your adopted tree.

ACADEMIC STANDARDS

SCIENCE

Practices
- Planning and carrying out investigations
- Analyzing and interpreting data

Concepts
- Patterns
- Cause and effect
- Natural resources
- Interdependent relationships in ecosystems

ENGLISH LANGUAGE ARTS

Practices
- Writing: production and distribution of writing

Concepts
- Language: vocabulary acquisition and use

MATH

Practices
- Use appropriate tools strategically

Concepts
- Measurement and data

SOCIAL STUDIES

Practices
- Applying disciplinary concepts

Concepts
- Geography: human–environment interactions

ASSESSMENT

Ask students to

- Describe three or more features of their adopted tree using drawings, photos, rubbings, pressed leaves and flowers, and/or twigs found on the ground.

- Describe seasonal changes by sketching or including photographs of the tree and its surroundings from season to season.

- Write or tell a life story from their tree's perspective. For example, a student might write a first-person essay in which the tree describes how it relates to the plants, animals, and people around it and shares what problems it has.

ENRICHMENT

- Have students create a picture of a tree with flip-up tabs portraying various elements of its life, including tree parts, potential inhabitants, or life among the roots. (See the diagram for an example, or visit plt.org/myk8guide for printable versions.)

- Make a painting or model of a large tree without leaves and use it as a focal point for various curriculum topics. Through the year, you might have students show how the tree is constantly changing: from fall colors and drifting leaves to a winter skeleton, then bursting buds, flowers, and bees, followed by green leaves and fruit. You can also use the tree to illustrate units of study about plants, wildlife, holidays, social studies, environmental issues, and so on.

- Raise money to buy a tree for the group to plant. Take students to a nursery to pick out the tree, then hold a tree-planting ceremony. (See the Plant a Tree activity [in Grades 6-8] for complete directions.)

NAME _____ DATE_____

SENSING MY TREE

My tree smells like:

My tree feels like:

My tree looks like:

My tree sounds like:

My tree is:

NAME _____ DATE_____

MY TREE'S LEAVES

Which tree has a shape most like your tree?

What shape are your tree's leaves?

Draw a leaf or make a leaf rubbing:

Color the circle to match
your tree leaves.

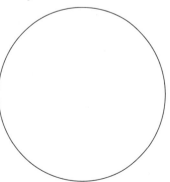

I LOVE MY
GREEN JOB

CAREER CORNER

**Trees are so beautiful! Many <u>ARTISTS</u> draw, paint, and take pictures of trees
to share them with others.**

ADOPT A TREE
CERTIFICATE

Name _____

Date _____

Type of Tree _____

Draw your tree and write a few words to describe it.

_____

_____

NAME _____ DATE _____

Here are some different ways to explore your tree. Use a journal to keep notes, drawings, and other observations.

- Make a sketch of your tree. Draw the shape of its trunk, branches, and canopy (treetop).

- Find out what kind of tree it is. Does it have any fruits, nuts, or seeds that help you identify it? Sketch what you find. Use a field guide or other reference guide to look up its name.

- Where is your tree? Draw a map to show its location.

- Draw a picture of your tree from various perspectives: from a distance, from a high place, or from underneath looking up.

- Investigate the health of your tree. Is it alive? How can you tell? Is it healthy? In what ways are people helping or hurting it?

- Write 10 words to describe your tree, and then use these words in a paragraph or poem about your tree.

- Draw a picture of a leaf from your tree. How does the leaf smell? How does it feel?

- Make a rubbing of your tree's bark using the edge of a crayon or a soft-leaded pencil. How does the bark feel? How does it smell?

- Are any animals on or near your tree? Don't forget to look for insects, spiders, and other small animals. Use binoculars or magnifiers for a closer look.

- Are there any signs that animals have used your tree in the past? Look for holes, nests, trails, and other animal signs and describe what you see.

- Create a model that shows how your tree interacts with the environment around it.

- Measure your tree. How long are its leaves? How big around is it? Use a ruler or measuring tape to find out.

- Each time you visit your tree, describe any changes you notice since the last visit.

- Take photographs of your tree every visit. Look at several of the different photographs at once. In what ways has your tree changed over time and in what ways has it stayed the same?

- Keep track of seasonal changes in your tree. When do the leaves start to fall? When do the leaf buds form on the branches? When do the fruits or seedpods ripen?

I LOVE MY GREEN JOB!

CAREER CORNER

FORESTERS take care of forests. They monitor forest trees over long periods of time to be sure that they are growing and healthy—just like you are doing with your adopted tree.

Every organism needs food, water, shelter, and space. A place that meets all these needs is called a habitat. Students will explore a nearby habitat—their backyard, schoolyard, or other outdoor setting—to look for signs of animals living there.

BACKYARD SAFARI

SUBJECTS
Science, English Language Arts, Visual Arts

PLT CONCEPTS
2.1, 3.2

STEM SKILLS
Investigation, Organization, Technology Use

DIFFERENTIATED INSTRUCTION
Hands-on Learning, Personal Connections, Student Voice

MATERIALS
Optional: Clipboards or writing surfaces, drawing paper, colored pencils or markers, magnifying glasses, camera

TIME CONSIDERATIONS
Preparation: 20 minutes
Activity: 50 minutes

OBJECTIVES

Students will

- Identify signs of animals living in an outdoor site.
- Describe how this habitat meets the needs of the animals living there.

BACKGROUND

A habitat is the place where an organism lives. A suitable habitat provides an organism with everything it needs to survive, including food, water, shelter, space, and whatever it needs to reproduce. Since the requirements of plants and animals can vary widely (think of a penguin, versus a tiger), suitable habitat for different animals or plants can differ tremendously in size and appearance. For example, a field is a suitable habitat for many types of grasses and forbs, as well as mice and rabbits that live among those plants; a single tree can be the entire habitat for many tiny animals that live in its bark and among its leaves; and a crack in a sidewalk provides habitat for the dandelions and ants that live there.

FOREST FACT

did you know

An important aspect of sustainable forestry is ensuring that there is appropriate habitat for a variety of animal species. Prairie warblers, for example, require a very young forest to survive, while red-cockaded woodpeckers require older and larger trees for nesting. Harvesting and replanting trees can create a diversity of conditions over time, enabling a richer mix of species to thrive across the landscape.

Even in the most concrete environment, you can usually find some signs of animal life. Most of the animals and animal signs that your students find will likely be insects and other small creatures. In an urban schoolyard, students may find spider webs, ants underneath rocks, or insects buzzing around. Students need to understand that all animals, large and small, need food, water, and shelter in order to survive. Remind students that people are animals too. Around the schoolyard they will find plenty of signs of "people life."

While most students enjoy looking for animals, some may be afraid of certain animals, such as spiders or worms. Be prepared for some students to act timid or scared during the activity. You might help by briefing students in advance on the kinds of animals they are likely to see, and by assuring them that most animals will be scared of them and are not dangerous to them. However, tell them it is smart to be cautious and warn them about animals they should not touch or pick up. (See Appendix B: Tips for Teaching Outdoors or more suggestions on teaching outdoors).

GETTING READY

- You may want to do the activity at a time of year when students are most likely to see animals outdoors, such as spring or fall.

- Collect any of the optional materials you choose. If desired, make copies of the Safari Count student page (or Safari Site Survey student page if you are doing the Variation).

 SAFETY CHECK! Always check the outdoor study site before taking students out. Look for potential hazards and risks. Either remove potential dangers or caution students about them. For younger students, arrange to have one or more parents, aides, or older students to help with the safari.

DOING THE ACTIVITY

1 **PERSONAL CONNECTIONS** Ask students whether they have ever heard the word "safari," and ask what kinds of things they might see on a safari. Point out that a safari doesn't have to be in a faraway place, and that they can even take a safari in their own backyard. Ask, "What might you see on a backyard safari?"

2 Tell students that they are going on a safari at your site. They will look and listen for signs of animals living or visiting there. Explain that students will need to search carefully to find animals, and that they will be more likely to find an animal if they are quiet. Ask students for ideas about where they might look and list their suggestions where all can see. Their suggestions might include on the bark and leaves of trees, in the cracks of sidewalks, among blades of grass, on utility wires, in the soil around plants, along the edges of buildings, under leaves, and on walls and fences. You might stimulate their imagination by having them pretend that buildings are mountains and cliffs, that the lawn is a jungle, or that the sewer is an underground river.

3 Point out to students that in addition to looking for actual animals, they should look and listen for signs of animals. Ask what kinds of signs they might find. Possibilities include insect egg masses, spider webs, leaves that have been nibbled, feathers, nests, animal tracks, bird or insect sounds, candy wrappers, or cigarette butts. Remind students that people are animals too, and they can record signs of "people life."

PROJECT LEARNING TREE
An initiative of SFI

SAFETY CHECK! Discuss appropriate outdoor behavior. All living things, including plants, should be respected and not injured in any way. Talk with students about following this rule: look, learn, leave alone. This includes leaving alone animals and their food, water, and shelter. (See Appendix B: Tips for Teaching Outdoors for more information about teaching outdoors.)

4 **HANDS-ON LEARNING** Divide students into pairs or small teams and hand out the Safari Count student page. Take them outside and give them a few minutes to find animals or signs of animals. Set boundaries so that students don't roam too far.

5 **STUDENT VOICE** Bring the group together and have students share their experiences and compare their findings. Focus them on the following questions:

- What animals did you observe living in the yard or outdoor site?

- What evidence did you find of other animals?

- What do these animals need to live? (food, water, air, shelter, space)

- How do these animals get food and water?

VARIATION: GRADES 3–5

1 As in the activity, invite students to observe animals and signs of animals at the site. Have students use the Safari Site Survey student page for recording their observations.

2 Discuss students' findings, focusing on how the animals living at the site get the food, water, shelter, and space they need.

3 **STUDENT VOICE** Ask students whether there are any animals they would like to see—or see more of—at the site (for example, birds, bees, butterflies, or squirrels). Have student teams research the habitat needs of those animals and possible ways to attract them to the site, such as providing feeders for birds or squirrels, or planting flowers for pollinators.

4 Assist the group in developing a plan for attracting the animals, based on their research. Their plan should include the benefits of attracting the animals, how they would address any potential problems, the steps they propose, the materials needed, and costs. Help them get any necessary permission and then put their plan into action.

ACADEMIC STANDARDS

SCIENCE

Practices
- Constructing explanations and designing solutions

Concepts
- Biodiversity and humans
- Natural resources
- Systems and system models

ENGLISH LANGUAGE ARTS

Practices
- Speaking and listening: presentation of knowledge and ideas

ASSESSMENT

Ask students to

- Draw a picture or diagram, write a story, or make a diorama showing an animal that lives in the yard or other site and how it gets food, water, or shelter.

- Inventory animals living in an area other than the one in the activity, such as their own backyards, the local park, a different part of the playground, or a nearby forest. You may want to assign some of the questions in Step 5 for them to answer.

ENRICHMENT

- Extend the safari to a larger outdoor setting, such as around the block or neighborhood. Students might focus their investigations by looking for birds and tallying the numbers of different kinds of birds, looking for evidence of animals eating or being eaten by something else, looking for evidence of animals using water, or sketching trees and looking for evidence of how trees help animals (including people).

- Give students a hula hoop to place on the ground and then count how many kinds of plants or animal species they find within it. Repeat in difference places around your site to compare different microhabitats.

- Compare the local site you chose with a local forest. Do these two locations have any of the same animals or trees?

PROJECT LEARNING TREE
An initiative of SFI

NAME _____ DATE _____

Look for animals and signs of animals. Write down each kind of animal or draw a picture of it. Count how many of each kind you see.

Animal or Animal Sign	How Many?

CAREER CORNER

I LOVE MY GREEN JOB!

<u>**WILDLIFE BIOLOGISTS**</u> (buy-ALL-uh-jists) study animals to find out what they need to live. They may watch birds, mammals, or reptiles in forests and other habitats.

NAME _____ DATE_____

Look for animals and signs of animals. Write down each kind of animal or draw a picture of it.
Count how many of each kind you see.

WHAT What animals or signs of animals do you see? List them or draw a picture.	WHERE Where do you see each animal or sign of an animal?	HOW How might that animal get the food, water, and shelter it needs to live here?

CAREER CORNER

WILDLIFE MANAGERS keep track of the animals that live in a natural area to make sure there is enough of the right habitat. They conduct surveys—like this one— to find out the types and numbers of animals in the area.

Camouflage is an essential survival strategy in the natural world. Students discover the value of protective coloration as they pretend to be birds in search of colored bugs.

BIRDS AND BUGS

SUBJECTS
Science, Math, Physical Education

PLT CONCEPTS
2.1, 2.2, 2.3

STEM SKILLS
Collaboration, Data Analysis, Nature-based Design, Organization

DIFFERENTIATED INSTRUCTION
Hands-on Learning, Nonlinguistic Representations

MATERIALS
60 small objects in assorted colors (e.g., pipe cleaner segments, colored pieces of yarn, paper shapes, or punched holes) to represent "bugs" (if you are doing this activity outdoors, we recommend using biodegradable items such as colored pasta, beans, popcorn, or breakfast cereal); a large piece of chart paper; crayons or markers. Optional: clothespins or tweezers for picking up bugs, camera.

TIME CONSIDERATIONS
Preparation: 20 minutes
Activity: 50 minutes

OBJECTIVES

Students will

- Identify signs of animals living in an outdoor site.
- Describe how this habitat meets the needs of the animals living there.

BACKGROUND

Many animals are "color-coordinated" with their surroundings. For example, snowshoe hares and grouse-like birds called ptarmigans (TAR-mih-guhns) change from brown in summer to white in winter. A box turtle's dappled shell and a fawn's white spots mimic blotches of sunlight on the forest floor, helping them blend in with the background. And the two-toned appearance of many fish—dark on top and light on bottom—helps them match the background of dark river bottom or pale sky. Any coloration, body shape, or behavior that helps an animal hide is called **camouflage**.

Blending in with the environment is a great **adaptation** to avoid being eaten, but some predators use it too. Camouflage helps them avoid being spotted by a potential meal. For example, a lion's tawny coat matches the grasses of the African savanna, and a leopard's spots match the patchy sunlight in a tree's branches.

Insect-eating birds consume a wide variety of insects and other invertebrates, such as beetles, grubs, spiders, mosquitoes, and butterflies. Their coloring may resemble their surroundings, or they may have warning coloration that stands out, the opposite of camouflage, to tell predators that they are poisonous or unpalatable.

GETTING READY

- Find one or more large, open areas (indoors or outdoors) for doing the activity. Collect 60 small, colored objects consisting of equal amounts of at least three colors. These will represent bugs. Make sure you have at least one color that matches the area's surface (e.g., gray for asphalt, green for grass, or brown for carpet). You'll need 20 each if you have three colors, 15 each of four colors, 12 each of five colors, and so forth.

 SAFETY CHECK! Use easily **biodegradable** objects in outdoor settings (see Materials).

- Optional: Create charts in advance for recording the results for Steps 4 and 6. Consider laminating the charts so you can reuse them.

- Before students arrive, scatter the "bugs" throughout the area(s).

1 Ask the group to think about how a bullfrog's green color or a polar bear's white color helps it survive. Invite students to give other examples of animals that blend in with their surroundings and talk about how this can help animals. Ask students what it is called when animals blend in with their surroundings (camouflage).

2 Ask students for their ideas about how they might investigate the benefits of camouflage. After discussing their ideas, explain that the group will do an investigation together.

3 Divide the group into teams, with the same number of students on each team. Guide students to the area where you scattered the bugs. Tell students that various types of tasty bugs are scattered here and that they are hungry birds. Show them what the bugs look like and ask them to predict what color bug might have the best camouflage in this environment.

TAKE IT OUTSIDE

Repeat this activity in an outdoor setting that offers a different-colored backdrop. For example, if your first simulation was on carpet or tile, try grass. If your first simulation was on grass, try soil, mulch, or asphalt. Discuss how the results differ and have students offer reasons for why.

4 **HANDS-ON LEARNING** Arrange teams in relay race lines. Explain that the teams will race to see who can get every bird fed. When you say, "Go," the first bird in each line should "fly" to the prescribed area and pick up the first bug he or she sees. You might have teams use a clothespin or tweezers (representing a beak) to pick up bugs. Each bird flies immediately back to the line and tags the next bird, who does the same thing. When the last bird returns, everyone on the team sits or raises a hand.

 SAFETY CHECK! If you use food items, remind students not to eat them.

PROJECT LEARNING TREE
An initiative of SFI

5 NONLINGUISTIC REPRESENTATIONS When all teams have completed the relay, spread a piece of chart paper on the ground. Make a chart with columns that correspond to the different colors, as in Example 1. Have students place their bugs in the appropriate color column. Have students count and record the number of each color. What color was easiest to find? How does this help the birds survive? What color was hardest to find? How does this help the bugs survive? What color bug has the best camouflage for this environment and why?

You may want to take a picture of the chart for students to use later in graphing.

EXAMPLE 1 RECORDING SHEET: BUGS COLLECTED BY COLOR

RED	GREEN	BROWN	GRAY

6 Have teams repeat the simulation to find the remaining bugs. Record results as before, discussing any similarities and differences.

7 Before leaving the study area, make sure students have recovered all the bugs.

8 Have students create pictographs or bar graphs to represent the data they collected. Help students interpret the graphs.

EXAMPLE PICTOGRAPH

BUGS COLLECTED

RED	🪲 🪲 🪲 🪲
WHITE	🪲 🪲 🪲 🪲 🪲 🪲
BROWN	🪲
BLACK	🪲 🪲

VARIATION: GRADES 3–5

1 ⬅ **HIGHER-ORDER THINKING** Lead students in the above activity, except have them record their findings in a chart that identifies the order in which they found the bugs. Make a chart with as many columns as there are students on each team, as in Example 2. Each column will represent the student's position in line. The students should each place their bug in the column that corresponds to their position in line (1st, 2nd, and so on).

EXAMPLE 2 RECORDING SHEET: BUGS COLLECTED BY POSITION IN LINE

1ST	2ND	3RD	4TH	5TH	6TH	7TH	8TH

2 Have students total and record the number of colored bugs in each column (e.g., 1st—4 reds, 2nd—3 reds and 1 green, and so on). Is there a pattern to the order in which the bugs were found? What might the pattern tell us?

3 You may also want to challenge the students to create their own graphical display for analysis.

4 Repeat the simulation for different conditions, and have students collect, organize, and interpret their data from the repeated rounds.

ACADEMIC STANDARDS

SCIENCE

Practices
- Analyzing and interpreting data
- Developing and using models
- Constructing explanations and designing solutions

Concepts
- Patterns
- Structure and function

MATH

Practices
- Reason abstractly and quantitatively

Concepts
- Counting and cardinality
- Measurement and data

ASSESSMENT

Ask students to

- Review pre-selected pictures of local flora and fauna and describe how their coloration helps these animals survive.

- Select another background that they believe would make it more difficult to find the bugs, and repeat the simulation to test their selection.

ENRICHMENT

- Have students use assorted art supplies to design and create their own camouflaged creatures. They should suggest advantages of their creature's camouflage and the environments that suit it best.

- Some animals are very brightly colored, standing out against their surroundings. Invite students to research how bright colorations help some animals survive.

- Have students pretend they are wildlife biologists and assemble a presentation (slides, a poster, or written report) about different types of camouflage, such as concealing coloration, mimicry, or scent camouflage.

In early spring, many trees sprout bright green leaves. Where do the leaves come from? How do they form? Students investigate these questions by observing tree buds throughout the year.

BURSTING BUDS

SUBJECTS
Science, Math, Visual Arts

PLT CONCEPTS
4.1, 5.3

STEM SKILLS
Data Analysis, Nature-based Design

DIFFERENTIATED INSTRUCTION
Hands-on Learning, Higher-order Thinking, Nonlinguistic Representations

MATERIALS
Trees, paper, pencils. Optional: Pocketknife, flagging tape or other markers, ruler, camera

TIME CONSIDERATIONS
Preparation: 20 minutes

Activity: Three to four 50-minute periods spread out over the school year, particularly in the fall and spring

Note: This activity includes observing a tree or shrub every few months throughout the year. In temperate climates, this observation begins in the fall.

OBJECTIVES

Students will

- Observe tree buds over time.
- Describe the developmental stages of leaf buds throughout the year.

BACKGROUND

When a deciduous tree's leaves drop in the fall, its leaves for the next spring are already being formed. The immature leaves, stems, and sometimes even flowers are located on the twigs in packages called **buds**.

The buds are made of tough scales that form a waterproof case around these immature tree parts. In spring, as temperatures warm and daylight lengthens, sap rises from the roots to the branches; the scales fall off the buds; and the tree's leaves, stems, and flowers begin to unfurl and grow. During the summer, the tree begins to develop new buds for the following year.

For many animals, tree buds are a concentrated food source. In winter, animals such as grouse, deer, squirrels, and rabbits feast on buds.

GETTING READY

- This activity works best in late fall to early spring.
- Find one or more deciduous trees that have branches low enough for the students to see. Shrubs can work, but the buds are smaller than those of trees. If students have adopted trees (see the activity Adopt a Tree), consider using the adopted trees for this activity.

 SAFETY CHECK! Check for any hazards at the site(s), such as deep holes, sharp objects, or poisonous plants.

- Plan to share the *Twig Diagram* electronically or otherwise enlarge it.

PROJECT
LEARNING
TREE
An initiative of SFI

FOREST FACT

In preparation for winter, trees in temperate climates, such as the box elder (*Acer negundo*), form resting buds that are resistant to frost.

DOING THE ACTIVITY

1 Ask students if they know what happens to deciduous tree leaves in the fall. Ask them where they think a tree's new leaves come from in the spring. Encourage students to share their ideas. Ask students how they might find out where new leaves come from. Help them design an investigation or use the following suggested procedure.

2 **HANDS-ON LEARNING** Take the students outside to look closely at tree branches. Hold a branch so that the students can examine the tree's buds. Have the students point out different features they notice on the branch (bark pattern, leaf scars, buds, thorns, etc.). Then use your fingernail or a pocketknife to split a bud in half lengthwise to reveal the tiny leaves tucked inside. Ask the students to describe what they see.

3 **NONLINGUISTIC REPRESENTATIONS** Show students the *Twig Diagram*. Review it together and identify the different parts.

TWIG DIAGRAM

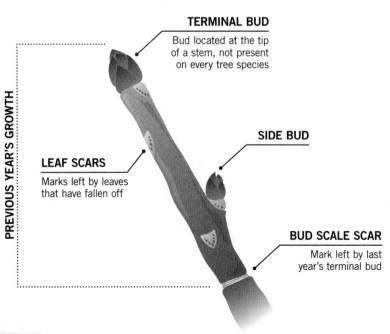

TERMINAL BUD
Bud located at the tip of a stem, not present on every tree species

SIDE BUD

LEAF SCARS
Marks left by leaves that have fallen off

BUD SCALE SCAR
Mark left by last year's terminal bud

PREVIOUS YEAR'S GROWTH

4 Explain that students will observe buds over time. Take the group outside (see Safety Check!), and have each student choose a live twig to examine. Invite students to take notes about what their twig and its buds look like. Students should draw a picture of the twig with a close-up of one or more buds. Have the students mark their twigs with flagging tape or other markers so they can return to the same twig each time they make their observations.

5 Have students visit the tree and observe the twig and buds at least once in the winter. They should look for changes in the bud and any signs of animal activity. Have them make notes and draw pictures of what they see. They can also take pictures to include in their records.

6 Have students visit their trees several times in the spring and record their observations during each visit. Students may measure the stem growth on several different twigs. If their twig or buds are no longer there, have students come up with a hypothetical scenario of what could have happened to them, and write or draw pictures of their story.

7 **➤ HIGHER-ORDER THINKING** Lead a discussion about students' observations and findings, asking:

- What does this investigation tell you about how tree leaves form?
- How could you find out whether the process or its timing are the same every year?
- Why is this information important?

VARIATION: GRADES 3–5

1 Engage students in a community science project called Budburst, in which they observe the timing of annual events in trees or other plants (such as first leaf, first flower, or first ripe fruit) and share it with a network of scientists, students, teachers, and volunteers. Visit budburst.org for more details.

2 Choose between two Budburst protocols:
- A one-time observation, which involves observing a plant at a single point in time. Students identify the current status of the plant and the date of the observation.
- A life-cycle observation, which involves watching a plant over a growing season. Students note the dates on which the plant reaches each specific phase.

3 After observations are conducted, invite students to research how changes in climate (such as increasing number of winter ice storms or shorter winters) may impact bud growth. For example, trees may bud earlier than they once did, or early spring thaws may "trick" trees into having their leaves emerge earlier, making them vulnerable to later frosts.

ACADEMIC STANDARDS

SCIENCE	MATH
Practices	**Practices**
• Planning and carrying out investigationss	• Reason abstractly and quantitatively
Concepts	**Concepts**
• Structure and function	• Measurement and data
• Patterns	

ASSESSMENT

Ask students to

- Create a visual representation of the observations they made.

- Write a description of how buds change into leaves.

ENRICHMENT

- In early spring, have students bring in small twigs. Use a knife to make cross-sections (both lengthwise and widthwise) of a few buds on each twig and have students compare the buds of different trees. Have them use magnifying glasses to enhance their observations.

- Before buds open in spring, cut a few branches from flowering trees: apple, dogwood, maple, oak, etc. Place the branches in water and observe them for several days. What happens? Ask students why the buds on these branches open before the buds on the same kinds of trees outside. Older students can collect small twigs from a tree and design an experiment to test their hypotheses.

- Students can cut one bud off their "observation" tree every 1–2 months between fall and spring. Quickly freeze or dry the buds to stop their growth. Students can arrange the buds chronologically and mount them on poster board as an exhibit. Note: To avoid damaging the tree's health, each student should use a different tree and select buds from different twigs.

- Point out that new tree buds are a tasty treat for deer, which can be a problem when they eat all the buds off trees planted to reforest or restore a habitat. Ask students to think of ways that people might prevent this kind of deer damage.

Students observe differences over time to learn that change in the environment can occur quickly, slowly, or not at all.

DID YOU NOTICE?

SUBJECTS
Science, English Language Arts, Social Studies, Visual Arts

PLT CONCEPTS
5.1, 5.3

STEM SKILLS
Communication, Creativity, Data Analysis

DIFFERENTIATED INSTRUCTION
Cooperative Learning, Personal Connections, Student Voice

MATERIALS
Crayons or colored pencils for timelines

TIME CONSIDERATIONS
Preparation: 30 minutes

Activity: One 50-minute period

Variation: Two to three 50-minute periods

OBJECTIVES

Students will

- Identify changes in themselves over time.
- Summarize those changes in the form of a timeline.
- Describe changes they observe in the environment around them.

BACKGROUND

It has been said that change is really the only constant in the universe. Some changes happen quickly, such as a tree falling in a storm. Others, like the slow erosion of mountains into the sea, happen so gradually that we are hardly aware of them.

History is a record of changes, whether it is the history of a person, tree, forest, society, or nation. Humans have recorded the history of people, places, and things for thousands of years. Historical information may be stored in books, photographs, movies, computer records, government documents, on websites, or in people's memories, through family traditions and community stories.

An individual person's history is an example of a **life cycle**. A life cycle is defined as all the changes a living thing experiences in the course of its life. In some organisms—like humans—these changes are slow and gradual, but in others, change can happen rapidly. The basic stages of all life cycles include birth, growth, reproduction, and death. Reproduction is necessary for the continuation of all species.

In this activity, students use history to look for patterns in their own growth and in the environment around them. In doing so, they use the same logic that foresters use to manage forested lands.

GETTING READY

- Make copies of the My Life Timeline and Time on the Line student pages.
- Create a blank chart for recording group observations, with the headers "Birth to Age Four," "Since Age Five," and "Since This Morning."

PROJECT LEARNING TREE
An initiative of SFI

FOREST FACT

Knowing the history of a forest is essential to all forest managers, land-use planners, and urban foresters. These professionals need to know how the forest has grown over time and how land-use patterns have evolved, in order to make the best decisions for the future.

DOING THE ACTIVITY

1 **PERSONAL CONNECTIONS** Ask students how they have changed since they were born. Invite them to share major changes that occurred between their birth and their fourth birthday. (Possible answers include that they grew taller, started eating real food, learned to use the toilet, learned to walk, learned to talk, etc.) Record their responses under the heading "Birth to Age Four" in the group chart (see Getting Ready). Then ask students how they know these things. Can they remember learning them? Did someone tell them? Did they see evidence in family photographs?

2 Ask students to name ways they have changed since they turned five years old. Record their answers under the heading "Since Age Five." (Possible answers include going to school every day, playing with friends, learning to read, etc.)

3 Ask students to think about ways they have changed since they woke up this morning. Record their answers under the heading "Since This Morning." (Possible answers include hair getting brushed, stomach getting full after eating breakfast, teeth getting cleaned, etc.)

4 Discuss how some of these changes are observable (such as learning to walk), while other changes are harder to observe (such as gaining knowledge). Point out how changes are sometimes linked to a specific date or time.

5 Explain that a timeline can be used to show how some change happens quickly, while other change happens slowly. Show an example of a timeline. Using the information from Steps 1–3, have students draw or write their personal changes on the My Life Timeline student page.

6 Display timelines around the room. Invite students to conduct a "gallery walk" to look at all the different timelines and identify changes that occurred slowly and quickly.

TAKE IT OUTSIDE

Have students create a personal timeline using sidewalk chalk on the playground, sidewalk, or asphalt. When all students are finished, invite them to explain, one at a time, what their timeline shows. Take pictures of the timelines for a more permanent record.

7 Lead a discussion about change, encouraging students to identify changes that occur in the environment around them. Ask questions such as:

- What about you has stayed the same over time? What has changed?
- What kinds of changes happen quickly? What changes happen slowly?
- What would happen if people didn't change at all?
- What changes do other living things go through?
- What changes do places around you go through?
- What changes do forests, gardens, or other natural areas go through?
- Do you think change is a good thing or not? Why do you think so?

VARIATION: GRADES 3–5

1 Ask students to think about ways their community has changed over its history. How is it different today than 100 or 500 years ago? How might students investigate these changes? How might they show them?

2 Have the group create a timeline mural or slideshow to show the history of the local community, with different sections focusing on different time periods. For example, sections might show different decades or centuries, ending with present day. Or, students might think creatively and design a slide showing how their community will change in the future.

3 ⊘ **COOPERATIVE LEARNING** Divide the group into teams, assigning each a section of the timeline or part of the slideshow. Challenge students to gather information about their community's history from more than one source (such as visiting a museum or library, interviewing residents, or searching the internet).

4 Give each team time to collect information. Each group should complete the Time on the Line student page, describing at least five events to include. Ask them to consider how these events changed the landscape, wildlife, and human lifestyles over their time period.

5 Provide materials for each team to create their timelines.

6 ⊘ **STUDENT VOICE** Ask teams to explain the history of the changes they recorded. Discuss:

- What changes have occurred in the community's environment, wildlife, and human lifestyle?
- What caused some of these changes?
- Do you think these changes have made the community a better or worse place to live for humans, or have they made no difference?
- Did any of the changes start out being good, and then turn out to be bad? Did any bad changes turn out to be good?
- Can you identify any trends? What might these trends mean for the future?

ACADEMIC STANDARDS

SCIENCE

Practices
- Analyzing and interpreting data
- Obtaining, evaluating, and communicating information

Concepts
- Stability and change
- Growth and development of organisms

ENGLISH LANGUAGE ARTS

Practices
- Speaking and listening: presentation of knowledge and ideas

SOCIAL STUDIES

Practices
- Evaluating sources and using evidence

Concepts
- History: change, continuity, and context

ASSESSMENT

Ask students to

- Use their personal timelines to describe changes that have occurred over their lives and since this morning.

- Identify changes that occur quickly and slowly.

ENRICHMENT

- Have students create their own books about their personal history to share with their family and friends.

- Encourage students to bring in personal artifacts, such as photos of themselves at different ages, or a favorite toy, book, or article of clothing from their early life to share with the group.

- Invite students to search (always with a parent or caregiver) through the attic, basement, closets, shelves, and drawers for "really old stuff" relating to a sibling or another family member's personal history. Have students write or draw a real or imaginary story that compares and contrasts their personal timeline with the family member's.

NAME _____ DATE_____

1. Use words or a picture to show a change that has happened to you at each age.

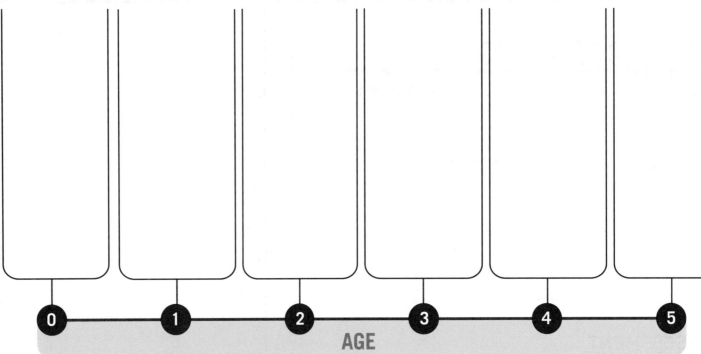

AGE
0 1 2 3 4 5

2. Use words or a picture to show changes that have happened to you since this morning.

CAREER CORNER

Do you like telling stories through pictures? A <u>FILMMAKER</u> creates movies to tell real-life stories about people and places.

NAME _____ DATE_____

Team Members: _____

Time Period Studied: _____

1. How many people lived in this area at the beginning of this time period?

2. What was the most common form of transportation during this time period?

3. Describe five major events that happened in your area during this time period. For each event, note when it happened and explain whether it changed people's lives or the vegetation, wildlife, or way that land was used in the area.

DATE	EVENT	How did it change people's lives or the vegetation, wildlife, or land use in the area?

4. Explain whether you think these changes made the area a better or worse place to live—or whether the event made no difference.

CAREER CORNER

I LOVE MY GREEN JOB!

SOCIOLOGISTS (sew-see-ALL-uh-jists) study people and their communities. By looking for changes in your community, you are thinking just like one!

A plant is a biological system containing processes and components that enable it to grow and reproduce. By observing, collecting, and classifying seeds, students examine one aspect of a plant's reproductive system.

HAVE SEEDS, WILL TRAVEL

SUBJECTS
Science, English Language Arts, Math, Visual Arts

PLT CONCEPTS
1.1, 3.1, 4.1

STEM SKILLS
Collaboration, Nature-based Design, Problem Solving

DIFFERENTIATED INSTRUCTION
Cooperative Learning, Hands-on Learning, Multiple Solution Pathways

MATERIALS
A variety of seeds (see Step 2 of Doing the Activity), magnifying glasses, paper plates, pictures or video clips showing different dispersal mechanisms of seeds, dried lima beans or other large seeds, various natural craft materials, plush toy or puppet. Optional: Cups or other containers, blanket or other piece of cloth, old socks, masking tape.

TIME CONSIDERATIONS
Preparation: 30 to 60 minutes

Activity: One to two 50-minute periods

OBJECTIVES

Students will

• Sort and classify plant seeds.

• Identify different methods of seed dispersal.

• Model or design seeds that use varied dispersal methods.

BACKGROUND

Living organisms contain systems that enable them to grow and reproduce. All living things have some system for reproducing their species.

Most plants reproduce using flowers and seeds. Seeds develop within the ovary of the plant's flower after being fertilized by pollen from another plant of the same species or after being self-fertilized.

A **seed** is the small, hard part of a flowering plant from which a new plant can grow. It is an embryonic plant enclosed in a protective outer covering, often containing stored food for initial growth. For a seed to germinate and grow into a mature plant, environmental conditions must be just right. Each plant needs a certain amount of sunlight, air, water, and nutrients from the **soil**. If a seed simply drops from the parent plant and tries to grow in its shadow, it might compete with the parent for those essentials. Therefore, most seed-bearing plants have developed a way to disperse seeds away from the parent, giving the new plants a better chance to find what they need to grow.

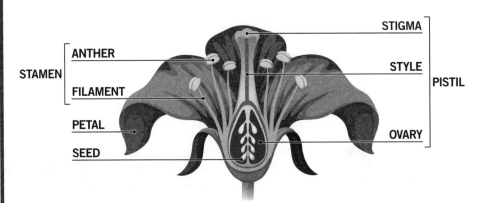

In flowering plants, flowers are the reproductive unit, containing several different parts. Seeds develop from ovules within the ovary of the plant's flower or cone. The fruit is the seed-bearing structure formed from the ovary after flowering.

PROJECT LEARNING TREE
An initiative of SFI

FOREST FACT

Prescribed burning, or planned fire, is an active forest management method that clears out fuel sources that would otherwise promote destructive wildfires, making the forest healthier. The heat of prescribed burns also promotes the regrowth and reproduction of some tree species.

Some plants rely on wind for seed dispersal. They produce very light seeds (or fruits) with sail-like or hairy outgrowths that enable them to be carried by the wind. For example, the maple fruit (called a **samara**) has papery wings that twirl like a helicopter, while a dandelion fruit has a fuzzy "parachute" that carries it on air currents. Orchid seeds are so tiny that they float in the air like particles of dust.

Many plants depend on animals to disperse their seeds. Some of these, like Queen Anne's lace and burdock, produce seeds with spines, hooks, or gooey coatings that catch on an animal's fur (or people's clothing) and are carried to distant places. Other plants, like peaches, apples, and raspberries, develop seeds within an attractive, tasty fruit. When the fruits are eaten by animals, the seeds are carried through the animals' digestive systems and deposited in a different location when the animal defecates. Still other plants like acorns and walnuts have attractive nuts that animals move to different locations for storage. Any forgotten nuts grow into new trees!

ANATOMY OF A BEAN SEED

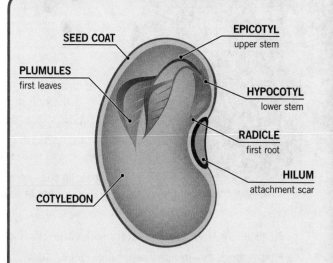

SEED COAT

PLUMULES
first leaves

EPICOTYL
upper stem

HYPOCOTYL
lower stem

RADICLE
first root

HILUM
attachment scar

COTYLEDON

Beans and other dicot seeds have two cotyledons inside the seed coat and typically contain these plant parts. Monocots, such as grasses and lilies, have just one cotyledon.

CATEGORIES OF SEED DISPERSAL

Acorns roll away from the parent plant.

Cherries are eaten by animals and carried away in their stomachs.

Burdocks stick to animal fur or people's socks.

Floats on air—dandelion, cottonwood, cattail, orchid

Flies through air—maple, ash, tulip poplar, alder

Floats on water—mangrove, coconut, cranberry

Bounces or rolls—acorn, pecan, tumbleweed (the whole plant rolls)

Eaten by animals—cherry, peach, pyracantha

Stored by animals—acorn, hickory, beech

Sticks to animals—burdock, cocklebur, wild barley, Queen Anne's lace

Ejected—locust, violet, witch hazel, impatiens, lupine

Released or opened by fire—lodgepole pine, jack pine, manzanita

Some plants mechanically eject their seeds away from their parent plant. For example, witch hazel seeds develop within a pod that squeezes the seeds as the pod dries. When the seeds finally shoot out, they can travel up to 40 feet (12.2 m)! Lupines, violets, and bean plants also disperse their seeds this way.

Still other plants depend on fire for dispersal. Their seeds are tough enough to survive a brief exposure to fire, and they benefit when fire burns away the undergrowth and clears the ground for them to grow. Some pine species around the world have **serotinous** cones, which are sealed by resin. When a fire sweeps through the area, heat melts the resin and allows the seeds to be released. Lodgepole pines and jack pines disperse their seeds in this way.

Understanding how plants disperse is important in forest management. To grow new trees, foresters must know the needs of the germinating seeds to determine whether they can regenerate on their own or whether they will need artificial regeneration, through manual seeding or the planting of saplings. This knowledge enables foresters to determine the ideal conditions for future forest growth.

GETTING READY

- If students will collect seeds, be sure to obtain any necessary permissions. Autumn is the best time to collect seeds from natural sources.

- Make copies of the Sorting Seeds student page.

- Soak a few dried lima beans overnight.

- Find a few seeds that show different seed dispersal mechanisms. (See the *Categories of Seed Dispersal* box for suggestions.)

- Find video clips showing different seed dispersal mechanisms.

- Gather craft supplies, such as glue, masking tape, string or yarn, toothpicks, pieces of cardboard, cotton balls, rubber bands, chenille stems, etc.

DOING THE ACTIVITY

1 Ask students what seeds are and what they do. (Don't worry if they have misconceptions at this point. The activity will help clarify them.) Slice open a soaked lima bean (see Getting Ready) to show them the inside. Review the seed parts as depicted in the *Anatomy of a Bean Seed* diagram (see Background). Ask: What are some seeds you've seen at home or other places?

2  **HANDS-ON LEARNING** Invite the group to help you collect seeds. Students might bring in birdseed, fruit seeds, seeds from trees in their yard, or seeds from plants in their garden. Consider taking students to a nearby natural area where they can find seed-bearing plants (check the site ahead of time for hazards, such as deep holes, sharp objects, or poisonous plants). Students can collect seeds by:

- Walking around an area. They can pick up seeds from the ground and collect them in a cup or other container.

- Dragging an old blanket (or other piece of fuzzy cloth) through the area. Then they can examine the blanket for seeds and seed parts. They can also wear old, wool socks over their shoes and walk around the area to pick up seeds and burs on their socks.

- Wearing masking tape bracelets (with the sticky side out). Small seeds or seed parts will stick directly to the bracelets.

3 **COOPERATIVE LEARNING** Divide the group into teams of 2 to 4 students and give each team a paper plate containing an assortment of seeds from the collection. Ask teams to examine their seeds and classify them (by color, size, shape, etc.). Students can use magnifying glasses to get a closer look. Have them record their findings on the student page and share with other teams how they classified the seeds.

4 Ask students whether they have ever seen seeds "move." For example, maybe they've blown dandelions and seen the seeds float in the wind, or had seedpods stick to their socks when they walked in a field. Show students the seeds or video clips you have collected showing different dispersal mechanisms. Ask students how different sizes and shapes can give seeds an advantage. If they don't mention it, point out that many seeds have ways to move away from their parent plant so that they have a better chance to grow.

5 Ask students about ways that animals help disperse seeds. Depending on their responses, you might point out that some seeds have structures that help them stick to animals' fur, or that encourage animals to eat or store them.

6 **MULTIPLE SOLUTION PATHWAYS** Challenge students to design a seed that can stick to an animal's fur. Students can start with a dried lima bean, adding craft materials to create a seed that will stick to a plush toy or puppet.

7 Invite students to test their designs by trying to attach their seeds to a plush toy or puppet and moving it a certain distance. Have them share their results with the group and discuss features of successful designs.

TAKE IT OUTSIDE

Many favorite backyard birds depend on seeds for food. Set up bird feeders made from milk containers, aluminum pie tins, or other upcycled materials to learn which birds like which seeds. Put a different type of bird seed in each feeder (sunflower, millet, safflower, etc.) and spend time each day observing the feeders, with binoculars if possible. Students should try to determine (1) which birds prefer which seeds, (2) what method each bird uses to eat seeds, and (3) why the bird uses that method.

VARIATION: GRADES 3–5

1 Ask students why it is important for seeds to travel away from their parent plant. Discuss how the size, shape, weight, and dispersal strategies of seeds affect the distance they travel.

2 Share video clips showing different seed dispersal mechanisms. Encourage students to examine the designs that help seeds disperse, identifying them by shape and structure.

3 ⬤➤ **MULTIPLE SOLUTION PATHWAYS** Challenge students to design seeds with special dispersal mechanisms. Students can use a dried lima bean as the base of their design, adding natural materials like wood, fiber, or paper to develop a seed that does one of the following (or another challenge of their choosing):

- floats in water for 5 minutes,
- sticks to an animal and gets carried for 10 feet, or
- floats in the air over a distance of 5 feet when blown lightly by a fan or a breath.

4 After designing their seeds, invite students to test their work. For example, you can test seeds designed to float by placing them in a bucket of water and timing for 5 minutes. Suggest that students improve their designs based on the test results.

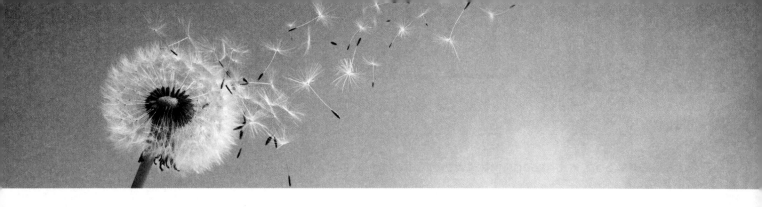

ACADEMIC STANDARDS

SCIENCE

Practices
- Analyzing and interpreting data
- Using mathematics and computational thinking

Concepts
- Structure and function
- Engineering design
- Patterns

ENGLISH LANGUAGE ARTS

Practices
- Speaking and listening: presentation of knowledge and ideas

MATH

Practices
- Use appropriate tools strategically

Concepts
- Measurement and data

ASSESSMENT

Ask students to

- Identify one or more categories of seed dispersal and sort seeds according to these categories.

- Create a display of local seeds that represent different categories of dispersal.

- Draw a picture of the seed they designed, describing its features.

- Describe the structure and function of seed parts.

ENRICHMENT

- Plant some of the collected seeds to observe plant germination in action.

- Drop some of the collected seeds (from Step 2) in front of a fan to demonstrate the effect of moving air on various seed designs. Note differences in movement, direction, speed, and rotations. Graph the distance each seed flies.

 SAFETY CHECK! Do this as a teacher demonstration, not a student activity. Be sure to keep fingers clear of fan blades.

- Not all plants reproduce from seeds. Some trees use vegetative propagation, in which tree roots or stumps sprout new trees. Demonstrate this in the classroom by growing new plants from pieces of carrots, potatoes, turnips, onions, or willow sticks.

- Explore different careers related to seeds, such as farmer or plant nursery worker. Seed conservation specialists help collect and store seeds, which is important for reforestation efforts. Some U.S. states and Canadian provinces even have forest nurseries where they grow trees from locally collected seeds, ensuring that the plants come from local species.

- Older students could investigate how seed dispersal helps invasive species establish themselves quickly in new areas. Many invasive plants produce lots and lots of seeds; for example, one purple loosestrife plant can produce as many as 2 million wind-dispersed seeds per year! Have students research the connection between seed dispersal and invasive plants in your area.

NAME _____ DATE_____

Sort seeds. Sort your seeds into two or three groups. All the seeds in a group must be alike in some way.

Create a bar graph. Label the categories on the bottom of the chart. Start at the bottom with 1. Place your seeds on top of the chart, one per box. Color in the boxes that contain seeds.

NUMBER OF SEEDS			
15			
14			
13			
12			
11			
10			
9			
8			
7			
6			
5			
4			
3			
2			
1			
CATEGORY			

CAREER CORNER

I LOVE MY GREEN JOB!

<u>BOTANISTS</u> (BOT-uh-nists) are scientists who study plants. They may look at the shapes of seeds and fruits to learn how these parts help plants live and grow.

A plant is a biological system that needs sunlight, water, air, nutrients, and space in order to survive and thrive. Students conduct inquiry-based experiments to explore these essential plant requirements.

HERE WE GROW AGAIN

SUBJECTS
Science, English Language Arts, Math

PLT CONCEPTS
2.1, 3.1, 4.1

STEM SKILLS
Collaboration, Data Analysis, Investigation, Organization

DIFFERENTIATED INSTRUCTION
Hands-on Learning, Higher-order Thinking

MATERIALS
A few house plants, about 50 seeds (try pea, bean, or sunflower), a large jar (16–32 ounces), paper towels, planting containers or cups with drainage holes, potting soil, masking tape and pens, rulers, a shallow tray to hold the containers, cups to measure liquid. Optional: Shallow plastic tubs to hold potting soil (to make scooping easier), waterproof marker.

TIME CONSIDERATIONS
Preparation: 45 minutes plus time for seeds to sprout (1–2 weeks)

Activity: Two 50-minute periods, plus time to measure plants over 2–3 weeks

OBJECTIVES
Students will

- Set up an experiment to determine what plants need to grow.
- Measure and compare plant growth under different environmental conditions.

BACKGROUND
A plant is a living system. To survive and function, it needs the right amount of sunlight, air, water, nutrients, and space.

SUNLIGHT
Green plants get their energy from sunlight through a process called **photosynthesis**, meaning "putting together with light." During photosynthesis, sunlight activates the **chlorophyll** in leaves. The plant uses the sun's energy to combine carbon dioxide from the air with water to make carbohydrates (starches and sugars), the plant's food.

All animals—including humans—need the food energy that comes from photosynthesis, whether they eat plants directly or eat animals that eat plants. Photosynthesis also releases oxygen, which animals need to breathe.

When something prevents a plant's leaves from getting enough sunlight, photosynthesis stops or slows, and plant growth slows down. If part of a leaf is covered, the plant stops producing green chlorophyll in that area, causing the spot to turn yellow. If an entire leaf gets no light, it will eventually turn brown and fall off. If a plant loses too many leaves, it will not be able to make enough food, and it will die.

AIR
Plants need air to live and grow. They use carbon dioxide from the air for photosynthesis. Their roots also need air to stay healthy and absorb water and nutrients.

WATER
Water is essential to life. Besides being a main ingredient for photosynthesis, water is a primary component of protoplasm, the basic material that constitutes plant structure. Water also helps transport nutrients from the soil into the plant's roots and through the plant's cells.

NUTRIENTS

Plants depend on a growing medium to provide nutrients and support. For most plants, this medium is **soil**. How well soil sustains plants depends on its texture (compact or porous), its water-holding capacity, its acidity, and its population of beneficial soil organisms. Different plants need different soil types to grow well.

SPACE

Plants need space to grow. If they do not have enough space or if they must compete with neighboring plants for nutrients, light, and water, plants may struggle or die.

Students will conduct an investigation to test whether plants really need these basic requirements. See Appendix L: Planning an Investigation for more information about how to design and carry out an investigation.

GETTING READY

- One to two weeks prior to the activity, soak **seeds** overnight and place them in a large clear jar on a layer of damp paper towels. Put the jar near a sunny window and monitor the seeds daily, keeping the paper towels moist. Seedlings will be ready for use in an experiment when they have developed leaves and roots. Hands-on alternative: Have students germinate their own seeds in advance as part of a homework assignment.

- Ensure that all planting containers have drainage holes. If not, carefully add them.

- Mark the soil fill line on each container (use a waterproof marker or masking tape).

- Label separate plastic trays to hold the planting containers, with one for each condition: Light, No Light, Water, No Water, Soil, and No Soil. Use additional containers if you are testing additional factors.

- Make copies of the My Plant Journal student page.

- Place sample house plants around the room.

DOING THE ACTIVITY

1 Show students the house plants. Ask what these plants need to live and grow. Write students' answers where all can see it. Be sure the list includes air, light, water, and soil.

2 Divide the students into teams. Explain that they will conduct an experiment to test what plants need. Assign each team one of the following factors to test: light, water, or soil. (It is too difficult to test plants' requirement for air.) Depending on students' answers in Step 1, you may include additional factors for them to test.

3 Demonstrate how to plant the seeds by filling the planting container with soil, gently packing the soil until it reaches the fill line, placing seeds in the middle of the soil at the appropriate depth (indicated on the seed packet), and slowly adding water until the soil is moist and not soaked.

4 HANDS-ON LEARNING Give each group two containers, four sprouted seeds, and masking tape. First, have them label each container with their names and the factor that they are testing, using masking tape. Labels should be "Light," "No light," "Water," "No water," etc. Have students plant two seeds in each container. The groups testing soil should plant two seeds in a container that has soil and place two seeds in another container that does not have any soil.

5 Have students place their containers on the appropriate plastic tray. Place all trays in a similar bright location (except the "No light" tray, which can be placed in a closet or simply covered with a box). Explain that they will begin to observe their containers once the seedlings have emerged from the soil. Be sure to keep the soil in all containers moist by watering when necessary (except the "No water" tray).

6 Once seedlings emerge from the soil, hand out the My Plant Journal student page. Help students write an investigation question related to the factor they were assigned. Have them predict the differences they might see in the containers after several days, and record their predictions and observations on the student page. Direct students to measure the height of each plant, using rulers or construction paper strips. These strips can be glued onto poster board to make bar graphs. These observations should continue every few days over a couple of weeks.

7 Support students in watering containers, measuring plants, and making observations every 2–3 days.

8 HIGHER-ORDER THINKING After the last observation, lead students in a results analysis. Ask:

- What differences did you notice in your plants over time?

- Which plants grew the tallest, and which were the shortest? Why might this be?

- What other characteristics besides the height of the plant did you notice, such as the number or color of leaves?

- Do you see any patterns in your results? If so, what?

- Based on the investigation results, what do plants need to live and grow?

VARIATION: GRADES 3–5

1 Ask students what factors they think are necessary for plant growth.

2 HANDS-ON LEARNING Have student teams devise experiments to test whether plants really need those elements to grow, using the seedlings you have started. Help teams develop a research question, think through a reliable method, and then predict the results. Make sure that they understand the need to have a control condition as well as experimental conditions. Then, help them conduct their investigations. Alternatively, teams can follow the *Variation: Experiment Model* (see box).

VARIATION: EXPERIMENT MODEL

CONTROL
Plant four of the same type of seedlings in four separate containers of potting soil. Label these containers "Control." Place them near a window or other light source. Water as needed to keep the soil moist.

TEST FOR LIGHT
Plant four of the same type of seedlings in four separate containers of potting soil. Label the containers "No Light." Place them in a dark cupboard or closet. Water as needed.

TEST FOR WATER
Plant four of the same type of seedlings in four separate containers of potting soil. Label the containers "No Water." Place them near a window or other light source.

TEST FOR SOIL
Put four of the same type of seedlings in four separate containers on a wet paper towel. Label the containers "No Soil." Place them near a window or other light source. Add water to keep the towel wet.

3 As the plants grow, have students measure and graph plant height. Encourage them to count the number of leaves and describe the leaf color (which will help them assess the vigor of the plants). Plot the daily or weekly measurements on a graph.

4 After several weeks of observation, analyze the findings. Ask the students:

- Which plants grew the most? The least?
- What other differences did you observe?
- What does a plant need to grow? How do plants meet those needs?
- What happens if a plant doesn't get enough sunlight? Water? Soil?
- Which parts of the plants seemed most affected by lack of sunlight? Water? Soil?
- If you were going to plant a tree on the school grounds, where might you plant it? Why? (Look for a place with the right conditions: sunlight, air, water, soil, and room to grow.)

TAKE IT OUTSIDE

Have students place their plants outside for the duration of the investigation (except for the "No light" ones). Direct access to sunlight will be beneficial for both the plants and the students!

ACADEMIC STANDARDS

SCIENCE	ENGLISH LANGUAGE ARTS	MATH
Practices	**Practices**	**Practices**
• Planning and carrying out investigations	• Speaking and listening: presentation of knowledge and ideas	• Reason abstractly and quantitatively
• Using mathematics and computational thinking		• Use appropriate tools strategically
Concepts		**Concepts**
• Matter and energy flow in organisms		• Counting and cardinality
• Interdependent relationships in ecosystems		• Measurement and data
• Patterns		
• Cause and effect		

ASSESSMENT

Ask students to

- Explain: what is the best way to grow bean plants?

- Complete a Claim–Evidence–Reasoning explanation based on their results. See Appendix K: Making a Scientific Argument for a sample graphic organizer. The Claim is students' answer to the question they were investigating. The Evidence is measurements or observations that support their claim. The Reasoning explains how the evidence supports their claim. For this investigation, students might say:

Claim: I think plants grow better with light.

Evidence: The plant that grew in the light had green leaves. The one that grew without light had yellow leaves.

Reasoning: This happened because plants need light to be healthy.

ENRICHMENT

- Have students take digital photos of their plant experiments every few days. Help them create a visual timeline of each plant's growth.

- Students can make "flip-it" books that show plant growth in animation. Give each student four index cards and have them cut the cards into quarters to make 16 cards. On the right edge of each card, students should draw a small picture of the plant, including stages from a seed to a mature plant. Stack cards in order and hold them on the left side between your thumb and forefinger. By flipping through the cards on the right side, you can watch the seed sprout and grow.

- Arrange to visit a nursery or orchard to see trees in various stages of growth. Learn about the unique needs of different species.

- Investigate what happens if a plant's leaves don't receive enough sunlight:

  » Cut several circles or squares of cardboard about ½ inch (1.3 cm) across.

  » Use tape to attach a cardboard circle or square to each of several leaves on a shrub, tree, or other plant.

  » After four days, remove the pieces of cardboard. (You will see a lighter-colored spot on each leaf where the cardboard blocked the sunlight).

My Plant Journal

NAME _____ DATE_____

Investigation question:

_____

Prediction: What differences will you see in your two cups after a week? Draw or write what you think.

_____

Look at your plants each day. Describe what you see.

DAY	DRAWING	DESCRIPTION
1		
2		
3		
4		
5		
6		
7		

CAREER CORNER

I LOVE MY GREEN JOB!

Do you like working with plants? <u>NURSERY WORKERS</u> sow, water, and care for plants. They know what plants need to be healthy.

GRADES K–2

VARIATION 3–5

Students learn about the papermaking process by trying it themselves. Students will find out that they can make their own paper and that their product is practical, as well as beautiful.

MAKE YOUR OWN PAPER

SUBJECTS
Science, English Language Arts, Social Studies, Visual Arts

PLT CONCEPTS
1.4, 2.5, 2.7

STEM SKILLS
Creativity, Nature-based Design

DIFFERENTIATED INSTRUCTION
Hands-on Learning, Student Voice

MATERIALS
Scrap paper torn into 1" x 1" (2.5 cm x 2.5 cm) pieces (paper towels, construction paper, and toilet paper work well); a large bowl; a wooden frame 5" x 7" (13 cm x 18 cm) or 8" x 10" (20 cm x 25 cm); nylon or wire screen; a stapler; a plastic basin at least 2.5 gallons (9.5 liters) in capacity and larger than the frame; cloth dishtowels, blender; sponge; strainer. Optional: Colored paper, liquid starch, rubber gloves, pieces of colored thread, or dried flowers.

TIME CONSIDERATIONS
Preparation: 30 minutes, plus time to gather materials
Activity: Two 50-minute periods

OBJECTIVES

Students will

• Describe the steps of the papermaking process.

• Identify the inputs and outputs of the papermaking process.

BACKGROUND

Paper is a simple material, essentially a mat held together by the roughness of fibers. It can be made from almost any fibrous material, such as cotton, hemp, flax, wood, or recycled paper. Despite its simplicity, paper has a tremendous effect on our lives. Imagine how different your day would be without paper!

We use paper for countless things, including books, stationery, copiers and printers, tissues and sanitary products, bags, containers, food packaging, gift wrap, wallpaper, disposable dishes, lampshades, and artistic media. Industrial uses include gaskets, liquid and gas filters, insulation, and friction devices.

The process for making paper was invented in China in the second century A.D. Until 1798, all paper was made one sheet at a time. During the Industrial Revolution, mechanical advances helped papermaking become a growing industry that provided countless products. Some modern machines can make a sheet of paper 26 feet (8.8 m) wide and nearly 40 miles (64 km) long in just one hour! While the technology has changed dramatically over the centuries, the basic steps are simple enough that you can try them yourself.

FOREST FACT

did you know

Papermaking begins with trees. About one-third of the paper used in the United States is made from trees that are thinned (harvested from a forest) to give other trees room to grow or from trees that were grown especially for papermaking. About one-third is made from the wood chips and sawdust created from milling lumber from logs. And one-third is made from recycled paper.

Paper Press

During the papermaking process, large mill machines strip away bark and shred logs into millions of chips the size of breakfast cereal. The wood chips travel on conveyors to gigantic cookers, where chemicals and steam are added. The mixture is heated and pressurized, breaking the chips into smaller and smaller pieces and finally forming a dilute water suspension of wood fibers called **pulp**. The pulp passes through screen cleaners and sometimes is bleached to whiten it. Dyes, pigments, or resins are sometimes added to give the paper or paperboard (thick paper used to make boxes) the appropriate finish.

The pulp is pumped through pipes to a paper machine where it is sprayed onto a wide, moving wire screen. After the water in the pulp drains through the holes, a damp mat of wood fibers remains; this is the paper. It is picked up from the end of the moving belt and dried over steam-heated rollers.

Sustainable practices can help to reduce the environmental impacts of commercial papermaking. These include:

• Sustainably managing forests to ensure the long-term health of trees.

• Using wood waste in mills to generate the electricity to run the mills, thus lessening the use of fossil fuels that emit carbon dioxide and other pollutants.

• Using smokestack systems to reduce both air pollution and odors created by the pulp-cooking process.

• Recycling the wastepaper produced in mills and using recycled paper in addition to new wood fiber.

• Monitoring mill wastewater to ensure that it does not pollute waterways.

For more about sustainable practices related to papermaking, see the activity What's in a Label? (in Grades 6-8).

It is easy to recycle paper, which helps reduce waste. However, paper cannot be recycled indefinitely. Each time paper goes through the manufacturing process, the fibers deteriorate. After undergoing repeated recycling, the fibers are no longer suitable for papermaking. So new trees are still needed for paper products, which is why sustainable forest management is so important.

GETTING READY

- Decide how you will conduct the activity. While you can demonstrate, ideally the students should participate. You might set up a papermaking station that you supervise and have students rotate through it. While you are helping the papermaking group, the rest of the group can do an alternative activity.

- Papermaking is a wet process, so use a workspace that won't be damaged by moisture. You might want students to wear "wet gear"—an apron, smock, or old clothing.

- Remove any plastic or staples from the scrap paper and tear it into small pieces (1-inch or 2.5-cm squares). Soak the paper in hot water in the large bowl for at least 30 minutes before you use it.

- Tightly staple or tack nylon or wire screening to the wooden frame, making a "deckle," which is the surface on which you will layer the fibers. Visit YouTube for helpful papermaking deckle tutorials.

DOING THE ACTIVITY

1 Ask students what they think paper is made of and how it is made. Ask what questions they have about paper, listing them where everyone can see. Ask them how they might find the answers to their questions. Suggest that one way is to make paper themselves.

2 Fill a blender halfway with warm water, then add a handful of soaked paper scraps. Blend at medium speed until you no longer see pieces of paper, and the pulp has a soupy consistency. You can blend in a piece of construction paper for color or stir in short pieces of thread, dried flowers, or herbs for texture.

3 Pour the mixture into the large basin and fill it with warm water, mixing thoroughly. Adding a few ounces of liquid starch will help make the paper firm.

4 **HANDS-ON LEARNING** Allow students to help you slide the deckle into the basin. Put some pulp onto the screen and, still holding the deckle underwater, gently move it back and forth to get an even layer of fibers on the screen.

5 **HANDS-ON LEARNING** Allow students to help you lift the deckle out of the mixture, keeping it flat. Allow it to drip until most of the water has drained off, leaving a uniform layer of pulp mixture on the deckle. Press the pulp gently with your hand to squeeze out excess moisture (wearing rubber gloves helps). Soak up any excess water from the bottom of the screen with a sponge.

6 Place a cloth (or other absorbent material) on a flat surface and turn the deckle paper-side-down. Lift the deckle gently, tapping the screen to release the paper onto the surface.

TAKE IT OUTSIDE

Papermaking works well in outdoor settings, where it is easier to conduct wet and messy projects. Encourage students to look outside for small leaves, flower petals, or seed pods to add to their paper.

7 Let the paper dry naturally overnight. Gently peel the paper off the surface when it is dry.

8 When you're finished making paper, collect the leftover pulp in a strainer and recycle it, or freeze it in a plastic bag for future use. Don't pour the pulp down the drain!

9 **STUDENT VOICE** Revisit students' initial questions about paper from Step 1. Ask them what they learned by actually making paper, and what questions they still have about paper or the papermaking process.

VARIATION: GRADES 3–5

1 Have students create paintings using paper pulp. Start by making different colors of pulp from construction paper scraps. Pour the pulp into small paper cups, pinching the rims of the cups to make pouring spouts.

2 Invite students to choose one color for the background, pouring a half cup of pulp onto the deckle screen. They should then carefully drip thin layers of other colors on top of the background to create a piece of artwork.

3 Have students research other ways that people use paper in addition to writing and art projects, such as cleaning, construction, packaging, or clothing. Students might also look for other fibers besides wood fiber that are used to make paper. Have them share the findings with the group in an oral, written, or visual report.

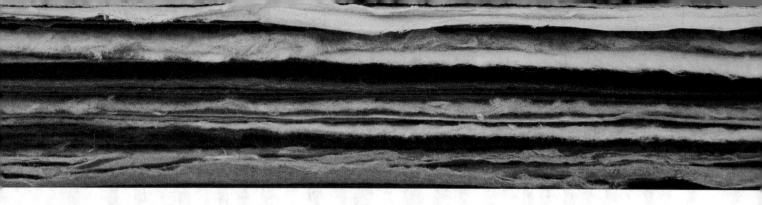

ACADEMIC STANDARDS

SCIENCE

Practices
- Asking questions and defining problems

Concepts
- Natural resources
- Engineering design
- Cause and effect

ENGLISH LANGUAGE ARTS

Practices
- Speaking and listening: comprehension and collaboration

SOCIAL STUDIES

Practices
- Applying disciplinary concepts

Concepts
- Economics: exchange and markets

ASSESSMENT

Ask students to

- Write about or visually organize the steps of the papermaking process and the materials needed.

- Tell or write a story about how paper is made.

ENRICHMENT

- Use different types of materials to make paper and compare the results. Students might try using newspaper, paper towels, or cotton balls. Which paper is the strongest? Most water-resistant? Best for writing? What other comparisons can you make about them? What other materials could you recycle to make paper instead of throwing them away?

- Create a book or bulletin board showing different kinds of manufactured paper, noting the characteristics, benefits, and limitations of each. Include samples of newsprint, gift wrap, parchment, wallpaper, packaging, food cartons, greeting cards, and so on.

- Make paper for thank-you cards, invitations, and stationery. Use homemade paper to write a poem (as in the Poet-Tree activity [in Grades 3-5]) for a gift or special occasion.

- If you live near a paper mill, plan a visit or invite a representative to talk to your class and help with the papermaking activity. Ask them to show samples of wood chips, pulp, and paper.

GRADES K–2

VARIATION 3–5

Students explore their sense of smell and discover why smell is important to animals, including beetles and humans.

PEPPERMINT BEETLE

SUBJECTS
Science, Social Studies

PLT CONCEPTS
1.2, 2.3, 4.1

STEM SKILLS
Collaboration, Investigation, Nature-based Design, Problem Solving

DIFFERENTIATED INSTRUCTION
Cooperative Learning, Hands-on Learning, Literacy Skills, Nonlinguistic Representations, Personal Connections, Student Voice

MATERIALS
Small bottle of concentrated flavoring (peppermint, cinnamon, winter green, etc.) and cotton balls, or spray cologne or other spray scent; a ball of yarn; flagging materials or rags to mark boundaries.

Variation: Several different flavorings or scents, different colors of yarn, flagging materials or rags to mark boundaries.

 SAFETY CHECK! Read the labels on all items and choose only those that are safe for students to inhale. Remember to teach proper procedures for smelling unknown substances.

TIME CONSIDERATIONS
Preparation: 30 minutes

Activity: 50-minute period

OBJECTIVES

Students will

- Model how animals use their sense of smell to respond to the environment around them.
- Identify the importance of the sense of smell in people's daily lives.

BACKGROUND

Taste and smell are chemically activated senses that are closely related. In fact, when we taste something, much of what we are actually sensing is smell. For a substance to be smelled and tasted, it must first dissolve on the olfactory mucous membrane in the nasal passages. That's why a person whose nasal passages are blocked because of a cold cannot smell or taste food very well.

The ability to respond to chemicals (through smell or taste) is probably one of the earliest senses that organisms evolved. It is especially important in the insect world. When foraging worker ants find food, they leave a scent trail for other ants. The ants touch their abdomens to the ground and secrete a substance that only members of the same species can detect, using their antennae. The better the food source, the more scent markings the ants leave on the trail. If another animal accidentally crosses the scent trail and breaks it, the ants become disoriented and confused.

Bark beetles are another example of animals that rely on their sense of smell to survive. Bark beetles reproduce in the inner bark of trees. They are native to US forests and have caused tree deaths across millions of acres of forest on the West Coast and in the Rocky Mountains (the mountain pine beetle) and in the US South (the southern pine beetle). Their ability to smell is particularly important to them because they can't fly very far. When a bark beetle infests a tree, it releases a special chemical called a pheromone, that other beetles can smell, which tells them where a tree is located. As the tree becomes too crowded to support additional beetles and their offspring, the beetles begin emitting a different pheromone, which essentially sends a "no vacancy" message to other beetles.

One of the best odor-detecting animals is the salmon. After salmon hatch in a stream, they swim downstream to the open ocean, where they live for two to five years. When it is time for them to reproduce, the salmon unerringly trace their

PROJECT LEARNING TREE
An initiative of SFI

original paths on a strenuous journey to their birthplaces upstream. It is believed that this incredible homing behavior is due to their ability to remember the specific water chemistry of their birth, and to isolate that from all other odors in the water between their birthplace and the ocean.

To define an area or territory, many animals (such as dogs, cats, wolves, ferrets, rabbits, and deer) mark objects with scent from special glands. They use scent marking to find a mate or mark an area that contains their family, shelter, or food supply. Animals often defend their territory from intruders, especially members of the same species.

GETTING READY

- Flag or mark boundaries in an area with trees. If your site has no trees or few trees, you could use structures such as playground equipment, fences, buildings, etc.

 SAFETY CHECK! Look for any hazards at the site, such as deep holes, sharp objects, or irritating plants. Look online or ask at a local nature center how to identify and avoid poison ivy, poison oak, or poison sumac, which are often found next to trees.

- Close to the time that the students will do the activity, "scent mark" trees that lie within the boundaries. Do this by moistening a cotton ball with flavoring and rubbing it on the bark or by spraying with a scented spray around the tree trunk at about the average nose level of the students. Depending on the number of trees in your site, mark at least one tree for each group or pair of students, but do not mark all the trees.

- Cut lengths of yarn that are long enough to tie around the tree trunks. Provide several lengths of yarn for each group of students. For very young students, provide rocks at the base of the trees or other structures so they can anchor their yarn under the rock instead of tying it.

DOING THE ACTIVITY

1 ⬤➡ **PERSONAL CONNECTIONS** Ask your students why their sense of smell is important. Did they ever have a cold and lose their sense of smell? How did it feel? Could their sense of smell save them from dangerous situations? (It can help people detect gas, smoke, or rotten food.)

2 ⬤➡ **STUDENT VOICE** Ask students for examples of different animals that rely on their sense of smell. Students with pets might share firsthand accounts about their pets relying on smell more or less than people do. Ask them what purposes smell serves for these animals. (It helps them find food, detect danger, find a mate, and identify another animal's territory.)

3 Tell students to imagine an insect called the "peppermint beetle" (or name it after whatever scent you are using, e.g., "licorice beetle," "lemon beetle") that lives in the area they will visit. This flying beetle is famous for the peppermint scent it occasionally marks on the trunks of trees. They will work in teams to find the trees that this imaginary beetle has marked.

4 ⬤➡ **NONLINGUISTIC REPRESENTATIONS** At the activity site, divide the group into pairs, and give each pair several lengths of yarn. (If your site has relatively few trees, use larger teams so that you have more trees than teams.) Tell each team to use their noses to find trees that the beetle visited. If they find a tree that all team members agree is scent-marked, the team should tie the yarn around the tree. Teams should continue searching for scent-marked trees; they need not check trees that have already been identified with yarn.

5 When all the scent-marked trees have been found, have the students walk the scent trail left by the peppermint beetle. Ask the students to make inferences as to why the peppermint beetle marked those trees. Could it be to attract a mate, or define a territory? Where might the peppermint beetle's trail lead? To a food source? Its home? Or nowhere in particular?

VARIATION: GRADES 3–5, Bark Beetle Infestation*

1 Follow the procedure described in Doing the Activity, except use several different scents to represent different species of beetles. Explain that each student is one of several species of bark beetles and must find the scent associated with their own species. Then, provide the students with different colors of yarn to mark their own paths.

2 ⬤➡ **NONLINGUISTIC REPRESENTATIONS** Allow students to take only a certain number of steps to check out trees. This will allow them to check multiple trees that are close by, but only a couple of trees that are far away. This introduces the concept that beetles have a limited distance they can travel to find a suitable host tree. You might try the activity once with a "normal" search range, and then redo the activity doubling the search range, to simulate a favorable wind that carries the beetles with it.

3 ⬤➡ **LITERACY SKILLS** Have students research an invasive beetle, such as the emerald ash borer, and describe its effects on North American forests. What effects, if any, does the beetle's spread have on humans' use of forest products?

*This variation was developed in partnership with Wyoming PLT.

PROJECT LEARNING TREE
An initiative of SFI

ACADEMIC STANDARDS

SCIENCE

Practices
- Developing and using models
- Analyzing and interpreting data

Concepts
- Structure and function
- Information processing
- Patterns

SOCIAL STUDIES

Practices
- Applying disciplinary concepts

Concepts
- Geography: human-environment interactions

ASSESSMENT

Ask students to

- Recall where they found the peppermint scent and share ideas about how they, as peppermint beetles, used their sense of smell to respond to the environment around them. Students may make a labeled model, such as a map or illustration, or may tell or write a story about how and why peppermint beetles use the peppermint scent.

- Consider ways that people use their sense of smell. Have students describe how their sense of smell is important to them. Ask them if they could use their sense of smell to find food. For example, could they find a pizza in the kitchen with the lights out? Why is the smell of a food important? (Makes it taste better, tells us if it's fresh.) Why do people use things like perfume or air freshener? (To make their environment more pleasant.)

- Set up an investigation to collect and analyze data to determine which of three to six scents other students can identify most easily.

ENRICHMENT

- Have students write a story from the perspective of a peppermint beetle, including why and how it created a trail of scents. Encourage them to be imaginative in their telling of the story.

- Challenge students to create a peppermint beetle using art materials or app. Ask them to describe its characteristics, including a sense of smell (or scent glands).

- Grow an herb garden that includes aromatic plants native to your area (search the internet or visit a local garden center to find suitable plants). As the plants grow, students can compare their scents and research possible uses for the plants.

- Make "mystery scents" to test how well students can recognize smells. Put a wad of cotton in each of several small plastic containers with lids. Put a different "smelly" substance into each container, such as a few drops of vanilla, vinegar, food flavorings, cloves, lemon peels, or garlic. Poke a hole in the lid of each container and tape the lids down. Label the jars A, B, C, etc. Let the students smell each one and have them write down what they think each smell is and where they've smelled it before. You can also try making pairs of containers with the same scent and see if students can match up the pairs. Afterward, ask the students if certain smells triggered certain memories.

Even though students may be very familiar with trees, they may not have thought much about the actual structure of a tree. In this activity, your students will go outdoors or view pictures to take a closer look at trees and their parts.

THE CLOSER YOU LOOK

SUBJECTS
Science, English Language Arts, Visual Arts

PLT CONCEPTS
4.1

STEM SKILLS
Creativity, Data Analysis, Nature-based Design

DIFFERENTIATED INSTRUCTION
Higher-order Thinking, Nonlinguistic Representations

MATERIALS
Drawing paper, crayons or markers.

TIME CONSIDERATIONS
Preparation: 30 minutes
Activity: 50 minutes

OBJECTIVES

Students will

- Compare their drawing of a tree from memory with an observation of a real tree.
- Identify characteristics of a tree's form and structure.

BACKGROUND

There are more than 50,000 species of trees in the world, and they have a lot of variety. For example, tree heights can range from just 15 feet (5 m) tall at maturity, in the case of bluejack oaks, to over 360 feet (110 m) tall, for coast redwoods. Tree leaves may be needle-shaped, broad and flat, or made of small scales. Tree bark may be smooth, rough, shaggy, or deeply furrowed. Branches may spread out to form a huge, broad crown or may rise narrowly like a column.

GETTING READY

- Locate several different kinds of trees that your students can observe closely.

 SAFETY CHECK! Check for any hazards at the site(s), such as deep holes, sharp objects, or poisonous or irritating plants.

- If there are no trees in your area, bring in a live potted tree or one or more cut trees (like Christmas trees). If this is not possible, collect pictures of trees that students can use to make their observations in Step 3. (Try the internet, books, or calendars for good color pictures of trees.)

- Make copies of the Seeing a Tree student page.

FOREST FACT

did you know

The tallest trees in the world are coast redwoods, which grow in natural forest stands along the Pacific coast of northern California and southern Oregon.

DOING THE ACTIVITY

1 Give students drawing paper and crayons or markers. Have them close their eyes and picture a tree. Encourage them to think about the overall shape of the tree, how the branches are connected, and the texture of the trunk and leaves. Ask them to draw a picture of the tree from memory. Save their pictures for later.

2 Ask students how they might draw a more accurate picture of a tree. Suggest that one way is to go outside and look at trees (or look at photographs of trees). Ask students to list different features they might look for when they make their observations. Hand out copies of the student page and encourage students to take notes or make sketches on their pages.

3 Take the students outside and have them examine the trees (or tree pictures) you located in Getting Ready. Encourage students to choose a kind of tree that is similar to the one they drew in Step 1.

4 ➡ **NONLINGUISTIC REPRESENTATIONS** If you have younger students, lead them to one or more trees and examine the trees together. Have them use their bodies to bend like the branches, flutter around like the leaves, stand tall like the trunk, or mimic other characteristics of the trees you examine.

5 When the students have finished their observations, have them draw a second tree picture. Encourage them to include as much detail as they can.

6 ➡ **HIGHER-ORDER THINKING** Hang each student's pair of drawings (from Steps 1 and 5) around the room. Let students compare each pair of drawings. Was anyone's second picture radically different from the first? Have students compare drawings done by different students. What characteristics were similar?

ACADEMIC STANDARDS

SCIENCE

Practices
- Analyzing and interpreting data

Concepts
- Structure and function
- Patterns

ENGLISH LANGUAGE ARTS

Practices
- Speaking and listening: presentation of knowledge and ideas

ASSESSMENT

Ask students to

- Use a graphic organizer (see sample below) to describe similarities and differences between their pictures drawn from memory and from observation.

- Write or present their answers to the question, "Did your second picture show a greater understanding of the tree's structure and form?" and support their answer with observations from their drawings.

SAMPLE GRAPHIC ORGANIZER

STRUCTURE	TREE FROM MEMORY	TREE FROM OBSERVATION
Tree Shape		
Trunk and Branches		
Bark		
Leaves		
Seeds, Fruit, or Flowers		
Plants or Animals		

ENRICHMENT

- Have students make bark or leaf rubbings of the trees they examined. Students can create a new picture of their tree (or add to the one they made in Step 5) using rubbings of the tree's parts; attaching actual flowers, nuts, or seeds from their trees; or rubbing leaves, stems, or bark against the paper so that their natural color comes off.

 SAFETY CHECK! Whenever possible, have students use leaves, seeds, or other tree parts that they find on the ground to make their rubbings, rather than picking those items off the tree.

- Have students make a model of a tree using construction paper, paper rolls, straws, tissue paper, and the like. Students should include and label all the tree parts they've learned about. Encourage them to be as creative as possible while still being accurate.

- Have students write about the tree they chose to draw and why they chose it.

- As students draw their trees, invite them to think about the function of the tree's leaves, branches, cones, and other structures. How do these structures help the tree survive? How do the size and shape of these structures relate to their function?

NAME _____ DATE_____

Look closely at your tree. Try to find each of the elements below. Draw or write what you see.

Tree Shape	**Trunk and Branches**	**Bark**

Leaves	**Seeds, Fruit, or Flowers**	**Plants or Animals**

CAREER CORNER

I LOVE MY GREEN JOB!

GRAPHIC ARTISTS use images and shapes to share ideas with others.
To teach others about forests, they may draw trees, plants, or animals.

From their leafy branches to their tangled roots, trees provide habitat for a host of plants and animals. Students will inventory the plants and animals that live in, on, and around trees and discover how plants and animals depend on trees in many ways.

TREES AS HABITATS

SUBJECTS
Science, English Language Arts

PLT CONCEPTS
1.1, 1.2, 2.1

STEM SKILLS
Collaboration, Data Analysis, Technology Use

DIFFERENTIATED INSTRUCTION
Hands-on Learning, Higher-order Thinking, Nonlinguistic Representations

MATERIALS
Part A: Paper tubes, materials for decorations, magnifying glasses, binoculars, digital cameras or electronic tablets, clipboards (or cardboard with paper clips). Optional: Collection of animal signs.

Part B: Journals or paper and clipboards.

Optional: Field guides (for trees, shrubs, insects, and birds), magnifiers, bug boxes, binoculars, digital cameras or electronic tablets.

TIME CONSIDERATIONS
Preparation: 15 minutes

Part A: 40 minutes

Part B: 40 minutes, plus time for data analysis

OBJECTIVES

Students will

- Observe animals and plants that depend on and influence trees.
- Identify interrelationships between different organisms that depend on trees.

BACKGROUND

A **habitat** is the place where a plant or animal gets all the things it needs to survive, including food, water, shelter, and space for having and raising offspring. A habitat may be as large as 100 square miles (259 km^2) of grassland for a lion or as small as single plant for an insect. A tree may serve as part of an organism's habitat, or it may be the organism's entire habitat.

Snags, or standing dead trees, provide optimal habitat for many different species. Tree frogs and beetles live under a snag's bark. Woodpeckers and other birds feed on the insects that live in snags. Chickadees nest in cavities created by woodpeckers. Squirrels and deer mice store food in them.

GETTING READY

PART A:

- Optional: Collect fallen leaves, twigs, bark, fruit, or nuts that show signs of plant or animal life. Signs may include chewed holes, tunnels, scrapings, egg cases, webs, galls, moss, lichen, or fungus.
- Gather (or make) paper tubes and collect art supplies for student-made telescopes.
- Make copies of the Tree Observation Bingo student page.

PART B:

- Find an area with several trees (any size) or shrubs for students to examine. If students have already adopted trees, use them. (See the activity Adopt a Tree.)

 SAFETY CHECK! Look for any hazards at the site, such as deep holes, sharp objects, or poisonous plants.

- Make copies of the What's the Connection? student page.

PROJECT LEARNING TREE
An initiative of SFI

FOREST FACT

Forests are home to 80% of all land-based plant and animal species!

DOING THE ACTIVITY

PART A: TREE HOUSE

1 Ask: What animals have you seen in or on trees? What were the animals doing in the trees? Do you think a tree can be a home for animals or other plants? How could we find out whether a tree can be a home? Suggest that one way to find out would be to look for animals and plants living in trees.

2 Lead students in making "telescopes" out of paper tubes, which can be decorated with tissue paper or paint, as a tool to study tree habitats. You might also provide magnifying glasses, binoculars, digital cameras, or tablets.

3 Optional: Show examples of plant or animal signs to the students (see Getting Ready). Ask students to describe what they see and what they think might have caused it.

4 **HANDS-ON LEARNING** Lead students to a tree and have them use their telescopes to look closely at and around the tree. Distribute copies of the Tree Observation Bingo student page to focus student observations. Allow students plenty of time to complete the worksheet and collect related data.

5 Lead a discussion on the findings. Ask students what they saw living on the tree's trunk and branches. Did they find any of the examples that you showed them earlier? What are different ways that animals and other plants depend on trees to live?

PART B: LIFE IN A TREE

1 Take students outside and show them several trees in the same area. Ask: Can you name some plants and animals that depend on these trees? How might we learn which plants and animals depend on or use them in some way? Point out that one way would be to look carefully at and around the tree and take an inventory of what they find.

2 Divide the students into groups of 2–3 and assign each group a specific tree part—trunk, branches, leaves, roots, etc. Challenge students to determine which plants and animals (including humans) visit the tree, live on it, and live in it. Encourage students to look for supporting clues, such as chewed leaves, bark holes, or carved initials.

3 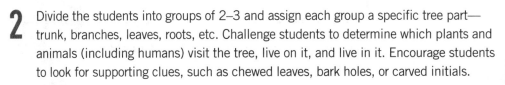 **NONLINGUISTIC REPRESENTATIONS** Distribute materials for journaling and close observation (see Materials). Have students draw, take pictures, or otherwise document all the plants and animals they find, especially those they cannot identify or have questions about. Invite them to use their sense of hearing to find plants and animals.

4 Optional: Use field guides to help students identify the organisms they find.

5 Using the What's the Connection? student page, have students identify how each plant and animal observed in Step 3 benefits from the tree, and how it affects the tree. They may need to conduct more research about the plants and animals they observed.

6 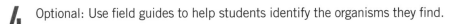 **HIGHER-ORDER THINKING** Have students organize their collected observations, data, and information into a booklet, portfolio, or other format.

7 Invite teams to share their observations with the whole group. Discuss:

- What plants, animals, or animal signs did you find on the tree's trunk?
- What did you find in the tree's branches?
- How does the tree benefit these plants and animals?
- Which of these plants and animals seem to harm the tree? Why do you think so?
- Do any of the plants and animals you observed seem to benefit the tree? In what ways?
- How might the plants and animals that live on a tree both need and affect the tree?

VARIATION: URBAN ENVIRONMENTS

1 If you do not have access to trees or shrubs, use human-built structures instead. For example, buildings provide habitat for many plants and animals (in addition to humans).

2 Have students work in small teams to observe living things inside and outside human-built structures, such as houses, buildings, bridges, schools, libraries, or community centers. Have student consider what aspects of the structure attract and support those organisms. Create a graphic organizer for inside versus outside the structure, and ask students list all the plants and fungi that grow on the inside (e.g., house plants, potted trees, mold, mildew) or the outside (e.g., moss, grass, lichens) and all the animals that make their homes on the inside (e.g., people, cats, dogs, goldfish, cockroaches, mice, houseflies) and outside (e.g., birds, ants, bees).

SAMPLE GRAPHIC ORGANIZER

	INSIDE	OUTSIDE
Plants		
Animals		

3 Have students consider how all those living things depend on the structure and how the structure is affected by them. Invite students to organize and share their observations as described in Steps 5–7 in Part B, adapting the questions for human-built structures.

ACADEMIC STANDARDS

SCIENCE	ENGLISH LANGUAGE ARTS
Practices	**Practices**
• Analyzing and interpreting data	• Speaking and listening: comprehension and collaboration
Concepts	• Speaking and listening: presentation of knowledge and ideas
• Biodiversity and humans	
• Natural resources	
• Patterns	

ASSESSMENT

Ask students to

- Conduct an imaginary interview with a tree (providing both questions and answers) or tell a story from a tree's perspective. These pieces should reveal how different plants and animals both depend on and affect trees.

- Explain how a plant or animal they observed benefits from and affects the tree, using evidence they collected to substantiate their claims.

- Describe the ways in which local animals (provide a list of native amphibians, reptiles, mammals, insects, and birds) may be connected to trees.

ENRICHMENT

- Read aloud *Welcome to the Neighborwood* by Shawn Sheehy, *The Busy Tree* by Jennifer Ward, or another story about animals living in or around trees (see plt.org/myk8guide for suggestions). Have the students make costumes for the different animals, using construction paper and artificial feathers. Read the book again, allowing the students to act out the animals.

- Invite students to examine their tree (or structure) at other times during the year. Have them compare their findings from season to season or to create a "Tree (or Structure) Habitat" mural. (This can be done in conjunction with the activities Adopt a Tree or Bursting Buds.)

STUDENT PAGE

Tree Observation Bingo

NAME _____ DATE_____

Look for signs of plants and animals living in and around your tree. Mark each sign you find with an "X." Then, answer the questions.

Location of Tree: _____   **Type of Tree:** _____

Chewed Leaf 	**Bite Marks on Nut or Fruit** 	**Hole in Trunk or Base of Tree** 
Animal on Tree 	**Other Sign of Animal or Plant Living in Tree:** _____ _____	**Nest** 
Plant Growing on Tree 	**Insect Eggs** 	**Bird Flying Around Tree** 

I LOVE MY GREEN JOB!

CAREER CORNER

<u>WILDLIFE BIOLOGISTS</u> (buy-ALL-uh-jists) study wild animals and their habitats to find out what they need to live. They may watch animals in trees, forests, and other habitats.

STUDENT PAGE

NAME _____ DATE_____

1. How do the plants and animals that live in and around the tree use it? Name as many ways as you can.

- _____

- _____

- _____

- _____

- _____

- _____

2. How might the tree be helped or hurt by the plants and animals that live on it or around it?

- _____

- _____

- _____

- _____

- _____

- _____

CAREER CORNER

I LOVE MY GREEN JOB!

FOREST ECOLOGISTS (ee-CALL-uh-jists) are scientists who study how forest plants and animals depend on each other to live. They may also explore how these living things use air, soil, and water to stay alive.

Students are often surprised to learn how many different products we get from trees. Use this activity to help students learn just how much we depend on trees in our daily lives.

WE ALL NEED TREES

SUBJECTS
Science, English Language Arts, Social Studies

PLT CONCEPTS
1.4, 2.5

STEM SKILLS
Collaboration, Leadership, Nature-based Design

DIFFERENTIATED INSTRUCTION
Cooperative Learning, Hands-on Learning, Personal Connections, Student Voice

MATERIALS
Small branch, wooden product, tree cookie (a cross-section from a tree trunk or branch), photos of tree products, three chart paper sheets. Optional: Tape or glue.

Variation: A variety of products from trees (see Getting Ready).

TIME CONSIDERATIONS
Preparation: 1 hour
Activity: 30 minutes
Variation: 40 minutes

OBJECTIVES

Students will

- Examine various products and determine which ones are made from trees.
- Classify products that come from trees.

BACKGROUND

Many products that we use are derived from trees. Wood is the most obvious. It provides lumber for houses, furniture, picture frames, paintbrush handles, and many more items. **Cellulose** is the major component of wood and most other plant fiber. Cellulose is used to make paper and paper products, including books, wrappers, cereal boxes, newspapers, and so on. It is also an ingredient in many other products.

Many other products come from trees in a less obvious way. For example, baseballs are made with a cork core surrounded by rubber. See the *"Wood" You Believe It Comes from Trees?* box for more examples.

Sustainably managed forests are a renewable source of raw materials. As trees regenerate and grow, they provide new wood, bark, sap, and other materials. They also provide services such as clean water and air, wildlife habitat, and carbon storage. Sustainable forestry involves a renewable cycle of planting after harvest and ensuring that forests are healthy, productive, and provide multiple benefits throughout their lifetime.

GETTING READY

- Collect photos of example tree products, one per student. Aim to get approximately equal numbers of three product categories: wood, food, and paper.

- In different parts of the room, display a large picture (or actual product) to represent each of the three categories. For example, a chair could represent wood products, an apple could represent food products, and a newspaper could represent paper products.

- Make a chart for each of the three categories, with a label and a picture to go along with it. Leave room for students to add their photos, if desired. Post charts around the room.

- For the Variation, collect 5–10 products from trees, using the *"Wood" You Believe It Comes from Trees?* list for ideas. You may want to include a few products that are not from trees, such as bamboo chopsticks, cotton balls, a plastic water bottle, peanuts, or raisins, to show your students. Make copies of the Tree Treasures student page.

FOREST FACT

did you know?

According to the U.S. Forest Service, forests and forest products in the United States offset nearly 16% of the country's carbon dioxide emissions by storing over 850 million metric tons of carbon per year.

"WOOD" YOU BELIEVE IT COMES FROM TREES?

Wood Products
- Fuel: Wood and charcoal
- Furniture
- Lumber
- Packaging
- Particle board
- Planks
- Plywood
- Wood panel veneers

Bark Products
- Cinnamon
- Cork
- Drugs and oils
- Dye
- Tannin (used for curing leather)

Cellulose Products
- Carpeting
- Cellophane
- Fiber board
- Imitation leather
- Paper products:
  » Books
  » Building paper
  » Industrial paper
  » Magazines
  » Newspaper
  » Toilet paper
  » Wrapping paper
  » Writing paper
- Rayon and other fabrics
- Shatterproof glass
- Sunscreen lotion
- Thickening agent (in shampoo)

Sap Products (Gums and Resins)
- Adhesives
- Chewing gum
- Cleaning fluids
- Cosmetics
- Crayons
- Electrical insulation
- Flavoring
- Paint thinner
- Perfumes
- Printing ink
- Rubber products
- Shoe polish
- Soap
- Sugar and syrup
- Varnishes
- Waxes

Fruit, Leaves, and Seed Products
- Cider
- Dye
- Fruits (apples, mangoes, oranges, etc.)
- Nuts (almonds, pine nuts, cola nuts, etc.)
- Spices (bay leaves, nutmeg, mace, etc.)

Note: Some of the products listed aren't always—or exclusively—made from trees.

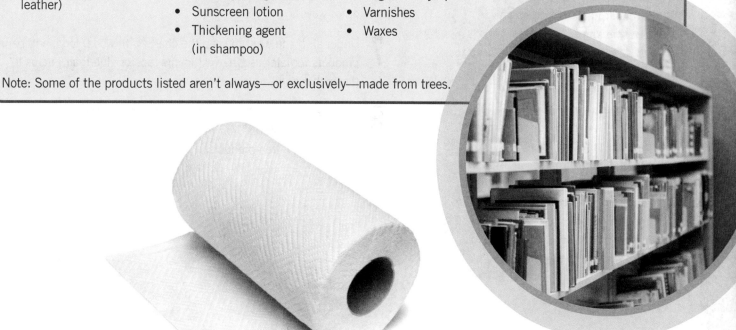

1  **PERSONAL CONNECTIONS** Ask students whether they've used anything today that comes from trees.

2 Hold up a small branch and a wooden object. Ask where each of these comes from. If you have one, show students a tree cookie (cross section), and explain that it also comes from a tree. Have students see and feel the texture of the wood. Can they identify similar texture and grain patterns in various wood products? Do they recognize that those products come from trees?

3 Ask students if they know where paper comes from. Describe in simple terms how trees become paper. (Paper is made by cutting down trees and chopping the wood into very small pieces, which are boiled in water until they turn into a mushy pulp. The pulp is then poured onto a wire mesh and squeezed with rollers to press out all the water.) Ask students if they can think of other things that come from trees.

4 Explain that wood, food, and paper are three of the main kinds of products people get from trees. Hand out the photos you collected. Explain that each photo shows one of these three important types of tree products. Tell the students to decide what type of tree product they have: wood, food, or paper. Then give them time to stand under the picture representing the appropriate category.

5 Have students look at the objects in each category and describe what properties the objects have in common. For example, the food items taste good, can be chewed, and provide nutrition.

6 **STUDENT VOICE** Invite students to come up with other ways to categorize the products, and then sort the products by those other ways.

7 Optional: If you want to keep the charts with wood, food, and paper products for later use, have students tape or glue their photos to these charts.

8 Ask if anybody can think of other products that come from trees. Then refer to *"Wood" You Believe It Comes from Trees?* to discuss some unusual tree products.

TAKE IT OUTSIDE

Challenge students to go on an outdoor scavenger hunt for tree products. In advance, scout the area to determine what students might find. Then, put together a list of objects for them to look for, including a few challenging items. Divide the group into pairs or small teams. Be sure to identify and communicate boundaries for the exercise before encouraging students to find as many items as they can. Inspire some friendly competition by offering a tree product reward to the team that finds the most!

VARIATION: GRADES 3–5

1 Designate four different stations around the room (or more, depending on the size of your group). Distribute the tree products you collected at various stations and label each one with a number.

2 Divide the group into four teams and tell them that each team will work together to determine which of the products are made from trees. All team members must agree and be able to explain why.

3 **COOPERATIVE LEARNING** Assign the following roles to the students in each group:

- Leader: Make sure that everyone in the team has an opportunity to speak as they try to reach decisions.
- Recorder: Record the team's decisions.
- Timekeeper: Make sure the team stays on track and gets everything accomplished in the time allowed.
- Reporter: Report their team's findings to the rest of the group.

4 **HANDS-ON LEARNING** Have the teams move around to the different stations and examine the products. After they have decided if an item comes from trees, they should record it on the Tree Treasures student page. Everyone on their team must agree with the decision and should be able to explain why each item is on their list.

> ⚠ **SAFETY CHECK!** Do not let students open any of the product containers.

5 Have Reporters share their lists with the rest of the group. Discuss the diversity of tree products. Ask students to explain why they included (or did not include) certain products. Students should realize by the end of the discussion that most (or all) of the products shared come from trees.

ACADEMIC STANDARDS

SCIENCE

Practices
- Analyzing and interpreting data

Concepts
- Natural resources
- Structure and properties of matter
- Patterns

ENGLISH LANGUAGE ARTS

Practices
- Speaking and listening: presentation of knowledge and ideas

Concepts
- Reading informational text: key ideas and details

SOCIAL STUDIES

Practices
- Applying disciplinary concepts

Concepts
- Economics: exchange and markets

ASSESSMENT

Ask students to

- Sort pictures of objects into three groups: wood, food, and paper.
- Identify two items (at school or home) from each category: wood, food, and paper.
- Write their responses to a question related to tree products, such as "What is something in our classroom that comes from trees, and how do you know?"

See Appendix K: Making a Scientific Argument for a sample template for sharing their responses.

ENRICHMENT

- Using self-stick notes or nametags, write the names of a variety of different tree products and attach one to each student's back. Tell students they must figure out the product on their backs by asking each other "yes" or "no" questions. Each student can ask another person only two questions about their own product before they must move on to another person. For example, "Is my product used at school?"
- Bring in a pruned tree limb with lots of branches, a discarded Christmas tree, or a small potted tree. Have the students decorate it with pictures of tree products. They can draw their own pictures, use the pictures from the activity, or find pictures on the internet or in magazines. They can also use actual small tree products, such as pencils, paper towel rolls, nuts, fruit, cellophane, etc. to decorate the tree.
- Discuss how a new awareness of tree products might affect students' behavior. For example, how might students and their families choose more sustainably harvested forest products to use at home?
- Try papermaking. See the activity Make Your Own Paper.

NAME _____ DATE_____

Look at each object and decide whether it comes from a tree. In the chart below, write the item number and your team's answer (yes, no, partly, or maybe). Explain your answer.

ITEM NUMBER	FROM A TREE?	EXPLAIN

CAREER CORNER

I LOVE MY GREEN JOB!

LUMBERMILL WORKERS cut logs into lumber for building materials such as flooring, windows, and doors. These workers may use computers to figure out the best way to cut each log and how to reduce wood waste.

ACTIVITY	3-5	K-2	6-8
Charting Biodiversity	O		
Discover Diversity	O	⇕	
Every Drop Counts	O		
Every Tree for Itself	O		⇕
Fallen Log	O		
Get Outside!	O	⇕	
My Green Future	O		
Peek at Packaging	O		⇕
Poet-Tree	O		⇕
Signs of Fall	O		⇕
Soil Builders	O		
Tree Cookies	O	⇕	
Tree Factory	O	⇕	
Tree ID	O		
Trees for Many Reasons	O		⇕
Trees in Trouble	O		⇕
Water Wonders	O		
Web of Life	O		

O = Core Activity ⇕ ⇕ = Grade-Level Variation

For more details, see Grade Level in the At-a-Glance Index.

GRADES
3-5
ACTIVITIES

explore your environment

Students explore the amazing diversity of life on Earth and discover how plants and animals are adapted for survival. This activity helps students understand why there are so many different species and teaches them the value of biodiversity.

CHARTING BIODIVERSITY

SUBJECTS
Science, English Language Arts

PLT CONCEPTS
1.1, 2.3

STEM SKILLS
Cooperation, Investigation, Organization

DIFFERENTIATED INSTRUCTION
Cooperative Learning, Higher-order Thinking, Literacy Skills, Student Voice

MATERIALS
Paper lunch bags or other containers (three per pair of students), resources on animals.

TIME CONSIDERATIONS
Preparation: 30 minutes

Activity: 50 minutes, plus time for research

OBJECTIVES

Students will

- Organize different species of plants and animals according to their physical characteristics.

- Determine how certain characteristics help species adapt to environmental conditions.

BACKGROUND

See the Background for the activity Discover Diversity.

GETTING READY

- Make one copy of the Match-Up Cards and Biodiversity Match-Up student pages for each pair of students.

- Find resources that students can use to research local wildlife, including websites, field guides, or other books. For a few places to start, see the resources for this activity at plt.org/myk8guide.

- See the Spice of Life game in the Enrichment section for an adapted activity that doesn't involve student research.

FOREST FACT

did you know

In the United States, roughly two thirds of at-risk and endangered species rely on private forestlands. Foresters employ sustainable practices to maintain or increase forest biodiversity by reforesting areas, restoring threatened species and habitats, and controlling invasive species.

DOING THE ACTIVITY

1 Ask students to name a wild animal that lives near them, such as a squirrel, a robin, or a spider. Encourage them to think about what characteristics—or adaptations—the animal possesses that might help it live where it does. For example, squirrels can climb trees, which enables them to gather acorns and other nuts for food. Point out another type of environment (such as forest, ocean, or desert) and ask what different kinds of characteristics animals living there might need.

2 Explain that students will learn how animals in different environments are adapted to their environments. Divide the students into pairs. Give each pair copies of the student pages and three lunch bags (or other containers). Have the students label the bags as follows:

- Where I Live
- How I Move
- What I 'Wear'

LITERACY SKILLS Make sure that students understand all the words on the student page.

3 Have students cut out the individual squares in the first column of the Match-Up Cards student page and put them into the bag labeled "Where I Live." Then have them cut out the squares from the second column and place them in the "How I Move" bag. The squares from the third column, which include different types of animal coverings, go into the "What I 'Wear'" bag. Have them shake the bags to mix up the squares.

4 To start, have one member of each pair take a square from each bag. Have students write the words in the top row of the Biodiversity Match-Up student page. They should take turns doing this until all the bags are empty.

5 COOPERATIVE LEARNING Explain to the students that they will complete the last columns of their charts by filling in the name of an animal species that has all three of the characteristics listed in a row. For example, if a row lists *forest, the ability to fly*, and *exoskeleton*, the students should do research to find one or more examples of an animal living in the forest that has these two adaptations. (A good example would be a forest-dwelling insect such as a katydid.) For each animal, they should also identify how that species is especially suited, or adapted, for the environment in which it lives.

6 Give the students time to research animals and fill in their charts. If they are not able to find an animal that fits a particular combination (for example, if the chart requires them to find an animal with fur that flies and lives in the water), allow them to pick a different characteristic for one of the columns.

7 HIGHER-ORDER THINKING After they've finished their research, have the students present their findings to the rest of the group. For each species, students should be prepared to say how that species is especially suited, or adapted, for the environment in which it lives.

VARIATION: PLANT ADAPTATIONS

1 STUDENT VOICE Have students do the activity using plants instead of animals. The group should decide on three categories for identifying plants, such as "Where It Lives," "How It Reproduces," "How It Depends on People and Other Animals," or "How It Protects Itself." Pairs should label their three bags with the categories they choose.

2 Students then should make four cards for each category. For example, if they choose the category "How It Reproduces," they could make cards for "Has Tasty Fruit" (for spreading seeds), "Has Bright Flowers" (for attracting pollinators), "Has Seeds That Float" (and can be carried by the wind or water), or "Grows New Plants from Roots" (for plants like ivy). They should put these cards in the appropriate bags.

3 Each pair should make a blank chart similar to the Biodiversity Match-Up student page, with plant categories instead of the animal ones. Each partner takes a turn picking a set of three cards from the bags, while the other partner fills in the appropriate words on the chart. Together, they should think of or research a plant that has those three characteristics.

TAKE IT OUTSIDE

Invite students to bring magnifying lenses and journals outside to record their observations of an animal. Encourage them to locate one, observe it up close, and draw a picture of it. They should also note other observations, such as the animal's behavior. (Depending on your site, students are most likely to find insects or small invertebrates like ants, pill bugs, or worms, but they may also find birds, mammals, or other animals.) Challenge students to determine which of the animal's characteristics or adaptations might help it to survive, grow, and reproduce. You may have students observe plants as a different option.

ACADEMIC STANDARDS

SCIENCE	ENGLISH LANGUAGE ARTS
Practices	**Practices**
• Obtaining, evaluating, and communicating information	• Reading informational text: integration of knowledge and ideas
Concepts	• Speaking and listening: presentation of knowledge and ideas
• Structure and function	

ASSESSMENT

Ask students to

- Look at the list of animals presented by the entire group and sort them into categories according to where those animals live and how they move.

- Choose three organisms and explain how they are suited to their environment.

ENRICHMENT

- Have the students use the cards to play a Spice of Life game.

  » Teams of two play against one another. Put the cards (plant or animal) into the appropriate bags from the activity.

  » Have students create six additional cards that say "Wild Card" and add two to each bag.

  » To play, each team should draw a card from each bag. The opposing team must try to think of an animal or plant that has all the characteristics printed on the cards. If a team pulls a wild card, they can pick any characteristic they want, provided it fits the category of the bag it came from.

  » Younger students can pick just one card per play and think of a plant or animal with that trait. They can alternate the bag from which they pick on each turn.

  » Develop rules for dealing with disputes. For example, if one team disagrees with another team's answer, they can look up the plant or animal in question to determine who is right.

  » Have the students keep track of their scores. A good answer wins one point, and a poor answer or no answer gets no points.

  » When the bags are empty, the game is over. Have the students add up their points to see which team is the winner.

- Invite students to "engineer an animal" for a specific environment. First, have them identify the environment and think of characteristics that might help an animal survive there. For example, forest animals might have physical structures that help them climb trees, like sharp claws or long limbs, or abilities to make use of limbs, branches or leaves, like prehensile tails or stomachs that can digest leaves. Challenge students to design and create a model of an animal characteristic that has at least one moving part, and to explain how that structure would increase the animal's chance of survival. Provide materials for students to use, such as egg cartons, paper clips, chenille sticks, scratch paper, etc.

- Explore cultural diversity by finding different common names (based on region or language) for the plants and animals that students researched in the activity. For example, depending on where you live, a pill bug may be called roly poly or tater bug. And a yellow poplar may be called tulip tree or tulip poplar.

- Explore adaptations of tree species that live in different environments. For example, palm trees that live in dry areas have spiny trunks that discourage animals from eating their leaves and fruit, and many tropical rainforest trees have leaves with "drip tips" that enable rain to run off quickly, reducing fungal and bacterial growth.

STUDENT PAGE

NAME _____ DATE_____

Where I Live	How I Move	What I 'Wear'
GRASSLAND	**SWIM**	**EXOSKELETON**
DESERT	**BURROW**	**FEATHERS**
FOREST	**CRAWL, HOP, WALK, OR RUN**	**SCALES OR MOIST SKIN**
WATER	**FLY OR GLIDE**	**FUR**

CAREER CORNER

I LOVE MY GREEN JOB!

NATURE PHOTOGRAPHERS help to document elements of our natural world with photos and video. They sometimes travel to remote areas, where they patiently wait to capture the perfect moment depicting wildlife and nature.

NAME _____ DATE_____

Where I Live	How I Move	What I 'Wear"	Who Am I?	How I Am Suited to Where I Live

CAREER CORNER

WILDLIFE CONSERVATIONISTS (con-sir-VAY-shun-ists) are scientists who study wild animals and their habitats. Wildlife conservationists may help control diseases and harmful insects to keep wildlife habitats healthy.

Students imagine that they are visitors from outer space, viewing life on Earth for the first time. By describing in minute detail all the life they find in a small plot of land, they will become more aware of the diversity and abundance of life on Earth and will better understand its importance.

DISCOVER DIVERSITY

SUBJECTS
Science, English Language Arts, Social Studies, Visual Arts

PLT CONCEPTS
1.2, 2.4, 4.1

STEM SKILLS
Investigation, Nature-based Design, Organization, Technology Use

DIFFERENTIATED INSTRUCTION
Cooperative Learning, Higher-order Thinking, Nonlinguistic Representations

MATERIALS
Hula hoops or stakes and rope, string, or strips of cloth for marking study plots; clipboards or other writing surface. Optional: tweezers and magnifying glasses, cameras, drawing paper, other materials for presentations.

TIME CONSIDERATIONS
Preparation: 25 minutes

Activity: One to two 50-minute periods

OBJECTIVES

Students will

- Describe plants and animals they find in a study site.
- Compare their data with others in the group to conclude what factors influence both abundance and a lack of diversity.
- Explain the value of having a diversity of life forms in a particular ecosystem.

BACKGROUND

Living organisms can be found just about everywhere on Earth: from the equator to the poles, from dry deserts to freezing water, from undersea thermal vents to miles in the air, and from lush forests to city sidewalks. Anywhere you look, in almost any environment you can imagine, there are organisms that are adapted to living there.

One of Earth's most valuable resources is its **biodiversity**, the variety of species that live there. Biodiversity is reflected in the wide range of ecosystems and species on Earth and in the genetic diversity within and among species. A **species** is a group of organisms classified together on the basis of genetic structure, that typically have a similar appearance and characteristic behaviors. To be considered the same species, organisms that reproduce sexually must be able to interbreed and produce fertile offspring.

Biologists estimate that Earth's current biodiversity is somewhere between 10 million and 1 trillion different species, living in a variety of ecological communities. We can't know for sure how many species there are because many live in inaccessible habitats, are too small to see, are hard to find, or live inside other living things. So far, biologists have classified about 1.7 million species and only have detailed knowledge of about one-third of those. We have not yet studied the roles and interactions of many millions of species.

FOREST FACT

did you know

Forests have the world's largest reservoir of plant and animal species and are home to 80% of the world's terrestrial biodiversity.

Humans, like other organisms, depend on this biological richness to live. Diversity within and among species provides us with a variety of food, wood, fibers, energy, raw materials, chemicals, and medicines and contributes hundreds of billions of dollars yearly to the world economy. Every species on Earth today represents stored genetic information that allows the species to adapt to certain changes in environmental conditions. We can think of biodiversity as nature's "insurance policy" against disasters, such as volcanic eruptions, floods, invasive species, or changing climate. A disaster might destroy wildlife species living in a particular area, but other individual species will survive and eventually repopulate that area.

CLASSIFYING LIFE ON EARTH

To classify Earth's organisms, scientists use a hierarchical system known as taxonomic classification. The broadest category is domain, followed by kingdom and then phylum, class, family, order, genus, and species. Species is the most specific category. In referring to a particular species, scientists use a scientific name that is made up of the genus and species names. For example, the scientific name for the human species is *Homo sapiens*, the genus name (*Homo*) and the species name (*sapiens*). Taxonomic classification uses Latin names and it is a universal standard: scientists around the world who speak different languages all use the same scientific names for species.

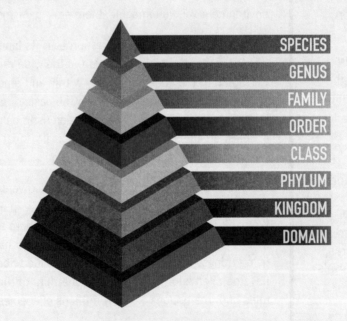

Recent advances in genetic sequencing are enabling scientists to learn more and more about the relationships among organisms. As scientists learn more, their classification of organisms changes.

The current classification system includes three domains and six kingdoms. The three domains are Archaea, Bacteria, and Eukarya. The kingdom Archaebacteria (ancient bacteria) is within the domain Archaea and the kingdom Eubacteria (true bacteria) is within the domain Bacteria. The other four kingdoms—Protista, Fungi, Plantae (plants), and Animalia (animals)—all lie within the domain Eukarya.

In any ecosystem, living (biotic) and nonliving (abiotic) elements constantly interact. For example, most plant species depend on soil for water and nutrients, and they need sunlight to manufacture food through photosynthesis. Some plants also depend on animals to pollinate their flowers, disperse their seeds, and fertilize the soil in which they live. Animals, in turn, depend on plants for food and shelter. Some animal species also depend on other animals for food and protection.

By looking at a real ecosystem in action, students will begin to understand how the intricate parts of that system work together to support the plant and animal species living there and help to maintain biodiversity.

GETTING READY

- Find an area at or near your site where you can set up study plots that are 2 feet x 2 feet (0.6 m x 0.6 m) to 4 feet x 4 feet (1.2 m x 1.2 m) in size. You can adjust the size to suit students' ages and your conditions. Try to find study plots that differ from each other in terms of plant type, sun or shade, and so on. For example, one plot might be in the shade of a tree, another on a grassy lawn, and another right next to the building. You can even put a study plot in an asphalt parking lot or on a sidewalk to show students that nature can be found anywhere (for example, they can find ants or small plants in the cracks). Obtain any necessary permission to use the study site.

 SAFETY CHECK! Check for any hazards at the study site, such as deep holes, sharp objects, or poisonous or irritating plants. (See Appendix B: Tips for Teaching Outdoors for more information about how to teach outside safely.)

- Measure and mark one study plot for each team of four students, using hula hoops or stakes driven into the ground with string or ribbon between them.

- Make copies of the Data for Deevoid student page.

- Depending on your time and setting, you may have students create more elaborate or simpler presentations of their findings. Gather any presentation materials or tools that they need.

- If you are in an urban area, see Appendix C: Urban Outlook for ideas for teaching this and other PLT activities with city kids.

DOING THE ACTIVITY

1 Invite students to imagine that they are scientists from a planet called Deevoid. Deevoid has an atmosphere, climate, and soil make-up that are similar to those on Earth, but it doesn't have many plants and animals. Scientists on Deevoid believe that the planet Earth is rich with a variety of life forms. To see whether that is true, several teams of scientists are on an exploratory mission to Earth. By studying Earth, the Deevoid scientists hope to discover ways to improve the quality of life on their own planet.

2 Explain that each team of scientists will record and describe all the life forms they find in a study plot here on planet Earth. When the scientists go back to Deevoid, they will present their findings at a scientific conference. Since Earth organisms are completely unknown back on Deevoid, the scientists must make careful observations while on Earth so they can describe their findings properly. They do not need to know the Earth names of the plants or animals they find.

3 Divide the group into teams of four students. Assign each team a study plot and hand out copies of the Data for Deevoid student page. Discuss safe and appropriate outdoor behavior.

 SAFETY CHECK! Point out any possible hazards of the site. Tell students to avoid handling any creatures, and to be especially careful of any animals that could bite or sting. They may turn over rocks and logs, but should not slide their hands under rocks and logs without looking. Also explain how to avoid any irritating or poisonous plants. Finally, remind the students not to harm any plants or animals, and to leave things exactly the way they found them.

4 Before they start their investigation, each team should describe their study plot and predict what forms of life, if any, they expect to find, writing this information on the student page.

5 **HANDS-ON LEARNING** Allow students ample time to examine their plots and record their data. Encourage students to look for signs of animals (such as chewed leaves or twigs, nests, or eggs) in addition to animals themselves.

6 **NONLINGUISTIC REPRESENTATIONS** Students may wish to use photos or videos to enhance their data collection.

7 **COOPERATIVE LEARNING** Ask each team to prepare a presentation of their observations. They may use drawing materials, video, or another form of expression. Their presentation should include a map that indicates the locations of plants and animals (or their signs) on their study plot, which they can draw by hand or using graphics software.

8 After all teams have presented their findings, discuss the group's findings:

- Did any organisms appear in several of the plots? Were any organisms unique to a single plot?

- Did some plots have a wider variety of animals than other plots?

- If so, what might be the reason for this?

- What environmental conditions do you think affect the number and kinds of organisms in a plot? (Guide students toward the observation that, in general, areas with a greater variety of plants have a greater variety of animals. For example, a plot on the edge of a wooded area would tend to have a greater variety of insects than a plot on a lawn.)

9 **HIGHER-ORDER THINKING** Ask students what they think the word "biodiversity" means and have them share their thoughts about why it might be a good thing—both in nature and for human communities. Discuss:

- What factors can increase or decrease biodiversity?

- Why might a lack of biodiversity be a problem?

- How does biodiversity on Earth benefit people?

- How might the people of Deevoid improve their planet's biodiversity? (Answers will vary but could include increasing the abundance and variety of vegetation, improving the soil, helping existing ecosystems recover from disruptions, and so on. Students may suggest bringing plants and animals from Earth to Deevoid to increase its biodiversity. Rather than dismissing this suggestion outright, encourage them to think about what happens here on Earth if a non-native animal is introduced to a new ecosystem, perhaps sharing an example of an invasive species in your area. Help students understand that this wouldn't be a good idea.)

- What additional information would students like to have about Deevoid to help determine steps that Deevoid could take to increase its biodiversity?

VARIATION: GRADES K–2

1 Give each pair of students a 3-foot (0.9-m) piece of string and two magnifying glasses. Have pairs place their strings on the ground somewhere in the study site. Alternatively, you could give each pair a wire hanger stretched into a circular shape, and have students place it on the ground.

2 Invite students to take a mini-hike along the mini-trail created by their string or inside the hanger. They should sit or kneel next to the string or hanger and "walk" with their fingers.

3 **HANDS-ON LEARNING** As students go on their mini-hike, encourage them to use their magnifying glasses to look for plants, animals, or interesting features along the way. Ask these questions:

- What are the plants like? Are they close together or far apart?

- What are the animals doing? Do you see any animals eating plants? How else do animals use the plants?

- What do you see animals doing with other animals?

4 Encourage pairs to share the highlights of their hike with the group. Challenge the group to identify what organisms and features are similar and what are unique among the various sites. What might explain some of the differences?

ACADEMIC STANDARDS

SCIENCE

Practices
- Analyzing and interpreting data
- Obtaining, evaluating, and communicating information

Concepts
- Biodiversity and humans
- Patterns
- Cause and effect

ENGLISH LANGUAGE ARTS

Practices
- Speaking and listening: presentation of knowledge and ideas
- Language: vocabulary acquisition and use

SOCIAL STUDIES

Practices
- Evaluating sources and using evidence

Concepts
- Geography: geographic representations
- Geography: human–environment interactions

ASSESSMENT

Ask students to

- Compare their study plot to another one, identifying differences between the two plots in terms of both living and nonliving components. Have them explain what this comparison tells them about biodiversity.

- Make a presentation about their study plot (as in Step 7). Use the Assessment Checklist on the right to assess the thoroughness of student presentations and completed student pages.

- Consider improvements that could be made to the study site and draw pictures of what the site might look like if all suggestions were carried out.

ENRICHMENT

- Write names of plants and animals on separate slips of paper. Mix them up, and let each person pick one. Tell the students to imagine they have a pen pal on a different planet. Have them write letters to their pen pals describing the animals or plants they picked, without saying the name of the organisms. Afterward, have the students read their letters aloud to the rest of the group, while the group tries to guess the organism.

- Conduct further investigations of the study plots. For example, students might compare soil samples from different plots, use a field guide to identify some of the plants, collect seeds and soil from the plots to try growing plants, or create detailed maps of the site.

- Have students write a story or draw pictures from the perspective of a hiker on their mini-trail (from the Variation), focusing on observations of the plants and animals along the trail.

ASSESSMENT CHECKLIST

Note: Descriptions may be in words, pictures, or both.

STUDY PLOT
Description of study plot includes:
- ❏ General site description
- ❏ Weather
- ❏ Non-living things

PLANTS
Description of plants includes:
- ❏ Where found
- ❏ Shape, size, and color
- ❏ Smell or texture
- ❏ Flowers, seeds, fruits, or other visible plant parts

More thorough descriptions include:
- ❏ Vein patterns on leaves
- ❏ Leaf or stem arrangement, leaf margins
- ❏ Actual leaf or plant rubbings

ANIMALS
Description of animals includes:
- ❏ Where found
- ❏ Shape, size, and color
- ❏ Number of legs or body shape/type
- ❏ Behavior or movement pattern

More thorough descriptions include:
- ❏ Sounds
- ❏ Other details

PROJECT LEARNING TREE
An initiative of SFI

Data for Deevoid

NAME ____________________ DATE ____________

Describe your study plot:

____

____

List the nonliving things in your plot:

____

Predict what life forms (if any) you will find in your plot:

____

Use the chart below to record the life forms you find in your plot. Use words, pictures, or both.

Plant, Animal, or Other	Where Found	Size, Shape, and Color of Life Form (or Sign of Life Form)	Other Observations	Number Found (Count or Estimate)

CAREER CORNER

I LOVE MY GREEN JOB!

TOUR GUIDES are experts on a specific place or region. They may lead visitors to national parks, local trails, or museums. When they are guiding visitors on a trail, they point out animals, plants, and other features and answer questions about the area.

It's easy to waste water and even easier to take water for granted. Water pours out of our faucets as though it were endlessly available. But the truth is that the supply of good quality, fresh water is limited. Fortunately, we can all conserve water instead of wasting it. This activity will help your group cut back on water waste.

EVERY DROP COUNTS

SUBJECTS
Science, English Language Arts, Math, Social Studies

PLT CONCEPTS
2.1, 2.7, 4.6

STEM SKILLS
Investigation, Leadership, Problem Solving

DIFFERENTIATED INSTRUCTION
Cooperative Learning, Multiple Solution Pathways, Personal Connections

MATERIALS
Empty beverage container (half-gallon or two-liter bottle), paper and pencils, measuring cup or other container, art supplies.

TIME CONSIDERATIONS
Preparation: 15 minutes

Activity: Three or four 50-minute periods

OBJECTIVES

Students will

- Monitor how much water they use in a day.
- Describe how water is wasted and why it is important to conserve it.
- Design, implement, and evaluate a plan for saving water.

BACKGROUND

Our society uses a lot of water. We use water at home for washing, flushing, watering, cooking, and drinking. We also use water for utilities, industry, and agriculture.

Only about 0.3% of Earth's water is available as drinking water. The rest is either saltwater, frozen in polar ice caps and glaciers, or located too deep in the ground to extract. If the world's water supply were represented by 26 gallons (98.4 liters), then our usable supply of fresh water would be only half a teaspoon (0.003 liters). Although natural systems, like forests, can continually recycle this fresh water, the rate at which we use it is important and can help ensure that our water resources remain available.

In addition to the amount of water available, the quality of that water is also vitally important. Contaminants—from sewage to agricultural and industrial chemicals—can threaten the quality of the water supply and can harm human health.

The United States has one of the safest water supplies in the world. However, water quality varies from place to place, depending on the condition of the source from which it is drawn and the treatment it receives. The U.S. Environmental Protection Agency requires that public water suppliers provide an annual report to their customers on the quality of the local drinking water. This report, sometimes called a consumer confidence report, gives people information on the water source and any contaminants present in the water.

Half of the drinking water in the United States is groundwater, which is water that fills the spaces between rocks and soil particles underground. The biggest source of groundwater supplies is precipitation that has trickled down into the soil. This trickle-down process takes time, and groundwater that is deep underground may require hundreds of years to be replenished or recharged. If we don't pay attention to the rate at which we're using water, the rate of groundwater recharge could fall behind the rate at which it is being used.

Whether our water supplies come from groundwater or from lakes, reservoirs, or forests that filter surface water, using too much water too fast or contaminating water sources can cause problems for people and wildlife.

FOREST FACT

Trees and forests absorb rainfall, filtering water to refill aquifers. The U.S. Forest Service estimates that 80% of the nation's freshwater originates from forestland.

Dams, reservoirs, and wells are ways to store fresh water and try to increase its availability. But if everyone made an effort to conserve water by making a few changes in their daily routines, huge amounts of water could be saved. For example, by installing a low-flow showerhead, each person could save up to 5,000 gallons (18,925 liters) a year!

GETTING READY

- For Part A, make copies of the Water Use student page.
- For Part B, find out how much your school or other facility pays per gallon or unit of water. (In the United States, a "unit" of water is one hundred cubic feet or 748 gallons of water.)

DOING THE ACTIVITY

PART A: WATER WATCH

1. **PERSONAL CONNECTIONS** Early in the day, ask students how much water they think they use in a day at your school or site. Record answers where the entire group can see them. You may want to show students an empty beverage container (a half-gallon or two-liter bottle) and tell them how much water it holds so they can visualize amounts of water. How do students use water at your school or site? Do students think they use less than the amount in the container in a day? If more, how many times more?

You may use a *Group Predictions of Daily Water Use* chart like the one below to record students' predictions. You might also have students work in pairs to calculate the percentages of students who fall within various prediction ranges.

GROUP PREDICTIONS OF DAILY WATER USE

Gallons (or liters)	5	10	15	20	25	30	35	40	45
Number of students									

FORESTS AND DRINKING WATER

Many communities throughout the United States rely on forests for their freshwater needs. When they are sustainably managed, forests can help communities maintain high quality water supplies by:

- Trapping sediments and contaminants, stabilizing soils, and protecting water from the results of erosion.

- Capturing moisture from rain, snow, and fog, which helps to make more water available.

- Improving the ability of soils to filter and store water.

- Cushioning communities from landslides, floods, droughts, and other effects of a changing climate.

2 Ask students to come up with ideas for determining the amount of water they actually use. Suggest that they could monitor their water use for the day. Distribute copies of the Water Use student page and have students record the number of minutes (or number of times) they use water for the rest of the day.

3 The next day, have students calculate the rate at which water comes out of the water fountain and sink faucet. Turn on the water to a typical flow rate, time how long it takes the water to fill the half-gallon or two-liter bottle or other container, and convert this rate to gallons or liters per minute. (For younger students, you may want to figure these rates for them in advance.) Have students use these rates to help them calculate the amount of water they use during the day.

4 Share with students the average rate of water used per toilet flush, shower, etc., from the *Typical Water Uses* chart below, or have them determine this figure by looking at the rating printed on the fixtures.

TYPICAL WATER USES

Gallons (or liters)	APPROXIMATE VOLUME OF WATER	
	Conserving Method	**Typical Method**
Washing Hands	Turn water off while lathering: 1 gallon (3.8 liters)	Leave the water running 4 gallons (15 liters)
Getting a Drink	Use a bottle or cup: 0.1 gallon (0.4 liter)	Use a drinking fountain: 0.25 gallon (0.9 liter)
Toilet	Use a low-flush toilet: 1.3 gallons (4.9 liters) per flush	Use a conventional toilet: 5 gallons (19 liters) per flush
Brushing Teeth	Turn water off except to rinse mouth: 0.25 gallon (0.9 liter)	Leave the water running: 4 gallons (15 liters)
Shower	Use a low-flow showerhead: 2 gallons (7.8 liters) per minute	Use a conventional showerhead: 5 gallons (19 liters) per minute

5 Have students compare their calculations with the predictions they made earlier. Discuss the differences between the two.

6 ⬤➡ **MULTIPLE SOLUTION PATHWAYS** Using the background information, lead a discussion about the importance of conserving water and on having good quality water. Have students brainstorm a list of ways that they can personally cut down on water waste. They might also suggest water-saving devices or practices for their school or other facility.

7 Once again, have students monitor their water use during the day, this time applying the water-saving methods they identified. The next day, have them calculate how much water they used and how much they saved and discuss their findings with the rest of the group.

8 Challenge student teams to estimate how much water could be saved in one day if everyone in the school or at the site (including the staff) worked to conserve it. How much could they save in a year?

PART B: ACTION PLANS

1 ⬤➡ **COOPERATIVE LEARNING** Have students work in small teams to create different parts of an action plan for conserving water at your school or other site. For example:

- Team A: Research the feasibility of installing faucet aerators in restrooms.

- Team B: Research toilet tank displacement devices (if your toilets have tanks) or other water-saving devices.

- Team C: Investigate water waste (from leaky faucets, running toilets, and so on) and work on solutions to these problems.

- Team D: Research and present environmental, social, or economic reasons for adopting water-saving practices.

Each team should estimate how much water and money their part of the action plan would save, using the rate your school or site pays per unit of water (see Getting Ready).

2 Have teams present their action plans to the rest of the group. Help students make a final action plan that includes each of the components as well as a final estimate of savings.

3 Have students present their action plan to school administrators or to their guardians.

TAKE IT OUTSIDE

Approximately 30% of residential water is used outdoors. Take students on an excursion outside to identify potential ways to conserve water. For example, students might examine outdoor water faucets and hoses for potential leaks, check to see if lawns or fields are being overwatered, or look at gutters and downspouts to determine whether rainwater could be collected and reused. They could also identify places where trees could be planted, to help provide a "buffer" to a stream or drainage ditch that captures pollutants before they wash into the waterway.

ACADEMIC STANDARDS

SCIENCE

Practices
- Obtaining, evaluating, and communicating information
- Using mathematics and computational thinking
- Constructing explanations and designing solutions

Concepts
- Human impacts on Earth systems
- Cause and effect

ENGLISH LANGUAGE ARTS

Practices
- Speaking and listening: presentation of knowledge and ideas

Concepts
- Speaking and listening: comprehension and collaboration

MATH

Practices
- Reason abstractly and quantitatively
- Model with mathematics

Concepts
- Operations and algebraic thinking
- Measurement and data

SOCIAL STUDIES

Practices
- Applying disciplinary concepts
- Communicating conclusions and taking informed action

Concepts
- Civics: participation and deliberation
- Geography: human–environment interactions

ASSESSMENT

Ask students to

- Design a water conservation brochure or web page for the general public. Encourage students to come up with a catchy slogan and graphic that makes the case for why people should conserve water and how nature can help conserve water (for example, by planting trees). The brochure or web page can also provide information about local agencies or organizations concerned with water conservation.

- Present what they learned about water conservation to younger students. They might create posters, skits, or other presentations.

ENRICHMENT

- Use PLT's *GreenSchools Investigations* to conduct a school-wide project to monitor and reduce your school's water consumption. Visit plt.org/greenschools to access PLT's five *GreenSchools Investigations*, which are focused on energy, environmental quality, school site, waste and recycling, and water. Each investigation provides a blueprint for students to create greener and healthier learning environments.

- Encourage students to monitor their water use at home for a week. First, they should estimate their use; then they can compare their estimates to the amount listed on their family water bill.

- Begin a collection of water proverbs from around the world, such as: "We never know the worth of water till the well is dry" (from France), or "Any water in the desert will do" (from Saudi Arabia). Search the internet for other proverbs.

- Students can investigate the quality of their community's drinking water by reading their local water supplier's Consumer Confidence Report. The U.S. Environmental Protection Agency requires local water suppliers to make these reports available to their customers each year. Check your supplier's website or epa.gov/ccr.

NAME _____ DATE _____

Record your water use for one day to calculate the total water used.

	Number of minutes (or times) per day	Rate (gallons or liters per minute or per use)	Total gallons (or liters)
Washing hands			
Getting a drink			
Flushing the toilet			
Brushing teeth			
Taking a shower			
Leaking faucet			
Other: _____			
Other: _____			
Other: _____			
TOTAL GALLONS (OR LITERS)			

CAREER CORNER

I LOVE MY GREEN JOB!

<u>WATER MANAGEMENT PLANNERS</u> design water systems that bring cities, towns, and farms the water they need without harming the environment. They study the landscape and use problem-solving skills to plan the best system.

This fun and active modeling simulation reviews the conditions that trees need to live and grow, while also demonstrating that trees must compete to meet their needs.

EVERY TREE FOR ITSELF

SUBJECTS
Science, English Language Arts, Math

PLT CONCEPTS
1.3, 2.1, 2.2

STEM SKILLS
Collaboration, Investigation, Organization

DIFFERENTIATED INSTRUCTION
Hands-on Learning, Higher-order Thinking, Student Voice

MATERIALS
Tree trunk or branch cross-section, 8" x 10" (20 cm x 25 cm) pieces of paper or white paper plates, markers or crayons, and 4–6 different colors of math cubes, poker chips, or construction paper.

TIME CONSIDERATIONS
Preparation: 15 minutes

Activity: 50 minutes

OBJECTIVES

Students will

- Model how trees compete to meet their essential needs.
- Describe how varying amounts of light, water, and nutrients affect tree growth.

BACKGROUND

What do trees need so they can grow? Some of their needs are the same as those of people and other animals. For example, trees need air, water, and food. But while people and animals eat their food, trees get food in a different way. Trees produce their own "food" by using the **chlorophyll** in their leaves to capture energy from the sun in a process called **photosynthesis**, which uses carbon dioxide from the air and water from rainfall. Just as people and animals need vitamins for growth, trees also need mineral nutrients, such as nitrogen and phosphorus, which they get from the soil.

If trees don't get enough sunlight, air, water, or nutrients, they may grow slowly or even die. You can see how well a tree grew in different years of its life by looking at growth rings in a cross-section of its trunk. In general, wide rings indicate good conditions for growth (plenty of resources), while narrow rings often indicate less favorable growth conditions (drought, insect damage, lack of nutrients, or competition with other plants).

Forest managers use a variety of strategies to ensure that trees get what they need to thrive. A process called **thinning** selectively removes some of the trees, allowing more water, sunlight, and nutrients for the trees that remain. Controlling the underbrush and other vegetation also reduces competition for limited resources. Since different tree species need different conditions to thrive, forest managers make decisions based on the types of trees that are growing and regenerating.

While trees may compete for limited resources, they sometimes also share resources or "cooperate" through underground fungi networks. In a forest ecosystem, for example, fir trees and birch trees might exchange nutrients through a network of fungi that live among their roots.

FOREST FACT

did you know

Did you know that the closer trees get to the equator, the faster they grow? In fact, growth rings in tropical areas are often associated with wet and dry seasons, instead of with the four annual seasons that we recognize. This means that some tropical trees show multiple growth rings in one year!

GETTING READY

- Obtain one or more cross-sections of a tree trunk or branch. These are often available from tree-trimming services or forest product companies. To help prevent the spread of invasive species, make sure to source local samples. If you are unable to obtain a cross-section, draw one where the whole group can see it. See the activity Tree Cookies for a sample drawing.

- Gather 4–6 different colors of math cubes or poker chips—such as blue, yellow, white, green, black, and red—with enough of each color so that each student can have two cubes or chips. Keep the colors separate to start. As an alternative, cut 3" x 3" (7.6 cm x 7.6 cm) squares out of different colors of construction paper.

- Make copies of the Tree Needs student page.

- Optional: Laminate growth ring drawings (from Step 3) to use in Steps 4–10.

DOING THE ACTIVITY

1 Ask students what they think trees need in order to grow. (They might mention water, sunlight, air, or nutrients. You may want to point out that most of a tree's mass is made of carbon, which comes from the air.) Ask: What do you think would happen if a tree doesn't get all the things it needs? How might we find out?

2 Suggest that students construct a model to help them understand how and why a tree might not get all its needs met. Propose the following model that students can adapt, using their own ideas. For this model, students will personify trees in an active simulation.

3 ⊘ HANDS-ON LEARNING To start, show students the tree trunk or branch cross-section (or drawing), pointing out the growth rings. Explain that the number of rings indicates the age of the tree trunk or branch at the time it was cut. Invite students to imagine that they are trees, and to draw a cross-section representing their age in growth rings on a piece of paper or a paper plate.

4 Have students spread out about 3 feet (90 cm) apart and stand (or sit in chairs) on their cross-section paper or paper plate. Explain that their goal as trees is to meet as many of their needs as they can.

5 Equally distribute the "tree resources" (colored math cubes, poker chips, paper scraps, etc.) among the students so that the resources are about 1–2 feet (30–60 cm) apart. Explain that in this model, each item represents a tree need. Assign each color a need from the ones identified in Step 1 (e.g., blue = water, yellow = sunlight, white = carbon from the air, and green = a nutrient such as nitrogen or phosphorus).

6 Give a signal to start the first round. Have student trees reach with their branches (arms) to gather the resources they need. Tell students that they must stay planted on their cross-sections, just as trees are rooted to the ground. They should not slide the paper along the floor or step off it.

7 Have students use the student page to record the numbers of each need collected. Discuss the results using the following questions:

- How many of each resource did each tree get?

- Are any trees missing one of the resources that they need? (Trees can fall down or look tired and droopy if they didn't get at least one of each resource.)

- What might happen to a real tree that couldn't meet one of its needs? (It might grow slowly or eventually die. Point out that different species of trees have different needs; some tree species might need more water than others, for example.)

- What might happen if a tree gets too much sunlight, water, carbon, or nutrients? (Every species has optimum levels. Too much or too little can cause the tree to become stressed.)

8 For a second round, have student trees stand (or sit) closer together on their cross-section papers or paper plates. Gather the "tree resources" and disperse them again. Have students collect resources again and record their results.

9 Compare the results of this round with those of the first. Students may notice that each tree gathered fewer resources. Ask what this tells them about trees that grow close to each other. (Such trees compete for needs. Often, they don't grow as well as trees that are more widely separated from one another.) Ask if any trees "died" because they did not have access to one or more of their resources.

10 Student Voice Invite students to suggest ways to set up additional rounds. Try several more rounds, comparing the results each time. Possibilities include:

- Students stand or sit closer together, but only half the group participates.

- Use fewer water resources (representing a drought).

- Use fewer sunlight resources (representing lack of sunlight for young trees because of overcrowding).

- Use fewer nutrient resources (representing poor-quality soil).

- Add a new colored resource to represent fire (red) or an insect infestation (black), such as bark beetles or gypsy moths. How might this new element affect the trees?

PROJECT LEARNING TREE
An initiative of SFI

11  **HIGHER-ORDER THINKING** As before, students should record their results for each round. Discuss what the results might tell students about strategies for managing forests (for example, thinning trees that are too close together).

12 After completing the activity, talk about the simulation as a model. What is it a model of? What are the strengths and limitations of this model? Challenge students to identify which of the model components represent matter and which represent energy.

VARIATION: GRADES K–2

Conduct the activity with the following enhancements:

- After each round, have students draw a "growth ring" on their paper to represent how much their tree grew that year, based on the resources they collected.

- **HIGHER-ORDER THINKING** Have students graph their results of the activity. Discuss what the results tell them about strategies for managing forests. Ask them to support their ideas with evidence (data) from the model.

- Add career opportunities to the model. For example, have students stand close together and assign one student the role of "forester," who decides which trees should be removed to help other trees grow. What impact does tree removal have on the other trees and the availability of resources? Other forest careers might include "wildland firefighter," "arborist," or "wildlife biologist."

- Integrate current events into the model. For example, a changing climate is affecting forest health by altering the availability of certain tree resources. What will happen to trees if climate change reduces the availability of water or impacts nutrients? Discuss as a group.

TAKE IT OUTSIDE

Take students on a walk through the neighborhood, a local park, or other nearby location to look for examples of the different scenarios they modeled in the activity. For example, they may see groups of trees growing close together (and one or more not getting enough sunlight) or a tree planted close to the pavement (and not getting enough water or space). Encourage them to look for examples of other plants or animals getting their needs met.

ACADEMIC STANDARDS

SCIENCE	ENGLISH LANGUAGE ARTS	MATH
Practices	**Practices**	**Practices**
• Developing and using models	• Speaking and listening: comprehension and collaboration	• Reason abstractly and quantitatively
• Analyzing and interpreting data		• Model with mathematics
• Constructing explanations and designing solutions		**Concepts**
Concepts		• Measurement and data
• Adaptation		
• Organization for matter and energy flow in organisms		
• Energy and matter		
• Systems and system models		

ASSESSMENT

Ask students to

- Name three things that trees need to live and describe one factor that affects tree growth.

- Write a story (or create a skit) describing 10 years in a tree's life. They should be sure to include events that affect the tree both positively and negatively.

- Select a specific round of the activity that the group played together, and use the data gathered to write a one-paragraph description of the conditions they experienced as a tree at that time.

- Draw a cross-section of a tree that shows 10 years of growth and varying growing conditions for each of the years. Challenge students to explain the conditions represented in the rings drawn (such as drought, competition, fire, cool spring and summer, insect infestation, abundance or lack of basic resources, forest thinning, animal damage, etc.)

ENRICHMENT

- Assign quantity requirements and values to tree needs in the modeling activity. For example, if a tree collects three or more of each resource, it could achieve superior growth. Two of each resource could provide average growth, while one or fewer of each could represent poor growth. Using these values as a basis, have students determine how many trees are growing very well, showing average growth, and growing poorly for each round. Older students can graph the results.

- Portray competition using root circles. Explain that in many tree species, the diameter of the spread of the tree's roots is roughly equal to the tree's height or the size of the crown. Have students measure themselves and then make a root circle (using chalk or string) with a diameter equal to their height or the spread of their arms. Conduct the activity as described, but have students only gathering water that lies within their circle of roots. Repeat the activity using the root circle restriction, but this time have trees stand in clumps. Afterward, discuss the effect of root competition.

- Examine what pollinators (or other organisms) need to survive. For example, in a version called "Every Bee for Itself," students could search for pollen, nectar, and shelter or other things that bees need. Students could design a "bee dance" that features different moves for each resource they have located.

NAME _____ DATE _____

For each round of the activity, describe the conditions (such as "trees spread out"). Then record how many of each tree resource you got.

	Sunlight	Water	Carbon from the Air	Nutrients	Other Need:
ROUND 1 DESCRIPTION: trees spread out **1**					
ROUND 2 DESCRIPTION: **2**					
ROUND 3 DESCRIPTION: **3**					
ROUND 4 DESCRIPTION: **4**					
ROUND 5 DESCRIPTION: **5**					
ROUND 6 DESCRIPTION: **6**					
ROUND 7 DESCRIPTION: **7**					

CAREER CORNER

I LOVE MY GREEN JOB!

ARBORISTS (AR-bur-ists) are "tree doctors" who care for trees to make sure they stay healthy throughout their lives. Arborists must know many different tree species and understand what they each need to thrive.

It's amazing how many things live in and on rotting logs. In this activity, your students will become familiar with some of those organisms by observing fallen logs or other decomposing pieces of wood. They'll gain an understanding of how decomposition takes place and a better appreciation for microhabitats and communities.

FALLEN LOG

SUBJECTS
Science, English Language Arts, Visual Arts

PLT CONCEPTS
1.1, 1.2, 2.1

STEM SKILLS
Data Analysis, Investigation, Nature-based Design

DIFFERENTIATED INSTRUCTION
Cooperative Learning, Hands-on Learning, Higher-order Thinking

MATERIALS
Clear containers with lids (plastic tubs, glass jars, or plastic baggies), paper, pencils, clipboards or sheets of cardboard with binder clips. Optional: cameras; field guides on insects, spiders, trees, or nonflowering plants; magnifying glasses; boxes with magnifying lids.

TIME CONSIDERATIONS
Preparation: 15 minutes

Activity: 50 minutes

OBJECTIVES
Students will

- Identify some of the organisms that live in, on, and under fallen logs or rotting pieces of wood.

- Explain how organisms depend on dead wood for survival.

- Describe the process of decomposition.

BACKGROUND

Throughout their lives, trees collect nutrients from the environment and use them to grow new bark, wood, branches, leaves, and so on. When a tree dies, its nutrients are recycled back into the environment through decomposition. **Decomposers**, such as wood-eating insects, fungi, and bacteria, invade dead trees, or sometimes the rotting portion of living trees, and break down the materials. Here's a look at some common things your students may find on, in, and around dead wood.

THINGS GROWING ON DEAD WOOD
Any decaying wood is sure to have fungi, moss, lichens, and other organisms growing on it. Wildflower, tree, and other plant seeds that land on a soft, decomposed log may also sprout and grow. Plants and fungi absorb nutrients from the decaying wood and, as they grow, penetrate the wood and break it apart. Lichens, as they grow, release a weak acid that breaks down the wood. Moss keeps the log moist, making it a suitable place for other plants and animals to live.

WOOD MUNCHERS
Termites, sow bugs, carpenter ants, and wood roaches are all examples of detritivores (animals that eat dead organic material) that eat or tunnel through wood. Many of them also eat other kinds of vegetable matter, such as dead leaves. As they chew their way through the wood, they help break down the log.

PREDATORS ON THE PROWL
Predator invertebrates, such as centipedes, beetles, and spiders, feed on the sow bugs, millipedes, and other detritivores found on decaying wood. Both the predators and the detritivores are eaten by birds, skunks, and other animals that tear into logs to find food.

FOREST FACT

Did you know that the closer trees get to the equator, the faster they grow? In fact, growth rings in tropical areas are often associated with wet and dry seasons, instead of with the four standard seasons. This means that some tropical trees show multiple growth rings in one year!

HIDEOUTS AND NURSERIES

Many creatures depend on decaying logs as places to hide from predators or to shelter from the elements. Patent leather beetles, click beetles, and other animals may spend the winter inside a rotting log. Some beetles, wasps, slugs, and other animals lay their eggs in decomposing wood. Salamanders may rest in the relative coolness and dampness of a fallen log during the day and then hunt for food at night. As these animals burrow into the log, they also help to break it down.

GETTING READY

- Find a place that has several dead logs, large fallen limbs, decomposing tree stumps, or rotting pieces of lumber that are fairly close together. Ideally, the logs or pieces of wood should be at least eight inches (20 cm) across and should be in different stages of decomposition.

 SAFETY CHECK! Check for any hazards at the site, such as deep holes, sharp objects, or poisonous or irritating plants. Also make sure logs will not move in an unsafe way when students examine them.

- Obtain appropriate permission to do the activity at the site.

- You may want to use this activity during a trip to a park, nature center, vacant lot, or wooded area.

- Make copies of the Fallen Log Observations student page.

DOING THE ACTIVITY

1 Begin by asking students why forests aren't piled high with fallen trees, branches, and leaves. What happens to trees after they die? Ask students for their ideas on how they could investigate this question.

2 **COOPERATIVE LEARNING** Take students to the site you have located (see Getting Ready) and divide the group into teams of three or four. Have teams investigate a question, such as:

- Has this tree or piece of wood been dead a long time or a fairly short time?

- What kinds of animals live in or under the log or piece of wood?

- Where do animals that live in or on rotting wood get the food they need?

- What kinds of plants live in or on rotting wood?
- How can plants that live in or on rotting wood survive without soil?
- Do the same kinds of plants and animals that live in or on rotting wood live under rocks or in leaf litter?

Distribute the student page and encourage teams to write down the question they are investigating and specify what evidence they could look for to help answer it.

3 Have each team choose a log or piece of wood to study. The teams can double up, if needed. Tell students to examine their log, making sure to minimize any disturbance to living things.

4 **HANDS-ON LEARNING** Direct students to record each kind of plant or animal they observe, where it was found, and evidence of animal activity such as insect or woodpecker holes, spider webs, animal dens, animal tracks, piles of sawdust, or patterns in the wood under the bark. Also have them look for any additional evidence to help answer their investigation question. Students may place creatures in the containers temporarily to get a better look at them. If they can't identify something, they should make a sketch or take a picture of it.

SAFETY CHECK! Establish safety rules such as "Don't touch any place you cannot see" and "Don't go beyond (a certain point)." Students should disturb their log or piece of wood as little as possible while they examine it. They should put any creatures they find into the containers only briefly for examination. Students must return the creatures to the places where they were found as quickly as possible. They should make sure the log or wood is in its original position when they finish.

5 Back inside, have the students use their notes, sketches, and photos to identify any creatures they were unable to identify in the field. Also have them revisit their investigation question and determine whether they found an answer. Then have them present their findings to the rest of the group.

6 **HIGHER-ORDER THINKING**
Discuss the following questions as a group.

- What happens to trees after they die?
- How do the animals you found on or in the log interact with it? (They eat the decaying wood, use it as shelter from rain and cold weather, lay their eggs there, etc.)
- What is decomposition? Why is it important for logs like the one you studied to decompose? (Decomposition recycles the nutrients stored in the log.)
- How does the forest ecosystem benefit from a fallen log? (The log provides habitat for plants and animals that, in turn, become food for other creatures. As animals and plants break down the log, its stored nutrients become available for other plants and animals.)

ACADEMIC STANDARDS

SCIENCE	ENGLISH LANGUAGE ARTS
Practices	**Practices**
• Asking questions and defining problems	• Speaking and listening: presentation of knowledge and ideas
• Planning and carrying out investigations	• Speaking and listening: comprehension and collaboration
Concepts	
• Cycle of matter and energy transfer in ecosystems	
• Patterns	
• Energy and matter: flows, cycles, and conservation	

ASSESSMENT

Ask students to

- Draw and label a series of pictures that shows what happens to a fallen tree over many years. Their finished pictures should show the tree with (1) little living on it, soon after it has fallen; (2) many things growing on it or living in it, as the wood breaks down; and (3) only a small hump of material or a young tree growing where the decomposing log once lay.

- Write a detailed report of what they learned when they investigated their question. They may use scanned images or photographs to illustrate their findings.

ENRICHMENT

- You may want to get permission to place some logs at your site so that students can observe changes over time. Position the logs on the ground, preferably in a moist shaded area, to allow decomposers to become established on the logs. Monitor the log over time to see how the decomposition process progresses. Record the different organisms you find each time you check on the log, and compare them to those found at other times.

- See the activity Soil Builders for additional explorations of decomposition.

- Standing dead trees, called **snags**, are especially good habitat for many kinds of animals. Find a snag on or near your site, and have students quietly observe how many different animals use it.

NAME _____ DATE _____

Your investigation question:

_____

_____

Closely observe your log or piece of wood. Record what you see and where you found it. Evidence of animal activity may include insect or woodpecker holes, spider webs, piles of sawdust, or patterns in the wood under the bark.

WHERE	PLANTS AND ANIMALS	EVIDENCE OF ANIMAL ACTIVITY
On the bark		
Under the bark		
In the wood		
Under the log or wood		

Record other evidence to help answer your question:

CAREER CORNER

<u>WOOD SCIENTISTS</u> study the physical, chemical, and biological properties of wood to improve the way we process it into different products. Wood is an amazing natural resource that we use for paper, construction lumber, particle board, and other products.

Regular and frequent time outdoors is beneficial for emotional, mental, and physical health, as well as for creativity, learning, and child development. In this activity, students will examine the physical and emotional effects of a task done outdoors versus indoors. They will design, plan, and carry out an investigation comparing the two settings, and analyze their results.

GET OUTSIDE!

SUBJECTS
Science, English Language Arts, Math, Health, Physical Education

PLT CONCEPTS
1.4, 1.10, 3.8

STEM SKILLS
Data Analysis, Investigation, Organization

DIFFERENTIATED INSTRUCTION
Higher-order Thinking, Nonlinguistic Representations, Personal Connections

MATERIALS
Stopwatch or stopwatch app, materials for chosen task (see Doing the Activity). Optional: calculators, dry erase markers, materials for student-designed investigation.

TIME CONSIDERATIONS
Preparation: 15–30 minutes
Activity: Two 50-minute periods (more for student-designed investigation)

OBJECTIVES

Students will

- Investigate the psychological and physical effects of working or playing outside compared with inside.

- Identify possible benefits of working and playing outside.

- Participate in an outdoor activity.

BACKGROUND

A growing body of research confirms that children are healthier, happier, more creative, and have better knowledge retention when they consistently play and learn outdoors. Some benefits of time outdoors for students include:

- Increased attentiveness and better recollection of information, even after they go back inside.

- Improved performance on tests and other external measures of knowledge gains.

- Greater feelings of competence and motivation to learn.

- Elevated mood and better ability to regulate emotions.

- Decreased stress and anxiety.

- More physical activity and improved physical health.

- Improved balance, coordination, and problem-solving skills through less structured play.

- More frequent and more effective conflict management, communication, and peer cooperation.

FOREST FACT

did you know?

Being outdoors brings you many health benefits, and so does bringing the outdoors in! Wood is a natural material used in **biophilic design**, which has been shown to reduce stress in humans. Exposure to wood indoors—whether in products, furniture, or design—offers many of the same benefits as being outdoors.

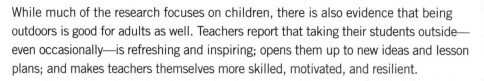

TYPICAL RESTING HEARTRATES

For most 5- to 9-year-old children, the resting heartrate averages between 70 and 115 beats per minute. For older children and adults, it averages 60–100 beats per minute.

While much of the research focuses on children, there is also evidence that being outdoors is good for adults as well. Teachers report that taking their students outside—even occasionally—is refreshing and inspiring; opens them up to new ideas and lesson plans; and makes teachers themselves more skilled, motivated, and resilient.

Researchers studying differences between indoors and outdoors rely on a range of measurements to draw comparisons. Two common assessments used are heartrate and mood.

MEASURING HEARTRATE

How slowly or quickly a person's heart beats is one measure of a physical response to an activity. With each beat, the heart pumps blood through the arteries, bringing oxygen and nutrients to cells throughout the body. The heartrate, or number of beats per minute, can be affected by movement or emotions: the more strenuous the movement and the more extreme the emotion, the higher the heartrate.

The beating heart creates a pulse, which you can feel on your wrist, neck, and other places where the arteries are close to the skin's surface. To measure heartrate, simply count the number of beats you feel at one of these pulse points over the course of one minute.

MEASURING MOOD

One way to determine the mental response to an activity is to measure mood changes. Mental health researchers use a variety of instruments to assess mood.

This activity includes two different surveys students may use to assess their mood. One uses simple emoji-like images to identify moods. The images are presented in four quadrants that range from low to high energy and from uncomfortable to comfortable.

The other survey is an adaptation of PANAS, or the Positive and Negative Affect Schedule, which enables students to quantify their mood. PANAS categorizes feelings as either positive or negative and has respondents rate the extent to which they experience each feeling during a given time frame. Since we can experience both positive and negative feelings at once, PANAS provides both a positive mood score (the shaded score) and a negative mood score (the unshaded score). The higher the number for either score, the more intense the mood.

DETERMINING THE EFFECTS OF OUTDOOR TIME

While both heartrate and mood may be influenced by many variables, such as time of day, air temperature, weather, or stress level, they do provide insight into the person's experience in each location. Researchers typically control for these factors by, for example, having people do the inside and outside tasks at the same time of day.

Note that with such a small sample over a short time, students may find no difference or only a slight difference in heartrate or mood between indoor and outdoor time. They may also find that being outside produces a more negative response than being inside. Any such results are valid. Science involves testing and retesting the same questions to confirm that the results are repeatable and devising possible explanations when the results are different than expected.

PROJECT LEARNING TREE
An Initiative of SFI

GETTING OUTSIDE

Many children have little to no exposure to the natural world. Whether due to overuse of electronic media or more people living in urban settings, children have become disconnected from nature and the outdoors. In many communities, particularly in low-income areas, there is limited access to parks and other green spaces, and children may not have safe places to play. Educators can play a key role in connecting or reconnecting children to nature by planning frequent and regular outdoor experiences. For more information, see Appendix B: Tips for Teaching Outdoors.

GETTING READY

- Decide whether students will design their own investigation or use the suggested procedure. In the suggested procedure, students select a task to conduct inside and outside for a given amount of time, and then assess their heartrate and mood in each location. For younger students, you may opt to do the variation instead.

- If students use the suggested procedure, make copies of the student pages. Each student will need one copy of the Measuring Heartrate student page and two copies of either the Mood Meter or What's Your Mood? student pages. If you want to reuse the student pages, laminate them and have students use dry erase markers to fill in their responses.

- Plan to do the indoor and outdoor task on different days so that the effect of each task is clearer. If possible, avoid doing the outdoor task on a severe weather day.

- If students will be measuring their pulse, have them practice a couple of times before doing the investigation.

DOING THE ACTIVITY

1 **PERSONAL CONNECTIONS**
Introduce the activity by taking a quick poll, asking:

- Which do you think is more fun: playing inside or outside?

- Which do you think is better for your brain: being inside or outside?

- Which do you think is healthier for your body: being inside or outside?

- Which makes you happier: being inside or outside?

- Where do you spend more of your day: inside or outside?

NONLINGUISTIC REPRESENTATIONS Optional: For each of the questions, invite students to indicate their answer using simple sign language. For "inside," they can make a cup shape out of the nondominant hand and place the fingers of the other hand into it. For "outside," they can reverse this action, taking the fingers out of the cup shape.

2 Ask students how they might be able to determine whether being inside or outside is healthier for their mind or their body. Encourage them to suggest ways they might investigate this question.

3 If students design their own investigation, help them determine what to test and how to measure results. Make sure that they understand the importance of testing just one variable at a time (for example, doing the same activity for the same amount of time both inside and outside, rather than varying the activity or the time). Help them plan and then carry out their investigations.

4 If students follow the suggested procedure, provide an overview of the investigation and guide them through the investigation steps:

- As a group, students select a task or series of tasks to do both inside and outside. See the *Testing … One, Two, Three* box for ideas.

- As a group, students decide how long to spend on the task inside and outside, such as 5 minutes or 10 minutes. If possible, conduct the two tests at least a day apart so that the effect of each is clearer.

- In each location, students:
  - » Take their pulse prior to doing the chosen task, using the Measuring Heartrate student page. (If students have trouble measuring their pulse, they can simply find their pulse and state how fast or slow it is.)
  - » Conduct the chosen task for the selected amount of time, using a stopwatch to mark time. Record their pulse again after doing the task.
  - » Complete the Mood Meter or What's Your Mood? student page after doing the task.

- Students calculate their scores on the What's Your Mood? student page according to the directions.

- Students tabulate the entire group's heartrates and scores.

5 🔄 **HIGHER-ORDER THINKING** Invite students to compare the results of their investigation for inside and outside locations, asking questions such as:

- What differences, if any, do you notice in heartrate or mood scores (or other measurements)?

- What might a higher heartrate in either location mean? (It can indicate more stress, anxiety, or excitement in one location than in the other.)

- If there wasn't much difference in the scores, what could that mean? (With such a small sample size over a short period of time, students may not find much difference between the two locations. Help them understand that science involves testing and retesting a question to confirm that the results are repeatable. You might ask students how they could expand the study; for example, they could conduct it for more time or with more students.)

- What might these results tell us about being inside versus outside?

- What other things might have affected the results?

- Why do people like to be outside? Why do they like to be inside?

- What could we do to make inside feel more like outside? (For example, people use wood, plants, and other natural elements to bring the feeling of the outdoors in. Windows that open and skylights help, too.)

- How else might we investigate the differences between being inside and outside? What new questions do you have after conducting this investigation?

TESTING ... ONE, TWO, THREE

Students may choose from the following ideas for their investigation or devise their own.

PHYSICAL TASKS

- Jumping jacks, jumping rope, or running in place
- Stretching
  - » Toe touches: While standing, bend over at the waist and reach for the toes, or as far as is comfortable.
  - » Side bends: Stand up straight with your arms at your sides. Slowly move the fingers of one hand down toward the outside of that knee, while bending at the waist. Switch sides.
  - » Reach for the stars: Stand on your tiptoes and reach as high as you can.
- Yoga poses
  - » Mountain pose: Stand tall with legs slightly apart and feet facing forward. Straighten the arms alongside the body.
  - » Tree pose: Stand on one leg. Balance on that leg as you press the sole of the other foot against the standing leg's calf or thigh. (Optional: Spread arms overhead as if growing like a tree.) Repeat on the other side.

MENTAL TASKS

- Draw a self-portrait.
- Read aloud a passage from a book.
- Complete a crossword puzzle or word search.
- ABC Shape Hunt: Look for letters of the alphabet suggested by objects in and around the area, like the letters S and A in these pictures. (Note that printed or typed letters, such as on signs or books, don't count.)

TAKE IT OUTSIDE

With students' help, make a list of outdoor spaces at your site that could be used for learning. Visit each space and identify any potential obstacles to using it more frequently as an "outdoor classroom." Obstacles may include aspects of the space itself, noise level, accessibility, or exposure to weather. Additional concerns might include decreased attention spans due to the distracting environment or reduced levels of physical comfort. Brainstorm ways to overcome one or more of the obstacles. Discuss what it would take to conduct learning activities outdoors on a more regular basis, such as once a week or once a month.

VARIATION: GRADES K-2

1 Ask students which they enjoy more—being inside or outside. What's the same about the two places, and what's different?

2 Have students sit quietly in a circle inside with their eyes closed.

- Challenge them to use their ears to listen for sounds. (If the room is too quiet, you might need to make some noises yourself in different areas of the room.) After a brief time, ask what they hear. They can point in the direction each sound is coming from or imitate specific sounds they hear.

- Invite students to use their sense of touch and notice what they feel. They might notice the texture of the floor or the temperature of the air on their skin. After a few moments, encourage them to describe what they feel.

- Challenge students to use their noses to detect any smells. Have them describe the smells they experience. Would they categorize them as good or bad? Why?

3 Take students outside and have them sit quietly in a circle, repeating the bulleted steps. You may have them complete the Seeing Without Eyes student page.

4 Lead a discussion about what students observed. Which place had the most interesting sounds? Touches? Smells? In which place did students feel more relaxed? More excited?

PROJECT LEARNING TREE
An initiative of SFI

ACADEMIC STANDARDS

SCIENCE

Practices
- Planning and carrying out investigations
- Analyzing and interpreting data

Concepts
- Structure and function
- Cause and effect
- Patterns

ENGLISH LANGUAGE ARTS

Practices
- Speaking and listening: presentation of knowledge and ideas

Concepts
- Writing: text types and purpose

MATH

Practices
- Reason abstractly and quantitatively
- Model with mathematics

Concepts
- Number and operations in base ten
- Measurement and data

ASSESSMENT

Ask students to

- Write a journal page describing what they learned from the activity and whether their opinion on spending time outside has changed.

- Write a "prescription" for an outdoor activity that includes:

  » a description of the activity

  » the recommended frequency for doing the activity (such as once or twice a week)

  » the benefits of doing the activity outside

  Encourage students to follow their own prescriptions by including outdoor activities in each week's schedule. Also encourage them to share their prescriptions with their families.

ENRICHMENT

- To help students compare the esthetics of indoors versus outdoors, have them imagine being nature photographers. Students pair up and one person plays the role of "photographer," while the other is "the camera." Blindfold the student playing the camera or have them simply close their eyes. The photographer chooses something to take a picture of, positions their partner in front of it, and removes the blindfold for 10 seconds while the camera captures the image. Have the students switch roles and do this activity both inside and outside. Discuss differences students notice between the two locations.

- Have students brainstorm future careers that would allow them to work outside. See PLT's *Green Jobs: Exploring Forest Careers*, available at plt.org/greenjobs, to find out about more opportunities to work outdoors.

- Encourage students to plan and lead an outdoor activity for younger students to get them excited about being outdoors.

- Challenge students to keep a log of how much time they spend outside in a week and what activities they do. Discuss whether and how they could increase their time outdoors.

- Biophilic design aims to increase connections between building occupants and the natural world. Invite students to look for examples of biophilic design at your site, in their neighborhood, in magazines or books, or online. Encourage them to create drawings or dioramas of spaces that incorporate biophilic design elements.

NAME _____ DATE_____

To take your heartrate:

1. Find your pulse by placing two fingers either on the soft part of your neck or on the palm side of your wrist.

2. Use the flat parts of fingers and press firmly, but not too hard.

3. Using a stopwatch, count how many heartbeats you feel in 15 seconds. Multiply that number by four to get heartbeats per minute.

Measure your heartrate before and after doing your chosen activity, both inside and outside. Record the number of beats per minute in the chart below.

Activity: _____

Length of time doing activity: _____

	INSIDE		OUTSIDE	
	Heartrate before activity	Heartrate after activity	Heartrate before activity	Heartrate after activity
Heartbeats in 15 seconds				
Multiply by 4	X 4	X 4	X 4	X 4
Heartbeats per minute				

CAREER CORNER

I LOVE MY GREEN JOB!

ENVIRONMENTAL HEALTH PROFESSIONALS work to improve the public's health. They identify, track, and reduce environmental risks that could hurt people, like pollution or harmful chemicals. They may test air, water, and soil to make sure these are safe.

PROJECT LEARNING TREE K–8 ACTIVITY GUIDE © SUSTAINABLE FORESTRY INITIATIVE

NAME _____ DATE _____

How are you feeling?

Angry

Afraid

HIGH ENERGY

Surprised

Excited

Nervous

Worried

Happy

Cheerful

← UNCOMFORTABLE   COMFORTABLE →

Bored

Tired

Calm

Sleepy

LOW ENERGY

Sad

Lonely

Thoughtful

Relaxed

CAREER CORNER

I LOVE MY GREEN JOB!

ENVIRONMENTAL FILMMAKERS tell stories through film that show people different points of view on a topic or theme. These films can help to increase people's understanding of and feelings for nature.

NAME _____ DATE_____

In each row, circle the number that best describes how you feel right now.

		NOT AT ALL	A LITTLE	SOMEWHAT	A LOT	VERY
1	Interested	1	2	3	4	5
2	Worried	1	2	3	4	5
3	Excited	1	2	3	4	5
4	Upset	1	2	3	4	5
5	Strong	1	2	3	4	5
6	Guilty	1	2	3	4	5
7	Scared	1	2	3	4	5
8	Angry	1	2	3	4	5
9	Eager	1	2	3	4	5
10	Proud	1	2	3	4	5
11	Grumpy	1	2	3	4	5
12	Alert	1	2	3	4	5
13	Ashamed	1	2	3	4	5
14	Motivated	1	2	3	4	5
15	Nervous	1	2	3	4	5
16	Ambitious	1	2	3	4	5
17	Focused	1	2	3	4	5
18	Stressed	1	2	3	4	5
19	Energetic	1	2	3	4	5
20	Afraid	1	2	3	4	5

Scoring Your Mood

1. Add up all the numbers you circled in the SHADED rows: _____

2. Add up all the numbers you circled in the UNSHADED rows: _____

- If your SHADED score is higher than your UNSHADED score, you are feeling more positive than negative. If the UNSHADED score is higher, you are feeling more negative.

- Most people can experience different feelings at the same time. For example, you might be both nervous and excited about doing something new.

- The larger the number for either score, the stronger your feelings at that moment.

Source: Adapted from Positive and Negative Affect Schedule – Short Form (PANAS – SF).

I LOVE MY GREEN JOB!

CAREER CORNER

OUTDOOR RECREATION LEADERS plan and guide hikes, games, crafts, and other outdoor activities in parks and camps. They teach groups how to do the activities and organize and set up any equipment needed.

NAME _____ DATE_____

Write or draw what you notice with each sense, inside and outside.

	Sound	Touch	Smell
Inside			
Outside			

CAREER CORNER

I LOVE MY GREEN JOB!

PARK RANGERS teach forest visitors about the forest and explain the rules. They keep visitors safe in the forest and help protect the forest from activities that could damage it.

All kinds of people work in the forest—from foresters, to loggers, to scientists. Everyone depends on properly managed forests for recreation, essential products, wildlife and biodiversity, clean water and air. This activity provides students with an overview of forest-related careers.

MY GREEN FUTURE

SUBJECTS
Science, Social Studies

PLT CONCEPTS
1.6, 2.6, 5.7

STEM SKILLS
Communication, Creativity, Organization

DIFFERENTIATED INSTRUCTION
Nonlinguistic Representations, Personal Connections, Student Voice

MATERIALS
Art supplies.

TIME CONSIDERATIONS
Preparation: 15 minutes
Activity: 50 minutes

OBJECTIVES

Students will

- Explore a variety of jobs that are directly related to forest resources.
- Describe how various professionals work together to care for forests.

BACKGROUND

Our society depends on forests for timber and other forest products, as well as for wildlife, clean air, water, and recreation. Many people in a wide range of forestry professions work to ensure that forests provide all the things we need and want from them.

Forestry is more than just planting trees, fighting wildfires, or harvesting logs, although managing those tasks may be part of a forester's responsibilities. It also includes work in computer modeling, mapping, statistical or budget analysis, and education. Some foresters specialize in individual aspects of the forest, such as soils, water, or wildlife. Others are engaged in harvesting, milling, engineering, or marketing forest products such as lumber, paper, and pulp.

Urban and community foresters focus on the trees and forests that grow in and around cities, towns, and communities. These trees provide a number of benefits: reducing energy costs, managing stormwater, enhancing human health, providing food security, and increasing climate resilience. Urban and community foresters pay close attention to factors that affect those forests, such as growing space, soil and water quality, water availability, and vandalism.

GETTING READY

- Make copies of the Who Works in This Forest? student page.

For more forest-related jobs, see PLT's *Green Jobs: Exploring Forest Careers*, available at plt.org/greenjobs

FOREST FACT

Jobs in sustainable forestry help to maintain or restore ecosystems and ensure that forest products are sustainably produced. Worldwide, more than 54.2 million people work in jobs connected to forests.

DOING THE ACTIVITY

1 **PERSONAL CONNECTIONS** Ask students if they have visited, read about, or seen pictures of a forest. What kinds of jobs might be necessary to care for forests and obtain the things we need and want from them? Invite students to brainstorm and record a list of forest-related jobs.

2 Discuss with students how forests provide plant and animal habitats; paper and wood products; places for recreation; and air, soil, and water protection. Explain that people must manage forests so that they can continue to provide these things. Add more jobs to the list based on this discussion.

3 Pass out copies of the student page and point out that it describes people who work in and for forests. Students should read the brief descriptions and explain how each job helps care for the forest.

4 **STUDENT VOICE** Go over the student page with students. Have them share their reasoning for how the jobs are necessary. By the end of the discussion, students should realize that every job on the page is helpful in conserving and caring for forests. Also use background information as you discuss some other kinds of people who work with forests.

5 Write the following jobs where all can see: logging truck driver, paper manufacturer, architect, nature photographer, newspaper journalist, lumbermill worker, camp counselor, and tree nursery worker. Ask students which of these workers depend on forests to do their jobs. (All of them.) What role do forests play in each of these jobs?

6 **NONLINGUISTIC REPRESENTATIONS** Have students create a concept map showing how each job depends on forests. They may use art supplies or a graphic organizer app, placing the word "forest" (or a picture of a forest) in the center, and arranging the jobs radiating out from the center. They should include words or pictures explaining the connection to forests for each job.

7 Invite students to share their concept maps with the group.

TAKE IT OUTSIDE

Many people who work in and for forests are motivated by a deep connection to nature. Awaken this connection in your students by inviting them to go outside and look for one or two natural things that catch their attention or pique their curiosity. Encourage them to walk quietly or sit still, letting their attention wander. Even in the city, they might notice the moon rising or setting, flowers blooming, birds chirping, or a butterfly flitting past. Invite them to write or draw their observations and draft a question related to each of them. If you want to make a more direct connection from nature to careers, ask them to name the kinds of people who work to answer questions like the ones they identified.

ACADEMIC STANDARDS

SCIENCE

Practices
- Obtaining, evaluating, and communicating information

Concepts
- Human impacts on Earth systems
- Systems and system models

SOCIAL STUDIES

Practices
- Applying disciplinary concepts

Concepts
- Economics: exchange and markets
- Geography: human–environment interactions

ASSESSMENT

Ask students to

- Create a collage showing how people depend on forests. It can include pictures of forests, trees, streams or rivers, wildlife, people living near forests, forest products, people using forests or wood products, and people working in forests. Have the students explain their collages verbally or in writing.

- Choose one forest-related job they would be interested in doing and explain how it is connected to the forest.

ENRICHMENT

- Invite one or more people whose jobs are related to forests to speak to your group. Have students prepare a list of questions to ask each person about the work they do. Here are some possible questions:

  » Why did you choose this career?

  » What kind of training did you need?

  » What's your typical workday like?

  » How many other people do you work with?

  » What other kinds of people do you depend on to do your job?

  » What kinds of clothes do you wear to work?

  » What special equipment do you use on the job and what do you use it for?

  » Do you use any new technologies in your work?

  » What are the most rewarding things about your job?

  » What aspects of your job pose the biggest challenges?

  » Would you recommend this career?

  Afterward, have students draw pictures or write stories about the people and their jobs.

- As an alternative to a guest speaker, have students do an internet search for careers related to the forest.

PROJECT LEARNING TREE
An initiative of SFI

NAME _____   DATE _____

Wildlife Biologist: I study wildlife to understand what they need to thrive. I look at how birds, mammals, fish, reptiles, or amphibians depend on the forest and on each other. *Why is this job important? Explain.*

_____

_____

Wildland Firefighter: My job is to help protect and maintain the health of the forest by controlling and putting out wildfires. I also talk to the public about ways they can help prevent wildfires. *Why is this job important? Explain.*

_____

_____

Forester: Foresters, or forest managers, oversee forestlands. I develop plans for planting trees, monitoring trees for healthy growth, and making sure these activities follow environmental laws. *Why is this job important? Explain.*

_____

_____

Park Ranger: I teach visitors about the forest and help keep them safe in the forest. I also enforce rules and laws to keep the forest safe from activities that could harm the forest. *Why is this job important? Explain.*

_____

_____

Forest Engineer: I design and supervise the building of roads, trails, bridges, and other construction projects in managed forests. I also identify any impacts these projects may have on forests. *Why is this job important? Explain.*

_____

_____

Logger: I harvest timber for building materials, furniture, paper, packaging, and many other products. My job is to cut the trees in a way that keeps water clean and ensures the health of the forest. *Why is this job important? Explain.*

_____

_____

CAREER CORNER   I LOVE MY GREEN JOB!

CAREER COUNSELORS help people find jobs. They may work in schools, guiding students to explore a variety of career choices.

GRADES 3-5
VARIATION 6-8

Nearly everything we buy comes in some sort of package. Students examine the pros and cons of different packaging and design an "ideal" package.

PEEK AT PACKAGING

SUBJECTS
Science, English Language Arts, Social Studies, Visual Arts

PLT CONCEPTS
5.5, 5.6, 5.10

STEM SKILLS
Collaboration, Creativity, Problem Solving

DIFFERENTIATED INSTRUCTION
Cooperative Learning, Hands-on Learning

MATERIALS
A collection of consumer product packaging. Optional: Art supplies and recycled materials for making prototypes of better packaging.

TIME CONSIDERATIONS
Preparation: 20 minutes

Activity: One to two 50-minute periods

OBJECTIVES

Students will

- Identify different purposes of packaging and the pros and cons of certain packaging.

- Assess the packaging of different products and suggest ways to reduce or improve it.

- Design the ideal packaging for a given product.

BACKGROUND

Product packaging holds items in a convenient way and protects them from damage. The earliest forms of packaging were animal skins, earthenware vessels, and woven baskets. Later, between 2,500 and 3,500 years ago, glass bottles, fired clay vessels (amphorae), and finished leather were developed. Packaging as we know it today developed in the late 19th century and is produced by packaging machinery.

In addition to holding goods together, packaging also protects, preserves, and facilitates the distribution of many products. For example:

- Canning preserves food, maximizing shelf life and freshness.

- Glass bottles, plastic jugs, and coated paper cartons allow liquids like milk to be stored and poured easily.

- Cardboard boxes protect products like shoes or electronics from damage, or enable products to be shipped directly to consumers.

- Plastic or paperboard packaging safeguards foods and health-care products from contamination and tampering.

- Large packages enable consumers to buy in bulk, which is more economical and reduces overall packaging.

Packaging also provides a convenient surface on which to display information for consumers, as well as advertising space for the manufacturer.

Packaging requires natural resources and energy to produce, and if it is not recycled it creates waste after it is used. Plastic packaging waste is especially problematic, as plastic persists in the environment and doesn't decompose or rot. Instead, plastic breaks down into smaller and smaller pieces, called microplastics, which can get passed through the food chain. Most plastic today ends up in landfills, oceans, and waterways, where it contaminates habitats and impacts

Cellulose nanofiber, a sustainable alternative to plastic packaging, is made from wood chips. It can extend the shelf-life and quality of food, medicine, and cosmetics.

countless animal species. For information about **renewable** versus **nonrenewable resources**, see the activity Renewable or Not? (in Grades 6–8).

Particularly concerning are single-use items that are meant to be used just once and then discarded. Items like plastic drinking bottles, plastic bags, cups, and take-out containers currently make up a significant proportion of our society's waste.

Manufacturers and consumers have become more aware of the impact of packaging on the environment, natural resources, energy, and waste management. Some cities and states have passed laws that limit single-use bags, straws, stirrers, cups, or food containers. In addition, some companies have reduced or eliminated packaging of some products.

More and more companies are adopting a **circular economy** model, which is aimed at reducing waste and the continual use and discarding of resources. Companies following this model strive to manufacture products using sustainable materials and without creating waste and pollution, and to design them to be recycled or to break down into natural components. For example, they may use packaging materials that are **compostable**, **biodegradable**, or even edible, or that are from **recycled** sources or **sustainably managed forests**.

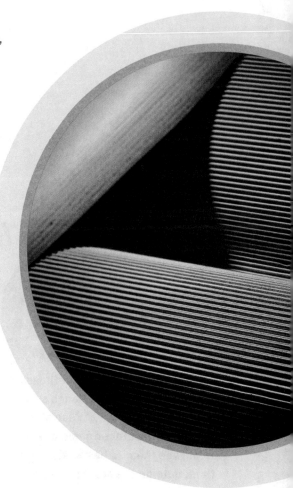

GETTING READY

- Collect a variety of consumer product packages or ask students to bring some from home. Packaging should be clean, empty containers or unopened products in their original packaging.

  SAFETY CHECK! Students should not bring in any dirty or unsafe containers (such as opened cans with sharp edges) or hazardous products (such as household cleaners). Collect the products in a box near the door and go through them to ensure that they are safe for the students to handle before using them in the activity.

- Select examples of packaging used for different purposes, such as advertising, maintaining freshness, preventing tampering, preventing damage during shipping, and convenience.

- Make copies of the Consumer Choices student page for each team or have it available electronically.

- Optional: Gather materials for students to make packaging prototypes, such as paper, cardboard, newspaper, greeting cards, or used wrapping paper.

1 Ask students why they think that many of the products we buy have packaging. Discuss different purposes that packaging might serve, listing their ideas where the whole group can see. (For example, students might say that packaging protects a product from damage, keeps it fresh, makes it easier to ship, or gives information about the product.)

2 Show the examples of packaging that you have selected. Ask students why they think each product is packaged the way it is, considering the purposes they identified in Step 1. For each example, ask them to name the pros and cons of the packaging.

3 **HANDS-ON LEARNING** Divide the group into teams to analyze a package they choose from the group's collection. Direct teams to work together to complete the Consumer Choices student page.

4 Have teams describe their analysis of one product to the rest of the group. As a group, discuss the teams' findings. Focus the discussion on the environmental impacts of packaging, including the resources that go into making it, its disposal, and how it affects habitats and organisms. (See Background for more information.)

5 **COOPERATIVE LEARNING** Invite teams to identify the properties of an ideal package, considering what they learned in their analysis and the group discussion. Then, challenge each team to design an ideal package for one of the products. Direct students to draw a picture of their proposed packaging or to create a prototype using art supplies or recycled materials.

6 Have teams present their proposed packaging to the group, explaining why it is ideal for their product.

TAKE IT OUTSIDE

Collect a variety of used cardboard shipping boxes and challenge student teams to design a way to use at least one box in an outdoor game or sport. Encourage them to be creative and to "think outside the box." (For example, they might make a maze, a giant chess game, or a canoe.) Let them use scissors, packing tape, or markers to create their designs.

PROJECT LEARNING TREE
An initiative of SFI

VARIATION: GRADES 6–8

1 Conduct Steps 1 and 2 of the activity and then lead a discussion about packaging based on students' observations. Questions may include:

- What different purposes does the packaging we've collected serve?

- Can you identify examples of too little or too much packaging?

- What resources are used to make this packaging? Where do they come from?

- How does the packaging affect habitats and organisms?

- What will happen to the packaging after the user is done with it?

2 Introduce students to the concept of a circular economy, which is an economic model aimed at eliminating waste through the continual reuse of resources.

3 Challenge students to research companies or organizations that embrace this model, and to report on the methods and materials these companies incorporate in the design, production, and use of their products and services.

4 Invite students to draw two flowcharts that compare the conventional flow of packaging material and use (which is more or less a straight line), and the flow in the circular economy model (which is typically a closed loop). Encourage them to include details from their research in their charts.

5 Point out that with repeated recycling, the fiber used to make boxes will eventually break down and new fiber from trees will need to be added to ensure that boxes are durable and strong. Ask students to consider how this fact might affect their flowcharts.

ACADEMIC STANDARDS

SCIENCE

Practices
- Developing and using models
- Constructing explanations and designing solutions

Concepts
- Defining and delimiting engineering problems
- Human impacts on Earth systems
- Structure and function
- Cause and effect

ENGLISH LANGUAGE ARTS

Practices
- Speaking and listening: comprehension and collaboration
- Speaking and listening: presentation of knowledge and ideas

SOCIAL STUDIES

Practices
- Applying disciplinary concepts
- Communicating conclusions and taking informed action

Concepts
- Economics: exchange and markets
- Geography: human–environment interactions

ASSESSMENT

Ask students to

- Present their packaging design. Evaluate students using criteria such as how well it suits the product, whether it meets the design criteria identified by the team, and how low its environmental impact is.
- Write a description of ideal packaging for a product.

ENRICHMENT

- Invite students to research forest products and other substitutes for single-use plastics. Ask them to do a side-by-side comparison of a product made from two different materials.
- Encourage students to find out how their community handles waste from packaging. For example, does their community recycle or compost? If so, what and how does it recycle or compost? Does it have laws or rules about single-use items?
- Take a "Supermarket Safari" trip to a local store to find at least one item in each of several different packaging categories, such as:
  - » packaged in ideal manner (as identified in Step 5)
  - » packaged with excessive materials
  - » packaged with single-use plastic
  - » packaged primarily to attract the consumer
  - » packaged in bulk
  - » packaged in something the consumer can reuse
  - » packaged with material from a sustainably managed forest
  - » packaged with material that has been recycled
  - » packaged with material that is recyclable
  - » packaged with material that is compostable or biodegradable

PROJECT LEARNING TREE
An initiative of SFI

Consumer Choices

NAME _____ DATE _____

Observe your product's packaging closely. Then complete the chart below. Use any information or labeling on your product to help your team.

Product Name: _____

Type of Product: _____

PARTS List each part of the packaging	PURPOSE What purposes does it serve?	MATERIALS What materials is it made of?
Outer wrapping	*Protects cardboard box*	*Plastic*

NAME _____ DATE_____

1. Is the packaging made from any of the following?
   - ❏ Compostable materials
   - ❏ Recyclable materials
   - ❏ Recycled materials
   - ❏ Sustainably managed forests

   How do you know?

   _____

2. After the product has been opened or used, what will happen to the packaging?

3. Can the packaging be reused? If so, how?

4. How might this packaging help or harm habitats or living beings?

5. How would you improve the packaging of this product?

I LOVE MY GREEN JOB!

CAREER CORNER

Do you enjoy working with materials and solving problems? <u>PACKAGING TECHNOLOGISTS</u> (teck-NAWL-uh-gists) design and make packaging for different products. By using thoughtful designs, they can help to reduce waste and pollution.

Writing and sharing poems gives students an opportunity to express their thoughts, feelings, and beliefs in creative and artistic ways. You can do this activity in combination with Adopt a Tree, to allow students to explore their adopted tree through poetry. You may also adapt the activity to explore parts of the environment other than trees and forests, such as art or architecture.

POET-TREE

SUBJECTS
Science, English Language Arts, Social Studies

PLT CONCEPTS
1.8, 1.10, 3.8

STEM SKILLS
Communication, Creativity, Nature-based Design

DIFFERENTIATED INSTRUCTION
Cooperative Learning, Higher-order Thinking, Literacy Skills, Personal Connections

MATERIALS
Paper; pens or pencils; clipboards, pieces of cardboard and paperclips, journals, or tablets that students can use to write outdoors. Optional: Large pieces of chart paper.

TIME CONSIDERATIONS
Preparation: 15 minutes

Activity: Two 50-minute periods

OBJECTIVES
Students will

- Express their environmental perspectives using various forms of poetry.
- Analyze their own and the poetry of others to discover meaning.
- Share their poetry with others.

BACKGROUND
Poetry is a great way for students to express their ideas about the environment. Giving students a specific poetic form helps them structure abstract ideas. Here are some sample poetic forms that work well, but you may use other forms if you wish. The poems provided were written by students and educators who completed this activity.

HAIKU
This Japanese form of poetry consists of three lines: the first line has five syllables, the second line has seven, and the third line has five again. The third line often contains a surprising or tension element.

EXAMPLE

Snails

Makes a slimy path
Sticking on the long thick grass
Hides from predators

By Leslie Heisler
Grade 3
Star of the Sea School
Virginia Beach, VA

CINQUAIN
This poetic style consists of five lines. Each line has a specific purpose and fixed number of syllables: (1) the title, in two syllables, (2) a description of the title, in four syllables, (3) a description of action, in six syllables, (4) a description of a feeling, in eight syllables, and (5) another word for the title, in two syllables.

EXAMPLE

Earth Worms
Squiggly squirmers
Aerating our topsoil
Happily helping our garden
Crawlers

By Lee Barnett, Amber Urban, and Margaret Meadows
Northside Elementary School teachers
Angleton Independent School District, TX

ACROSTIC

In acrostic poetry, the first letter in each line, when read vertically, spells out the name of something or conveys some other kind of message.

EXAMPLE

Towering
Reaching
Extending
Embracing the sky.

DIAMANTE

These poems are diamond shaped and consist of seven lines that have the following pattern:

Noun
adjective adjective
participle participle participle
noun noun noun noun
participle participle participle
adjective adjective
noun

EXAMPLE

tree
tall, sturdy
standing, towering, observing
branches, trunk, anchor, shelter
nurturing, swaying, caring
proud, happy
tree

By Jennifer Mammel
Grade 7
St. Paul Lutheran Church and School
Lakeland, FL

WINDSPARK

These poems have five lines with the following pattern: (1) "I dreamed,"
(2) "I was…" (something or someone), (3) where, (4) an action, and (5) how.

EXAMPLE

I dreamed
I was a tree
On a hillside
Playing with the wind
Joyfully.

FLUXUS

This poetry aims to elevate everyday objects and events to the level of fine art. To give it a try, write down nouns, adjectives, verbs, and adverbs on small strips of paper that are related to a chosen poem topic (for this activity, consider nature, trees, or the outdoors). Fold each strip in half, mix them, then randomly pull the strips from a pile and write the words in the order that you chose them, adding punctuation at will.

EXAMPLE

Green, refreshing, quiet, leaves.
Calmness… chirping… excitement!

SHAPE POETRY

The arrangement of words in this type of poetry (also called concrete poetry) form a picture of the poem's topic or what is happening in the poem.

EXAMPLE

branches
shade rubber
fruit clothes
paper wind barrier fuel
furniture resource nuts
treehouses maple syrup parks
multiple uses seeds oxygen
lumber habitat energy
building materials
baseball bats leaves
photosynthesis
roots
gum
cork
books
paint
cocoa
sponge

FREE VERSE

This type of poetry follows no set formula or style.

EXAMPLE

I am the tree that overcomes all.
I laugh at the wind.
I am one with the wilderness.

GETTING READY

- Decide which poetic form is most appropriate for your group to try. You do not need to teach all the forms. Make copies of the corresponding student page or relevant parts of it.

- Plan to take students outdoors to observe one or more trees at your site or in a nearby yard, park, or forest area. If possible, choose a location that has several different trees for students to observe.

- For each student team, prepare a sheet chart of paper with the name of one of the senses: Touch, Smell, Sight, or Sound. (If students have journals or tablets, they may use them instead.)

- Plan to have students share their poetic works. For example, students might create a literary magazine by making copies of their poems and stapling them together, produce an electronic book using word processing software, or host a poetry reading or open-mic event. Be sure to get students' permission to share their work beyond the group.

DOING THE ACTIVITY

1 **PERSONAL CONNECTIONS** Ask students to name some of the benefits they derive from trees and forests. Invite them to share their experiences, asking:

- What do you think about or how do you feel when you stand next to a tree or enter a forest?

- Do you have any favorite neighborhood trees?

- Are there any special wooded places you like to visit?

- Do you have any favorite stories about trees or forests?

- Are there any forest issues that you are worried about?

2 Use their responses to come up with a group list of characteristics and attributes of trees or forests. Explain that you will create a book of poetry together, expressing their ideas and attitudes about trees, forests, and the environment.

FOREST FACT

Edward Thomas wrote the poem "Aspens" in July 1915 and sent it to his friend and mentor, the American poet Robert Frost. While the poem describes the way aspen trees sway day and night, whatever the weather, the trees' continuous movement also represents a metaphor for human endeavors: like the aspens, we persevere.

3 **LITERACY SKILLS** Review the major parts of speech (nouns, verbs, adjectives, participles, etc.) that the students will need for the poetic form(s) they will be using. Write these parts of speech where the whole group can see them, and have students generate a short list of examples for each part of speech.

4 Present the poetic form(s) you have selected and give examples. Explain to students that there are many other types as well. Distribute copies of the student page Poet-Tree Forms or parts of it.

5 Take the students to visit nearby trees to gather "tree impressions." (This can be done indoors by looking through windows, if necessary.) Have them sit quietly under one or more trees for at least 10 minutes. Direct students to write descriptive words about how the tree looks, smells, and feels; what sounds they hear; what living things they see on the tree; and any other observations they make while sitting under the tree.

6 **COOPERATIVE LEARNING** Divide students into teams and give each team a sheet of chart paper with the name of a sense written on it (see Getting Ready). Have teams use their designated sense to generate words or pictures describing the tree. Ask a reporter from each team to share their words with the full group.

7 While you are outside or once you have returned inside, have students create poems about trees and forests. Encourage them to try more than one poetic form, using the student page as a guide. Then let the students share their poems with the rest of the group. Have them explain which poetic form they used and why they chose it.

8 **HIGHER-ORDER THINKING** Lead a group discussion, pointing out that people see trees and forests differently. Ask:

- Does your poem mention the influence people have on trees or forests?
- Does it mention the importance of trees or forest products to people?
- Does your poem refer to people's place in nature? How?
- Does the poem recognize different cultural connections to the forest?
- What other themes do our poems represent?

9 Have students review the poems they wrote and choose one they like best. Assemble everyone's favorite poems to share as planned (see Getting Ready).

TAKE IT OUTSIDE

Invite students to find a comfortable spot: it might be resting against a tree, lying in the grass, swaying in a hammock, or sitting on a bench. Let students know to be careful around trees, to avoid damaging the bark or compacting soil around the roots. Point out that spending time in a new place can help you make new observations, and tell your students that they will use this new position to make a sound map. Hand each student a 3" x 5" card and a pencil. Tell them to draw a small mark in the center of the blank (unlined) side to represent themselves. Explain that they should make a mark on their card for any sound they hear, showing the direction they hear it. The mark can be a word, a squiggle, a picture, or whatever helps them remember the different sounds. Suggest that they also close their eyes. Make an owl call or other sound signal to begin the sound mapping, and again after three minutes to end. You might also read or tell a story while you have students' quiet attention. Afterward, ask them to share what they heard.

VARIATION: GRADES 6–8

1 Invite each student to choose a nearby tree. Have students spend time with their tree, sitting against it, lying underneath it, walking around it, and observing it from various perspectives. During this time, they should write down words, ideas, and impressions that come to mind.

2 Guide students to convert their thoughts into a free verse poem. When the poem is finished, they should think of a word or phrase that sums up the "character" of their tree to serve as the title.

3 Have students take a photo of their tree that visually captures the essence of their poem. Encourage them to use creative perspective, lighting, photo filters, or other effects to produce visually striking images!

4 Invite the group to create a physical or virtual gallery, as appropriate, to share their work.

PROJECT
LEARNING
TREE
An initiative of SFI

ACADEMIC STANDARDS

SCIENCE

Practices
- Constructing explanations and designing solutions

Concepts
- Earth materials and systems
- Systems and system models

ENGLISH LANGUAGE ARTS

Practices
- Writing: production and distribution of writing

Concepts
- Writing: text types and purpose

SOCIAL STUDIES

Practices
- Applying disciplinary concepts

Concepts
- Geography: human–environment interactions

ASSESSMENT

Ask students to

- Save early drafts and multiple renditions of their work before it reaches the final product. Later, have students arrange these raw materials in a portfolio that shows the development of their poem, and submit the portfolio along with the final product.

- Write about a favorite family member, pet, or book using the same poetry forms from the activity.

ENRICHMENT

- Help students identify and contact appropriate local, regional, and national organizations that might publish students' poems, and encourage students to submit their work. For example, PLT's online newsletter, *The Branch* (plt.org/newsletter), often publishes "poet-tree."

- Through group discussion, make a list of environmental issues (local, regional, national, or global) that students are concerned about. Divide the group into teams of four, and have each team choose one of the issues to discuss. Team members should share their points of view with each other, making sure that each person gets a chance to talk. After about 10 minutes, individuals should write a short poem in any form that reflects their perceptions or opinions on the issue discussed. Afterward, discuss poetry's value for clarifying thoughts or perspectives. How might poems distort or energize an issue?

- Invite students to find poems about trees and forests to share with the group. Possibilities include "Stopping by Woods on a Snowy Evening" by Robert Frost, "Trees" by Joyce Kilmer, and "The Trees" by Philip Larkin.

- Have students imagine a world without trees. Encourage them to write a poem describing that world or how they would feel in a world without trees.

- Have students create a list of descriptive words showing pleasant feelings and thoughts about the world around them and name some of the places those words could describe.

STUDENT PAGE
Poet-Tree Forms

NAME_____ DATE_____

✂ -

HAIKU

Form	Your poem
1st line: Five syllables	
2nd line: Seven syllables	
3rd line: Five syllables (with something surprising or unexpected)	

✂ -

CINQUAIN

Form	Your poem
1ST LINE: Title in two syllables	
2ND LINE: Description of title in four syllables	
3RD LINE: Description of an action in six syllables	
4TH LINE: Description of a feeling in eight syllables	
5TH LINE: Another word for the title in two syllables	

STUDENT PAGE

NAME _____ DATE_____

ACROSTIC

Choose a word related to trees and forests and write each letter of the word in the boxes below. (The boxes should spell out your word when you read down.) For each line, write a word or phrase that starts with that letter.

Your Poem:

NAME _____ DATE _____

✂ -

DIAMANTE

Form	Your poem
1ST LINE: Noun (title)	
2ND LINE: Two adjectives	
3RD LINE: Three participles	
4TH LINE: Four nouns	
5TH LINE: Three participles	
6TH LINE: Two adjectives	
7TH LINE: Noun	

✂ -

WINDSPARK

Form	Your poem
1ST LINE: "I dreamed"	
2ND LINE: "I was …" (something or someone)	
3RD LINE: Where	
4TH LINE: An action	
5TH LINE: How	

NAME _____ DATE_____

FLUXUS

1. On small strips of paper, write down nouns, adjectives, verbs, and adverbs related to a chosen poem topic (like nature, trees, or the outdoors).

2. Fold the strips and mix them, then randomly pull the strips from a pile.

3. Write the words in the order they are chosen, adding punctuation where you would like.

Your poem: _____

_____

- ✂ -

SHAPE POEM

Write a poem inside the tree.

NAME _____ DATE _____

FREE VERSE

This type of poem doesn't follow a set form or style.

Your poem:

CAREER CORNER

POETS use words, metaphors, and rhyming patterns to express feelings or to describe objects or events. Poets help people see experiences more deeply. They may write poetry books, songs, or advertising jingles.

GRADES
3–5
VARIATION 6–8

Students will look for signs of autumn and conduct an investigation to discover why the leaves of deciduous trees change color in the fall.

SIGNS OF FALL

SUBJECTS
Science, English Language Arts, Visual Arts

PLT CONCEPTS
1.1, 5.1, 5.3

STEM SKILLS
Data Analysis, Investigation, Nature-based Design

DIFFERENTIATED INSTRUCTION
Hands-on Learning, Higher-order Thinking, Student Voice

MATERIALS
Part A: Crayons.

Part B: Coffee filters (or chromatography paper), tape, scissors, rubbing alcohol, at least six green leaves, three pencils, three glass jars not taller than 6 inches (15 cm).

TIME CONSIDERATIONS
Preparation: 20 minutes

Activity: Part A: 30 minutes
Part B: 30 minutes

OBJECTIVES

Students will

*   Identify and describe the signs of fall they observe outside.

*   Understand why leaves of deciduous trees change color in the fall.

BACKGROUND

Seasonal changes result from the angle of Earth's axis and Earth's movement around the sun. Angled toward the sun at 23.5 degrees, the Northern Hemisphere experiences its summer from the summer solstice, around June 21, to the fall equinox, around September 21. The summer solstice is when the sun's rays strike Earth at the farthest north point (making it the longest day of the year), and the fall equinox is the day when the sun's rays shine directly on the Equator (making the day and night equal in length).

When the sun's rays fall more directly (more or less perpendicularly), the Northern Hemisphere has longer and warmer days. At the same time, the Southern Hemisphere—angled away from the sun—experiences shorter and colder days, marking its winter. At the winter solstice, around December 21, the sun is at its farthest point south, making this the official beginning of winter in the Northern Hemisphere and summer in the Southern Hemisphere.

As winter approaches in temperate regions, animals prepare for the change. Some animals migrate to warmer areas where there is more shelter and food, while others gather food or add an extra layer of fat or fur to keep warm.

The colder temperatures and shorter days also trigger responses in plants. In deciduous trees, the cells at the base of each leaf stem begin to die, forming a barrier that keeps water and nutrients from traveling to the leaf.

Chlorophyll, the green pigment in the leaves, starts to break down, and other leaf pigments begin to show through or accumulate. Yellow or orange carotenoid (kuh-RAW-ten-oid) pigments are present in the leaves during summer, but they are concealed by the chlorophyll. As the level of chlorophyll decreases, these pigments become more obvious and the leaf appears more and more yellow. Red anthocyanin (an-tho-SIGH-a-nin) pigments are not usually present in summer, but they form as a result of chemical reactions that occur when temperatures drop and photosynthesis slows. These pigments are responsible for the deep red leaf colors of fall.

While early cool temperatures bring about the best fall colors, an early frost can diminish the show by killing the leaves outright, before the gradual shift in color can develop.

As the cells at the base of the leaf stem die, the leaf's attachment to the twig weakens. When the attachment breaks, the leaf falls to the ground. With its leaves gone, the tree is less likely to suffer damage from freezing. However, without leaves the tree cannot photosynthesize; therefore, deciduous trees remain dormant in the winter until the longer days and warmer weather of spring trigger new leaves to grow.

Unlike deciduous trees, evergreen trees keep their leaves throughout winter. This enables them to photosynthesize later into the fall and start earlier in the spring than deciduous trees. Evergreens have several different characteristics that help them survive cold, wind, and snow. First, the leaves themselves are narrow, which makes them less vulnerable to heavy loads of snow that would otherwise break a tree's branches. The leaves are also covered by a thick layer of wax, which keeps them from drying out through the long winter. In addition, the leaves contain chemicals that act as antifreeze, preventing ice from forming inside the leaves. These chemicals are what give evergreens their characteristic scent.

GETTING READY

PART A:

- In the fall, identify an area on or near your site with both deciduous and evergreen trees. It may be in a nearby wooded area, on the school grounds, at a local park or garden, or along neighborhood sidewalks.

 SAFETY CHECK! Check for any hazards at the site, such as deep holes, sharp objects, or poisonous plants.

- Make copies of the Signs of Fall student page. As an alternative, have students make journal pages for recording their observations.

- Optional: Make copies of the suggested template from Appendix K: Making a Scientific Argument for practicing scientific argumentation.

PART B:

- Collect at least two green leaves from three different deciduous trees. (You might want to do this while conducting Part A.) Avoid the hard waxy leaves that are common on ornamental shrubs. The best leaf choices are soft, green leaves from trees that typically show lots of fall color. Sweetgum, flowering cherry, and maple trees are good examples.

- Cut three 2" x 6" (5 cm x 15 cm) strips from coffee filters (or chromatography paper).

FOREST FACT

Fallen leaves are an essential part of a forest's ecosystem. The "leaf litter" shields the soil from hard rains, holding in moisture and preventing erosion. It also protects tree seeds that will germinate next spring, and nutrients that leach from the dead leaves nourish the seedlings.

did you know

PROJECT LEARNING TREE
An initiative of SFI

DOING THE ACTIVITY

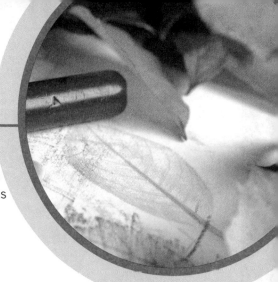

PART A: VISIBLE CHANGES

1 **HANDS-ON LEARNING** In the fall, take students on a walk through an area with both deciduous and evergreen trees. Challenge them to find as many signs as possible that indicate winter is approaching, describe their observations, and record them on the student page. Colorful falling leaves are easy to see, but encourage students to look for other signs too (e.g., birds migrating, squirrels storing nuts, people wearing sweaters, garden plants dying). Encourage them to notice nonliving things: puddles, ice, frost, and mud are indicators of a cooler or wetter fall climate.

2 Invite students to compare a deciduous tree (which loses its leaves in the fall) with an evergreen tree (which doesn't lose its leaves in the fall). What similarities and differences do they notice between the trees?

3 Distribute copies of the student page and colored crayons. Review the questions, then give students time to complete the questions and leaf rubbings.

4 **HIGHER-ORDER THINKING** Back indoors, ask students to describe the signs they found that winter is coming. Ask students which signs might be causes and which might be effects of the changing season, and record their ideas on a group list. Invite them to choose a related cause and an effect from the list, and to describe the evidence that they are related. You may have them use the template from Appendix K: Making a Scientific Argument.

PART B: INVISIBLE CHANGES

1 Ask students why and how some leaves change color in the fall. List their ideas where all can see. Invite students to state any questions they have about this phenomenon, adding their questions to the list. Encourage them to suggest ways they might investigate these questions.

2 Explain that one way to investigate how leaves change color is to separate the different colored substances or pigments found in the leaves. Have students help you tear two green leaves collected from a particular tree (see Getting Ready) into small pieces and place the pieces in a glass jar. Repeat for two additional jars, using leaves from different trees for each.

3 Add enough rubbing alcohol to each jar to cover the leaf pieces. Tape the end of one of the coffee filter strips you prepared to the midpoint of a pencil. Lay the pencil across the top of the jar so that the end of the strip just touches the rubbing alcohol (see illustration). The strip should begin to absorb the liquid.

⚠️ **SAFETY CHECK!** Keep rubbing alcohol away from flames or heated surfaces. Use safety goggles and provide suitable ventilation when handling rubbing alcohol.

4 When the alcohol has moved about halfway up the strips and colors are visible, remove the strips and lay them on clean paper towels to dry. This may occur in as little as one hour or it may take up to a few days.

5 **STUDENT VOICE** Invite students to describe what they see. They will likely notice green bands (chlorophyll) and yellow or orange bands (carotenoid pigments). Ask students what the demonstration tells them about why and how leaves change color in the fall.

6 You may want to point out that carotenoid pigments are always in the leaves but are usually masked by the green chlorophyll. In the fall, when the leaves no longer produce chlorophyll, the other pigments show through (see Background).

VARIATION: GRADES 6–8

1 Ask students why they think some trees' leaves turn yellow in the fall, while others turn red and still others stay green all year.

2 Introduce the protocol from Part B for separating out the three leaf pigments: chlorophyll, carotenoids, and anthocyanins.

3 Challenge student teams to plan and carry out an investigation to help them understand why different trees show different colors in the fall. They may use the protocol as the basis of their investigation (comparing leaves from different trees, for example) or another they choose.

4 Students should be able to explain their findings using scientific argumentation. See the Appendix K: Making a Scientific Argument for a sample template.

5 Encourage teams to share their findings with the group.

ACADEMIC STANDARDS

SCIENCE

Practices
- Constructing explanations and designing solutionsn

Concepts
- Variation of traits
- Structure and function
- Patterns
- Cause and effect

ENGLISH LANGUAGE ARTS

Practices
- Speaking and listening: presentation of knowledge and ideas

ASSESSMENT

Ask students to

- Draw a sequence of pictures of a local forest as it might change through the seasons. In each picture, they should include at least three signs of the season, including one human sign (e.g., people wearing warmer clothing), one wild animal sign (e.g., squirrels gathering nuts), and one plant sign (e.g., leaves changing colors).

- For Part B, explain: What happened to the filter paper? How does this experiment explain why leaves are different colors in the fall?

ENRICHMENT

- Try Part B with leaves that have already turned color. What differences do you find? (Leaves show very little, if any, green pigment.) How might this be explained? (Chlorophyll has broken down.)

- Take students outdoors to collect fallen leaves of many different colors. Challenge them to compile, analyze, and display leaf data based on the collection, perhaps on the basis of leaf color or size or tree species. Have students use different graph types—such as line, bar, or pie graphs—to display this information.

- A legend of some indigenous people of North America tells of celestial hunters who slew a great bear each fall, causing the forest leaves to turn red from the bear's blood. Invite students to create their own legends explaining why leaves change color in the fall.

- Take pictures of colorful fall trees, make prints, and create a collage. Or inventory nearby trees and document their color changes by taking pictures over time.

- Explore the importance of leaf pigments to plant and human health. For example, red leaves contain the pigment anthocyanin, which is a strong antioxidant. Create a list of high-antioxidant common foods.

NAME _____ DATE_____

1. What signs do you see that winter is approaching? List some changes that you see in living things and nonliving things.

2. Find a deciduous tree (one that loses its leaves). Make a leaf rubbing from one of its leaves on the back of this page, using a crayon that most closely matches the leaf color.

3. Find an evergreen tree with a needle-like leaf. Make a leaf rubbing from it on the back of this page, using a crayon that most closely matches its color.

4. From where you are standing, count all the deciduous trees and all the evergreen trees that you can see.

   Number of deciduous trees: _____

   Number of evergreen trees: _____

5. What differences do you observe between deciduous and evergreen trees?

I LOVE MY GREEN JOB!

CAREER CORNER

METEOROLOGISTS (me-tee-uh-ROL-uh-jists) use science and math to predict daily weather and long-term climate. They also work to understand how the atmosphere, weather, and climate affect the Earth and people.

Students explore differences in soil types and what those differences mean to people and to plants. They also investigate the role soil organisms play, both in building soil and in decomposition.

SOIL BUILDERS

SUBJECTS
Science, English Language Arts, Math, Social Studies

PLT CONCEPTS
1.2, 3.1, 4.2

STEM SKILLS
Data Analysis, Investigation, Nature-based Design

DIFFERENTIATED INSTRUCTION
Cooperative Learning, Hands-on Learning, Personal Connections, Student Voice

MATERIALS
Part A: For each team, a small plastic bag for collecting soil, trowel or shovel, toothpicks, sheet of white paper or white paper plate, magnifying glass, jar with lid, water, ruler.

Part B: For each team, one plastic container with lid (or plastic wrap), leaf litter and other organic material, eight sow bugs or pill bugs. Optional: Spray bottle of water.

TIME CONSIDERATIONS
Preparation:
Part A: 15 minutes
Part B: 15 minutes, plus time to collect living materials

Activity:
Part A: Two 50-minute periods over two days
Part B: Two 50-minute periods over the course of a week

OBJECTIVES
Students will

- Describe the physical characteristics of various soils.
- Investigate soil organisms to determine their role in the ecosystem.
- Explain the function of scavengers and decomposers.

BACKGROUND
Students often wonder why certain plants grow in some places and not in others. Climatic factors such as temperature, moisture, and sunlight are important, but subtle differences in soil also enable a plant to grow more successfully in one area than in another.

Soil, the foundation for life on Earth, is composed of mineral particles mixed with living and nonliving **organic** matter, water, and air, as well as fungi, bacteria, and other microbes. It is a dynamic, living ecosystem that sustains plants and animals, including humans. All soil originally started as parent material, a deposit of sediment or rock at the Earth's surface. Over time, a variety of factors—including sun, water, wind, ice, and living organisms—helped to transform the parent material into soil.

Soils are constantly changing. As soil ages, it is altered by water moving matter from one layer to another, by living organisms taking out nutrients and adding organic material, or by the formation of new minerals. Changes in climate also change soil, as they may cause an increase or decrease in precipitation, erosion, or available nutrients.

FOREST FACT

did you know

80% of the total carbon stored in Canada's boreal forest is in the soil. Microorganisms in the soil are essential for decomposing dead matter and storing carbon in soil humus.

Different soils are classified by their main parent material and by the size of the mineral particles.

- Sandy soil is made up of large round particles with relatively large spaces of air between them. Because sandy soil contains a lot of air or space between particles, it cannot hold water well and tends to erode easily and lose nutrients quickly.

- Silty soil is intermediate in texture between clay and sand. It feels smooth and is slippery to the touch when wet.

- Clay soil is made up of microscopic, flattened mineral particles. These tiny particles pack closely together, becoming sticky when wet and leaving little space for air and water. Because pure clay compacts tightly into a solid mass, water may be suspended above the clay (as in a swamp or a pond) or trapped below the clay, making it unavailable to plants. Clay reduces water movement so the soil feels moist.

The ratio of these components helps determine how well soil can sustain plants and withstand erosion, and which plants will grow well in that soil. A fairly equal mix of sand, silt, and clay is called **loam**. The table below describes the standards for common soil textures.

COMMON SOIL TEXTURES

	Particle Size	Feel	Nutrient-Holding Capacity	Air Space Between Particles	Water Availability
Sand	0.05–2.0 mm	Gritty	Low	Many large-sized spaces	Low
Silt	0.002–0.05 mm	Smooth	Medium	Many fair-sized spaces	Good
Clay	Less than 0.002 mm	Sticky	High	Few tiny spaces	Slow movement of water

Note: 1 mm is equal to 0.04 inches. To convert mm to inches, multiply by 0.04.

Some trees need soils that hold a lot of water, while others need drier soils. It is possible to determine the type of soil under a forest by evaluating the kinds of trees growing there. Although many factors determine which tree species grow where, certain species are closely associated with certain kinds of soils. For example:

- **Slow-draining soils** – cedars, red maples, silver maples

- **Moderately draining soils** – hemlocks, red spruces, balsam firs, aspens

- **Fast-draining soils** – white pines, white birches

Sow bugs, pill bugs, earthworms, and other soil organisms also help create soil conditions that are suitable for plants. By eating, digesting, and then excreting dead plant material, these organisms recycle nutrients back into the soil, where they are reused by plants. Soil organisms also help recycle food scraps, leaves, grass clippings, and other **biodegradable** organic wastes. When people compost their scraps and yard waste, they create the optimal conditions for this decomposition to occur and provide the necessary components for the process: soil (including microorganisms), organic wastes, nitrogen, water, air, time, heat, and mass.

PROJECT LEARNING TREE
An initiative of SFI

SOW BUG OR PILL BUG?

Turn over a rock or log, or lift up the leaf litter in a forest, and chances are you'll see small, gray, armored animals scurrying out of sight. These sow bugs (*Oniscus asellus*) and pill bugs (*Armadillidium vulgare*) are not "bugs" at all, or even insects. They are crustaceans, relatives of crabs and lobsters, and they feed on dead plant material. By eating, digesting, and then excreting dead plant material, scavengers and decomposers like sow bugs and pill bugs recycle nutrients back into the soil, where they are reused by live plants.

Though sow bugs and pill bugs look similar, there's one very easy way to tell the difference between them: pill bugs can roll into a ball to protect themselves, but sow bugs cannot. Both are found in the forest as well as in urban environments (gardens, roadside vegetation, garbage, wood piles, parks).

GETTING READY

PART A:

- Make copies of Making a Soil Shake student page.

- Scout around your site to find at least five locations where students can examine and collect different soil samples. Possibilities might include low or wet spots, baseball fields, garden areas, overgrown fields, lawns, forested areas, or under trees. Get necessary permission before taking any soil samples.

- If you do not have five different soils at your site, consider these options:

  » Ask students to bring in plastic bags of soil from different sites around their homes.

  » Use only two or three different sites, but obtain different soil types by digging deeper: for example, surface soil, soil from 6" (15 cm) deep, and soil from 12" (30.5 cm) deep.

  » Buy sterile sand (for gardening), and powdered clay (for pottery or sculpture) so you can make your own soil types. Use five different formulas to create a variety of soils, such as mixing equal parts of both, mixing three times more of one ingredient than the other, and so forth.

PART B:

- Make copies of the What's on the Menu? student page.

- Collect sow bugs or pill bugs from under rocks, logs, leaf litter, and other debris. You will need at least eight per team of students. Keep them in a large container with moist (not wet!) leaves until you're ready to use them. Also collect enough plastic containers for one per team. (Note: In temperate climates, sow bugs and pill bugs will be more difficult to find during the winter months. Schedule this activity for fall or spring, or considering doing the composting activity with worms instead of sow bugs or pill bugs, as described in the Enrichment section.)

 SAFETY CHECK! Sow bugs and pill bugs are not dangerous, so you can pick them up without worrying for your safety, but you do need to be careful not to hurt them. If you don't want to touch them with your fingers, try using a spoon to quickly scoop them up and place them into a container. Sow bugs and pill bugs cannot live indoors for a long time. You should collect them, have students make their observations, and then return the animals outdoors within a week.

DOING THE ACTIVITY

PART A: RECIPE FOR SOIL

1 **PERSONAL CONNECTIONS** Ask students what they think soil is made of. List all the elements that students name, whether they are correct or not. Discuss:

- Is soil the same everywhere? How do you know?

- What differences might there be between soils collected from different areas? (For example, color, texture, moisture, amount of different materials.)

- What do plants get from soil? (For example, air, water, nutrients, support to hold them.)

- Do different plants have different soil needs? (For example, some need dry soil, while others need wet soil.)

2 Divide the group into teams, and have each team collect and analyze a different soil sample. You can either assign locations or let them choose their own, making sure that teams collect from different locations. Distribute the bags and digging tools to each team. Direct each team to collect a sample of soil (at least one-half cup or 120 mL).

 SAFETY CHECK! Always have students wash hands thoroughly after handling soil, as it might contain contaminants.

3 **HANDS-ON LEARNING** Back inside, have teams transfer their soil sample to a sheet of white paper or a white paper plate. Have them use toothpicks and a magnifying glass to examine their soil and to sort the soil particles into different materials.

4 **STUDENT VOICE** After a few minutes, ask students whether sorting soil this way is easy or hard to do. Suggest that they brainstorm easier ways to sort the soil particles. If possible, try one or more of their alternative ideas.

5 Share with students that one method you know to separate different kinds of soil particles is to make a "soil shake." Distribute the Making a Soil Shake student page and have them answer the first two questions.

6 Show students how to make a "soil shake" by placing one-half cup (120 mL) of their soil into a jar with a lid and adding about 2 cups (500 mL) of water. Ask them to predict what will happen if they shake the closed jar and let it settle for a couple of minutes. They should record their predictions on the student page. Younger students may draw a picture of what they expect to see.

7 Have students close the lid tightly and shake the jar vigorously for a couple of minutes. Allow the soil to settle for at least two hours, but preferably overnight.

8 Students will be able to observe the layers that have formed in each jar. Since larger components settle out first, the soil particles will fall out in layers. Pebbles will fall first, then sand, silt, and clay. The organic materials (leaves, twigs, and stems) will float or be suspended in the water. Have students draw on the student page a picture of the layers formed by their sample. Encourage them to measure the layers and indicate the measurements in their drawings. Ask students to compare their picture with their prediction. Invite them to explain any patterns that they notice.

PROJECT LEARNING TREE
An initiative of SFI

9 Invite students to share their results with the group and to compare the different soil shakes. They might use graphic organizer software or presentation software to display their data in diagrams or tables. What similarities and differences do they observe? What might account for the differences?

10 Lead a discussion about students' results and what they tell us about soils. With younger students, you might discuss how soils are an important element of organisms' habitat, and that different soils mean that different plants and animals can live in a particular place. With older students, you also might discuss students' ideas about why there are different-sized particles in different soils.

PART B: SOIL ORGANISMS

1 Ask students how they think soil is made. Ask: What do you think are some ways that animals or plants might help to make soil? How might we investigate this?

2 Have the students pretend that they are teams of scientists who have been asked to solve a mystery. Explain that someone has found some strange-looking soil creatures and wants the scientists to identify what the animals eat. Suggest that perhaps these soil creatures can provide a clue about how animals can help make soil.

3 Give each team a couple of the sow or pill bugs you collected earlier so students can look at them. Ask students if they have ever seen these animals and what they know about them.

4 Tell students that the person who collected the animals found them under moist leaves near a house and under several large rocks in the backyard. Have students brainstorm a list of foods the animals might eat and make a group list where all can see it.

5 **COOPERATIVE LEARNING** Invite each team to pick two of the foods listed in Step 4 to see which one the animal prefers. Tell students that each team will set up a study container and use a data sheet to record their observations. Ask students how they might conduct a fair test in order to get the best results. If they are stumped for ideas, you might suggest some (for example, providing the same number of food pieces and same size pieces, and placing the food equidistant from the animals). Why might these things matter in a fair test?

6 Give one container to each team. Have students gather tiny bits of potential foods (leaves, vegetables, wood, grass, and so on) they are going to investigate. Tell them to make sure their samples are moist, but not soaking wet. They can moisten the food with a spray bottle if needed. Have them label their container with the names of the team members.

7 Give approximately eight sow or pill bugs to each team to put in their container. Place a moist crumpled paper towel in each container for the animals to hide under. Place the containers in a cool place away from direct sunlight. After the students have set up their containers, have them record their observations on their What's on the Menu? student page.

TAKE IT OUTSIDE

Explore different soils at your site using a soil percolation test, which measures how quickly soil absorbs water. Take a metal can with both ends removed and push one end of the can 1" (2.5 cm) into the ground by resting a board on top of the can and firmly tapping on the board with a hammer. Pour 1 cup (240 mL) of water into the can. Time—to the second—how long it takes the water to completely disappear from the can. Compare the result with other locations at your site

⚠ SAFETY CHECK! Do not allow students to use their bare hands to push the can into the ground. Have them use the board method described or wear work gloves.

Lead a discussion about the test results:
- Rank the sites by how long it took for the water to disappear (percolate).
- What does the data tell you about the soil's ability to filter water?
- What other differences did you note among the soils at different sites?
- What assumptions can you make about the soil based on the result of this test?
- Why might the soil's ability to filter water matter to plants and animals, including people?

SAFETY CHECK! Discuss with students how to handle the sow or pill bugs without hurting them.

8 Have students observe their sow or pill bugs and the potential foods several times over the next few days and record what they see on the student page. They may use a camera to document their observations. After making their observations, team members should leave the container open for a while to keep it from becoming too moist and making the food moldy. If the food does appear to be getting moldy, exchange it for fresh food. (You might also use the opportunity to discuss what mold is and how it functions as a decomposer.) If the paper towel seems dry, students should sprinkle a little water over it.

9 Have the teams organize and present their data to the rest of the group. After each team answers the following questions, discuss the answers with the entire group:

- Which foods did the sow bugs or pill bugs eat? Which did they prefer?

- Based on your experiments, what other foods do you think sow or pill bugs eat in the "wild"? (Answers will depend on what foods students studied during the activity, but should include similar plant materials.)

- How do sow bugs or pill bugs help make soil?

- How might sow bugs or pill bugs be important to a forest ecosystem? (By eating dead leaves and plants, they—along with other scavengers and decomposers—recycle nutrients back into the soil, making them available for plants. They keep dead material from piling up on the forest floor. Sow bugs and pill bugs are also eaten by other animals.)

ACADEMIC STANDARDS

SCIENCE
Practices
- Constructing explanations and designing solutions
- Planning and carrying out investigations

Concepts
- Earth materials and systems
- Cycles of matter and energy transfer in ecosystems
- Patterns

ENGLISH LANGUAGE ARTS
Practices
- Speaking and listening: comprehension and collaboration

MATH
Practices
- Reason abstractly and quantitatively
- Use appropriate tools strategically

Concepts
- Measurement and data

SOCIAL STUDIES
Practices
- Applying disciplinary concepts

Concepts
- Geography: human–environment interactions

ASSESSMENT

Ask students to

- Write a claim for either the soil shakes or soil organism investigation, using data from their investigation to support it.

- Describe the set-up and procedure for an experiment that would test how a variable (such as container location, amount of moisture, or temperature) affects the amount of a given food that sow bugs or earthworms eat. Give each student a variable to evaluate.

ENRICHMENT

- Challenge students to design an experiment to determine the "best" soil for young plants. For example, they might try sprouting seeds (radishes or ryegrass grow quickly) in different types of soil, while maintaining equal amounts of sun and water. They might use soil samples collected in Part A, as well as sterile sand, peat moss, and moist paper towels (no soil). See the activity Here We Grow Again (in Grades K-2) for a sample investigation.

- To demonstrate the drainage properties of different soil textures, use a flowerpot with drainage holes in the bottom. Place different soils in the pot and pour water into the pot, having the group count aloud until water leaks from the bottom. Try gravel, sand, loam, and, finally, clay.

- Set up a mini-compost container to observe another soil organism at work: earthworms. In a large watertight container, alternate layers of soil and organic waste (such as small bits of wood, vegetable scraps, or weeds), ending with soil. Avoid meat scraps, dairy products, fats, and oils. Sprinkle with enough water to moisten the material, but not make it soggy. Add one to two dozen earthworms and place the container at room temperature, but not in direct sun. Once a week, examine the organic material (wearing rubber gloves) and record the approximate amounts of each type.

 SAFETY CHECK! Collect earthworms from local soil (rather than purchasing them), and return them to the same location after the activity. (Earthworms sold at fishing, pet supply, or gardening stores are not always native to the region where they are sold. In fact, some areas of North America do not have any native earthworms. Non-native earthworms can damage forests and other ecosystems by destroying plant species and reducing biodiversity. Check with your state's Department of Natural Resources or Conservation for more information.)

Use the rich soil that the worms make to grow indoor or outdoor plants at your site. Be sure to decontaminate it first by storing it in the freezer for a month to prevent introducing unwanted organisms into your site.

STUDENT PAGE   Making a Soil Shake

NAME _____ DATE_____

1. **Describe where your soil is from.**

   - Where did you get it? _____

   - What was growing there? _____

   - What else did you notice? _____

   - Draw a picture of the site.

2. **Describe the soil.**

   - What color is it? _____

   - How does it feel? _____

   - How does it smell? _____

   - What do the largest soil particles look like? The smallest? _____

3. **Make a soil shake:**

   - Place about one-half cup (120 mL) of soil into a jar.

   - Add about 2 cups (500 mL) of water.

   - Put the lid on tight.

   What do you think will happen if you shake the jar and let it sit for a couple of hours or overnight?

   _____

   _____

NAME _____ DATE_____

4. **Shake the jar hard for a minute.** Draw what the soil and water mixture look like right after shaking.

5. **Let the jar sit untouched for a few minutes.** What do you notice happening? Write or draw what you observe.

6. **Let the jar sit untouched for several hours or overnight.** Draw what the contents of the jar look like after sitting for this amount of time.

CAREER CORNER

I LOVE MY GREEN JOB!

SOIL SCIENTISTS are really into dirt! They research how soil is related to plant growth or study how taking care of soil can improve forest health.

What's on the Menu?

NAME _____ DATE_____

| Date | SOW BUGS OR PILL BUGS | | FOOD: _____ | | | FOOD: _____ | | |
	How many?	What are they doing?	How much was put in?	How much remains?	What does it look like?	How much was put in?	How much remains?	What does it look like?

What do you think? How do sow bugs or pill bugs help make soil?

_____

_____

CAREER CORNER

<u>FOREST ECOLOGISTS</u> (ee-CALL-uh-jists) study the links between living and nonliving elements of forests. These scientists are interested in how different elements—including people—affect the health of the forest.

One way to learn about tree growth is to look at annual rings. Tree rings show patterns of change in the tree's life, as well as changes in the area where it grows. Students will trace environmental and historical changes using a cross-section of a tree, or "tree cookie."

TREE COOKIES

SUBJECTS
Science, English Language Arts, Math, Social Studies, Visual Arts

PLT CONCEPTS
5.1, 5.3

STEM SKILLS
Communication, Nature-based Design, Organization

DIFFERENTIATED INSTRUCTION
Hands-on Learning, Literacy Skills, Multiple Solution Pathways, Personal Connections

MATERIALS
Part A: Tree cookies. Optional: Magnifying glasses.

Part B: Large sheet of paper, string, tacks or pins, small paper labels, strips of paper 2" (5 cm) wide. Variation: White paper plates with ridges.

TIME CONSIDERATIONS
Preparation: 15 minutes (more if cutting tree cookies)

Activity: 50 minutes

OBJECTIVES

Students will

- Examine cross-sections of trees.
- Infer from a tree's rings what environmental conditions it might have experienced.
- Correlate the time it takes a tree to grow with events in human history.

BACKGROUND

By counting a tree's growth rings in the trunk, you can tell how old a tree was when it was cut. By counting the rings in a limb or branch, you can tell how old that part of the tree was. Every growth season, a tree adds a new layer of wood to its trunk and limbs. Each ring has two parts: a wide, light part (early wood) and a narrow, dark part (late wood). In temperate climates, the early wood grows during the wet, spring growing season. During the transition from the drier summer to fall and winter, growth slows and the late wood forms. The rings provide clues about the area's climate and weather over time, as well as evidence of environmental disturbances, such as insect pests, fires, and floods.

The shape and width of the annual rings often differ from year to year because of varying annual growth conditions. During a moist season with fast growth, a tree in a temperate region will produce a wider ring. During a drought, a colder-than-average winter, or an unseasonable frost, a tree will produce a narrow ring. **Dendrochronology** (which literally means "the study of tree time") is the science of learning about past climates by studying the ring patterns of very old trees.

FOREST FACT

You can see the growth rings of a tree without cutting it down! Foresters use a tool called an **increment borer** to see tree growth history and make management decisions. This tool drills a small hole into a tree and extracts a sample of the tree rings to analyze. The tree can heal this small hole, just as humans heal from small injuries.

Many factors can affect a tree's growth, and a tree's rings reflect its responses to these factors. Sometimes a disturbance will occur after the growth season has ended, producing a narrow or misshapen ring the following year. Scars may indicate fire or other bark damage. Lopsided rings, characterized by one narrow side and one wide side, may indicate that the tree was crowded by another tree, with the narrow rings on the side closer to the neighboring tree.

Tree rings provide viable data for foresters, forest ecologists, and climate scientists who are interested in environmental conditions. They may use core samples of the tree to study growth rings without cutting the trees down (see *Did You Know? Forest Fact*). The growth rings appear as lines on the core sample.

GETTING READY

- Obtain tree cross-sections or "tree cookies," or make your own. Tree cookies can be obtained from a local tree-trimming service, county or state forester, or utility, forest products, or firewood company.

- To make your own tree cookies, saw the trunk or limb of a fallen tree into sections that are 1–2 inches (4–5 cm) thick.

- Dry the tree cookies to prevent them from splitting. To dry, place them on foil in a kitchen oven set to "warm" for five hours; put them on a hot, sunny driveway for five days, or lay them on a dry, well-ventilated surface under low humidity for 10 days. Whichever method is used, be sure to turn the cookies over periodically so that both sides dry. Once they are dry, gently treat with sandpaper so that the rings are clearly visible.

 SAFETY CHECK! If you use an oven to dry the wood, use "warm" setting only. Higher temperatures can cause some wood species to give off fumes or to ignite.

- If you cannot obtain tree cookies, use the Tree Rings student page.

- Plan to share student pages electronically or make copies. Consider enlarging the Reading Tree Cookies student page so that the whole group can see it.

- See the activity Tree Factory for information about tree parts.

DOING THE ACTIVITY

PART A: COOKIE COUNTING

1 **HANDS-ON LEARNING** Distribute tree cookies (or share the Tree Rings student page) with students. Challenge them to estimate how old this part of the tree was when the cookie was cut. Have them describe how they estimated the age.

2 Give students a copy of the Reading Tree Cookies student page. Explain how to count the rings to find the age of a cross-section by counting only the light or only the dark rings. Count with the group the number of rings on the tree cookie parts cross-section on the student page, using the enlarged version if you made one. Then, have them count the rings of their tree cookie to determine its age.

3 **LITERACY SKILLS** List the following terms for all to see: outer bark, phloem (FLOW-uhm) or inner bark, cambium (KAM-bee-uhm), xylem (ZEYE-luhm) or sapwood, and heartwood. Have the students label the diagram on the student page with these terms, and challenge students to identify these parts on their own tree cookies.

4 Explain the different kinds of markings that tree cookies display (see Background; tree cookies might show scars from a forest fire, narrow rings from insect attacks or drought, etc.). Have students look at the three tree cookies on the bottom of the Reading Tree Cookies student page and interpret what might have happened to the tree. Discuss responses and review the answers provided in the "Answers to Reading Tree Cookies student page."

5 Optional: Distribute magnifying glasses, and have students look for small holes in the sapwood and heartwood of the tree cookie. The tiny channels enable water and nutrients to travel up the trunk and branches of the tree.

TAKE IT OUTSIDE

Locate one or more tree stumps (or fallen trees cut to clear a trail or road) near you. Encourage students to analyze the tree rings visible in each stump to determine the age and growing conditions of the tree.

PART B: TREE STORIES

1 On a large piece of paper, have students draw a life-size cross-section of a redwood tree trunk (or other large tree native to your area). An average mature redwood is about 6 feet (1.8 m) in diameter. Draw an appropriate number of growth rings for the tree's size, about 2–4 rings per inch (2.54 cm) in diameter. Remember, there should be some variety in the growth rings to reflect changing environmental conditions. As a group, decide on the year the tree began growing and the year it was cut.

2 **MULTIPLE SOLUTION PATHWAYS** Divide the group into teams. Assign each team to research certain information about the tree. Topics should include (1) significant events in the tree's lifetime, such as years of drought, flood, or fire; (2) significant world events during the life of the tree; (3) significant events in state or national history during the life of the tree; and (4) significant events of people in your community during the life of the tree. Each team should identify at least five dates for events, using the internet and other resources to obtain information.

3 Have each team select a color and make labels for their events that feature that color. Students can staple the cross-section to a bulletin board, place labels around the outside margin, and connect the labels with string to a tack inserted at the appropriate year.

4 Optional: Using a three-foot of strip of paper, make a "core sample" for the same tree (see Background). Mark lines on the tape that correspond to the tree's rings (from the bark to the tree's center). Add the core sample to the bulletin board and again use string to connect the event labels to the appropriate places on the core sample.

5 Invite teams to present the events they researched and describe how their events relate to the life of the tree.

VARIATION: GRADES K–2

1 Show students a tree cookie and explain how it was obtained from a tree. Let students feel and examine the tree cookie.

2 Point out the growth rings and explain what they can tell us about the tree (see Background). Show students how to count the rings to determine the tree's (or limb's) age and let them practice.

3 Using a paper plate, demonstrate how to create a "tree cookie" using the bumpy perimeter as the bark, the smooth inside edge as the cambium, and the center circle as the heartwood.

4 **PERSONAL CONNECTIONS** Have students use a paper plate and crayons to create a tree cookie the same age as themselves. Have them identify when important events in their lives took place, such as when they were born, when they started school, and so on. Use this information to write or narrate a "My Life as a Tree" autobiography.

ANSWERS TO READING TREE COOKIES STUDENT PAGE

1. Heartwood

2. Xylem

3. Cambium

4. Phloem

5. Outer bark

6. Drought or insect attack. The narrow rings signify growth-inhibiting factors.

7. Crowding. The lopsided rings show what happens when a tree is too close to another tree. The narrow rings are on the side that is closest to the other tree.

PROJECT LEARNING TREE
An initiative of SFI

ACADEMIC STANDARDS

SCIENCE

Practices
- Obtaining, evaluating, and communicating information

Concepts
- Structure and function
- Stability and change

ENGLISH LANGUAGE ARTS

Practices
- Reading informational text: integration of knowledge and ideas

MATH

Practices
- Reason abstractly and quantitatively

Concepts
- Measurement and data

SOCIAL STUDIES

Practices
- Evaluating sources and using evidence
- Communicating conclusions and taking informed action

Concepts
- History: change, continuity, and context

ASSESSMENT

Ask students to

- Examine a tree cross-section (or photograph of one) and write a possible scenario that accurately interprets the growth ring pattern displayed.

- Read "The Forest Tree's Tale" on the Tales of Two Trees student page and draw what the tree's growth rings might look like. Make sure students have indicated the events in the tree's life at points that match the timeframe in the story.

- Read "The Urban Tree's Tale" on the Tales of Two Trees student page and extend the story to include what would happen in the tree's sixth, eighth, fifteenth, and twentieth years. Students should include events that affect the tree's growth, both positively and negatively, and should draw a tree cookie showing appropriate growth rings to support their story.

ENRICHMENT

- Introduce the idea that forests can be sustainably managed in ways that protect their health and allow for the production of timber and other forest products. Develop a list of actions that foresters might take to encourage sustainable tree growth. For example, foresters might assess tree health, check for disease or pests and treat as necessary, remove selected large trees to allow smaller trees to grow (using the cut trees for timber), or harvest mature trees (and replant). Discuss how these actions affect tree growth and ring patterns.

- Invite a forester to talk with your group about how he or she uses core sampling to learn about trees and the forest environment and make forest decisions. Ask the forester to bring an increment borer and demonstrate its use on a tree at your site (be sure to obtain all necessary permissions).

- Locate a nearby tree to adopt. See the activity Adopt a Tree (in Grades K-2) for more information.

NAME _____ DATE _____

Estimate how old this part of the tree was when it was cut. How do you know?

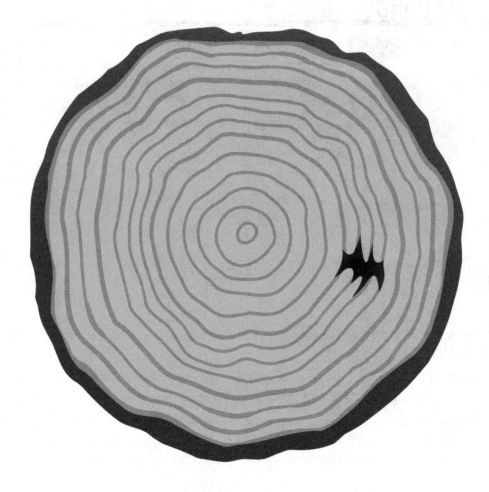

CAREER CORNER

FORESTRY TECHNICIANS help foresters monitor the health of forest trees. One way they do that is to take core samples from living trees to see the pattern of the trees' growth rings.

Reading Tree Cookies

STUDENT PAGE

NAME_____ DATE_____

Use the image at the right to label the tree cookie parts:

1_____

2_____

3_____

4_____

5_____

How old was this tree when it was cut? _____

Cookie clues: What happened to the tree where the arrow points?

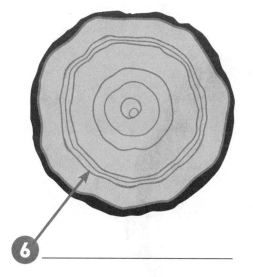

6_____

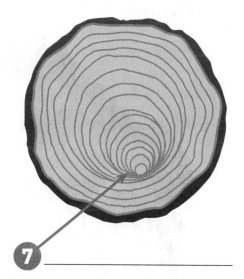

7_____

CAREER CORNER

I LOVE MY GREEN JOB!

<u>CLIMATE SCIENTISTS</u> study long-term weather patterns. One way they learn about weather that happened in the past is to look at tree growth rings. In warm, wet years, trees grow faster—and have wider growth rings—than in cool, dry years.

NAME _____ DATE_____

Draw growth rings in the blank tree cookies to match each story.

The Forest Tree's Tale

Once upon a time, a tree grew in the forest. **In its first 10 years**, it grew slowly because the large trees overhead blocked the sunlight.

In its 11th year, a large tree next to it blew down in a storm. This allowed sunlight to reach the little tree, and for the next 10 years it grew rapidly.

In its 21st and 22nd years, there was a severe drought, and the tree could not get enough water. This stress caused the tree to grow very slowly for three years.

In its 25th year, favorable conditions returned, and the tree grew normally for 15 years.

In its 40th year, wildfire raged through the forest. The tree's thick bark enabled it to survive, but it was deeply scarred. It grew slowly for several years after that.

Year 45 was particularly bad. Bark beetles got under its skin, fungus entered its body through woodpecker holes, and caterpillars ate most of its leaves. For five years, the tree hardly grew at all and became very weak.

In its 50th year, it blew down in a storm. A science teacher found the fallen tree and used a chainsaw to make a big tree cookie from the trunk.

NAME _____ DATE _____

The Urban Tree's Tale

Once upon a time, a tree seedling was planted on an urban street close to a school.

In the first two years after the tree was planted, there was not much rain. Since the tree's root system was not very developed, it grew very slowly.

In the third year, there was lots of rainfall and the tree grew rapidly.

In the fourth year, a car backed into the trunk of the tree, tearing off parts of the bark and leaving some of the trunk exposed.

In the fifth year, students from the school adopted the street tree. They watered it weekly and placed trunk-protecting mesh around it so that it could heal from its injury.

Add to Urban Tree's Tale, describing events for each of these years that follow. Add these rings to your drawing.

In the sixth year... _____

_____

In the eighth year ..._____

_____

In the 15th year ..._____

_____

In the 20th year ..._____

_____

Source: Jessica Kratz, Greenbelt Conservancy, Staten Island, NY.

CAREER CORNER

I LOVE MY GREEN JOB!

URBAN FORESTERS plant, care for, and protect the trees in a city. Urban forests provide shade, improve air quality, reduce energy use, absorb carbon dioxide, and add beauty to the community.

By modeling the parts of a tree and creating a "tree factory," students will learn about the structure of a tree.

TREE FACTORY

SUBJECTS
Science, Physical Education, Performing Arts

PLT CONCEPTS
4.1, 4.2

STEM SKILLS
Collaboration, Creativity, Nature-based Design

DIFFERENTIATED INSTRUCTION
Hands-on Learning, Nonlinguistic Representations, Personal Connections

MATERIALS
Slips of paper, paper sack, yarn or string. Optional: tape. Variation: Leaves, magnifying glasses.

TIME CONSIDERATIONS
Preparation: 20 minutes

Activity: 50 minutes

OBJECTIVES

Students will

- Describe the structure of a tree.
- Explain how different parts of a tree help the tree function.

BACKGROUND

From a tree's tiny root hairs buried in the ground to the highest leaves in its crown, each part of a tree plays a role in helping it to function. Here's a rundown of the various parts of a tree and what each one does:

LEAVES

Leaves are the food factories of a tree. Using energy from the sun, which they capture with a pigment called **chlorophyll**, leaves convert carbon dioxide and water into oxygen and sugar (which they use for food!).

This process is called **photosynthesis**. The gases needed for and generated by photosynthesis enter and exit through tiny holes called **stomata**, under the leaves. Water vapor also exits through the stomata in the process of transpiration.

TRUNK AND BRANCHES

The trunk provides support for branches, which in turn support the tree's leaves. The trunk and branches contain the tree's "plumbing"—the tubes that transport water and nutrients to the leaves and sugar from the leaves to the rest of the tree. They also contain the growing layer of the tree that makes the trunk, branches, and roots of the tree thicker each year.

Here's a look at a tree trunk from the inside to the outside and a description of what each layer does (see diagram):

- **Heartwood** forms the central core of the tree, is made up of dense dead wood (former xylem), and provides strength for the tree.

- **Xylem** (ZEYE-luhm), also called sapwood, carries water and nutrients up from the roots to the leaves. Older xylem cells become part of the heartwood.

- **Cambium** (KAM-bee-uhm), a very thin layer of growing tissue, makes cells that become new xylem, phloem, or cambium.

- **Phloem** (FLOW-uhm), also called the inner bark, carries water and the sugar made in the leaves down to other parts of the tree, such as roots, stems, buds, flowers, and fruits.

PROJECT LEARNING TREE
An initiative of SFI

FOREST FACT

Trees help support many other living organisms, including lichens, which appear most often on the tree trunk. Lichens function as bioindicators, as their presence often indicates good air quality.

did you know?

- **Bark** protects the tree from injury caused by insects and other animals, by other plants like ivy, by disease, and by fire. Bark characteristics vary from species to species. For example, it may be thin, thick, spongy, rough, smooth, covered with spines, and so on, depending on the type of tree.

ROOTS

A tree's roots help anchor the tree in the ground. They also absorb water and nutrients from the soil. Trees have **lateral roots** that spread out from the tree and cover a broad area. Some trees also have a taproot that grows straight into the ground. As a tree's lateral roots grow away from the tree, they branch into finer and finer roots called rootlets. The rootlets themselves are, in turn, covered by even finer root hairs. These root hairs absorb approximately 95% of the water and nutrients absorbed by the tree.

GETTING READY

- Write the following parts of a tree on separate slips of paper and put them in a sack. There are enough parts here for a group of 30 students. You may need to adjust the numbers depending on the size of your group. For much smaller groups, you could create a "cross-section" view of the tree with just one or two students representing each part.

    Heartwood: 1
    Xylem: 3
    Tap root: 1
    Lateral roots: 3
    Cambium: 5
    Phloem: 5
    Bark: 8
    Leaves: 4
    Total = 30 slips of paper

- Make four branches for your tree by cutting yarn or string into four 6-foot (1.8-m) lengths. Cut four additional lengths of yard or string to represent the phloem, using a different color, if possible.

- ⬗ **NONLINGUISTIC REPRESENTATIONS** Read over the activity steps. Depending on students' physical or language abilities, adjust the movements or chants for the different tree parts.

- Find a large, open area where the students can build the tree.

- For the Variation, you will need an outside area that has a tree and enough space to allow the students to spread out and sit on the ground.

1 Ask students what people need to survive (such as food, water, air). Identify parts of the body that help process those basic needs (such as a nose and lungs to breathe, mouth to eat). Explain that trees are like people in many ways.

⊗ **PERSONAL CONNECTIONS** Throughout the activity, as new terminology is introduced, relate it to the human body to provide connections (heartwood = skeleton; xylem, phloem, cambium = veins; taproot = feet; lateral roots = toes; bark = skin; leaves = hands).

2 Ask the group to think about trees and what they need to survive (such as food, sun, water, air, and space). List their ideas where the whole group can see them. Ask them how the tree gets these things, especially since trees can't move around the way most animals can. You might ask questions such as

- How do trees get the water they need?
- Where does the water come from?
- How does it get into the tree?
- How does it get around to all the parts of the tree?
- How do trees get the food they need?
- How do they keep from blowing over in the wind?

3 ⊗ **NONLINGUISTIC REPRESENTATIONS** Invite students to create a model of a tree by acting out the tree parts they just discussed. Have each student pick one slip of paper from the sack to find out what role to play in the model. Take students to an area with lots of space to build the tree.

4 Ask students what makes up the center of the tree and gives the tree strength (heartwood). The student portraying **heartwood** should stand in the center of an open area, tighten his or her muscles, and chant, "I support; I support."

5 Ask students what part transports water to all parts of the tree (xylem). Have the **xylem** students join hands to form a small circle around the heartwood. Have these students chant, "We carry water; we carry water," as they raise their joined hands up and down.

6 Ask students where the water in the xylem comes from (it's absorbed by the roots). Then have the **taproot** sit down with his or her back against the xylem, and have the **lateral roots** lie down on the ground with their feet toward the xylem and their arms and fingers spread out to represent root hairs. Have the roots make sucking noises.

PROJECT LEARNING TREE
An initiative of SFI

7 Ask students where the water in the xylem travels (to the leaves). Then have the heartwood hold the ends of four pieces of yarn or string that you cut earlier. Give the other ends of the pieces to four different students who represent *leaves*. Ask the leaves what they do all day (make food through photosynthesis). Have the leaves flutter their hands and chant, "We make food; we make food."

8 Ask the leaves what happens to all the food they make using sunlight, air, and water (it gets transported to the rest of the tree). Ask everyone what part of the tree transports the food from the leaves to the rest of the tree (phloem). Have the *phloem* students join hands and form a large circle around the tree. Give the leaves the other four pieces of yarn or string you cut and give the other ends to six different students who represent the phloem. Then have them simulate the role of the phloem by reaching above their heads and grabbing (for food), and then squatting and opening their hands (releasing the food) while chanting, "We carry food; we carry food."

9 Ask students if they've left out an important part of the tree. What layer produces new xylem and phloem to keep the tree growing and healthy (cambium)? Have the *cambium* students form a circle between the phloem and the xylem. Tell them to sway from side to side and chant, "We make new cells; we make new cells."

10 Ask students what final component of their tree is missing—it's something that protects the tree (bark). Have the *bark* students lock arms and form a circle that comes out from the center of the tree. Ask them to look tough. Have them march in place chanting, "We protect; we protect."

11 When the tree is completely assembled, have all students act out and chant their parts simultaneously. If you want, you can end the session by telling the students their tree is old and falls over. Let everyone carefully fall down.

VARIATION: GRADES K–2

1 Ask students to name what living things need to survive (sun, air, water, food, and space). List their ideas where everyone can see them. Explain that they will find out how members of one group of living things (trees) get what they need to survive.

2 Have students sit down around a tree. Ask how trees get the water they need.

- Where does the water come from? (From rain, snowmelt, dew, or groundwater.)

- How does it get into the tree? (It's absorbed by the roots.)

- How does it get to all the different parts of the tree? (Tiny "pipes" in the xylem carry water to the trunk, branches, and leaves.)

As the students discuss each question, have them act out the answers. For example, they can simulate rain falling by patting their hands on their legs or the ground, they can simulate roots by lying on their backs with their arms and legs spread out as they make slurping sounds, and they can simulate xylem chanting, "We carry water; we carry water."

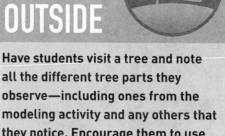

TAKE IT OUTSIDE

Have students visit a tree and note all the different tree parts they observe—including ones from the modeling activity and any others that they notice. Encourage them to use evidence from their observations to identify the main parts of a tree above ground. Make sure not to hurt the tree by damaging the bark or compacting the soil around its roots.

3 Next, ask students where trees get the food they need to survive. Do they chase after animals? Grab things with their branches? (No! They make their own food in their leaves by using energy from the sun.) Then have the students imitate how the leaves make food. Have them hold their arms up and alternately curl and straighten their fingers ("leaves") while chanting, "We make food; we make food."

4 ⬤ **HANDS-ON LEARNING** Explain that the leaves also "breathe" by taking in gases from the air and releasing other gases through tiny holes in their undersides (stomata). You might pass around some leaves and magnifying glasses so students can look for these holes.

5 Have students stand up in a circle around the trunk of the tree. What does the trunk do for the tree? (It provides strength, supports the branches and leaves, and contains all the "pipes" that transport water and food to different parts of the tree.) Then have the students act out the trunk of the tree by standing straight and tall and by looking strong. Have them chant "We support; we support."

6 Have students feel the bark of a living tree and describe what it feels and looks like, making sure to avoid damaging the bark. Then ask them how bark might be useful to a tree. (It protects it from insect pests, chewing animals, and disease.) Have students act out the role of bark by holding hands and forming a circle with all students facing out from the center. Have them chant, "We protect; we protect."

7 Have students look for seeds, fruits, nuts, or cones on the tree, but make sure they don't pick anything directly off the tree. Ask them what these parts of the trees do (they produce new trees). Then have them act out a seed growing into a tree by scrunching down into a ball (the seed) and then slowly straightening and standing up until their arms are raised over their heads.

8 Ask students what keeps the tree from blowing over (roots). Then divide the group into two parts. Have all students lie down with their arms and legs spread out, and have one group make slurping sounds (to simulate the roots absorbing water) while the other group chants: "Stay in place; stay in place" (to express how roots anchor the tree).

9 Finally, call students together to build a model tree. Divide the students into three groups. One group, the roots, should stand close together with their arms entwined and chant, "We drink up water; we drink up water." The next group, the bark, should make a circle around the roots, join hands, and chant, "We protect; we protect." Members of the last group, the leaves, should stand at various distances around the bark and chant, "We make food; we make food" while flexing their fingers.

ACADEMIC STANDARDS

SCIENCE

Practices
- Developing and using models
- Engaging in argument from evidence

Concepts
- Structure and function
- Systems and system models
- Energy and matter

ASSESSMENT

Ask students to

- Create a model of a tree, label all the tree parts they've learned about, and explain what each part does. Provide art supplies such as drawing paper, scissors, construction paper, toilet paper rolls, straws, aluminum foil, scissors, and tissue paper. They may explain orally or create labels. Encourage them to be as creative as possible while still being accurate.

- Write a story or draw a cartoon sequence that shows how a tree gets the water and food it needs to live. The stories should include all the tree parts from the activity and an explanation of what the parts do.

ENRICHMENT

- Take photos of students doing the activity. Have students create a story about their tree using the images and a presentation app.

- Have the students look at cross-sections of a tree (tree cookies) and identify the heartwood, xylem, phloem, and bark. (The cambium is a very thin layer in between the xylem and phloem and may be too difficult to see.) You may also want to do the activity Tree Cookies.

- Ask students how a tree is similar to a factory. (It takes in raw materials—sunlight, air, and water—and manufactures products—leaves, fruits, nuts, and flowers.) What different departments are found in a "tree factory," and what jobs are done by each? (For example, in the "roots department," the tree gets anchored to the ground and water is absorbed from the soil, and so on.) Have students draw a cut-away diagram of a tree factory in which you can see the jobs that are done by each department.

- Point out that trees have inspired many metaphors and similes that describe people and their behavior, such as "shaking like a leaf" or "tall as a tree." Challenge students to create new metaphors and similes based on different parts of a tree.

- After exploring how a tree works, have your students consider how they benefit from trees. Have students draw a small tree in the center of a page, on a piece of paper or using a graphic design app. Have students draw eight lines radiating from the tree like the spokes of a wheel. On each line, have them write or draw something the tree gives to them (such as beauty, shade, furniture, pencils, paper, apples, something to play on, etc.).

Tree species can be identified by looking at several different features: leaves, bark, twigs, flowers, fruit, and seeds. Even the overall shape of a tree can give clues to the tree's identity. Students learn more about trees through these identifying features. Afterward, they can play an active game that tests their knowledge of different types of trees.

TREE ID

SUBJECTS
Science, English Language Arts, Visual Arts

PLT CONCEPTS
2.4, 4.1

STEM SKILLS
Investigation, Nature-based design, Organization

DIFFERENTIATED INSTRUCTION
Hands-on Learning, Multiple Solution Pathways

MATERIALS
Part A: Tree leaves, copies of identification sheets (see Getting Ready), pencils. Optional: Tree field guide or identification app, clipboards.

Part B: Leaves, slips of paper. Optional: Paper sacks.

TIME CONSIDERATIONS
Preparation: 60 minutes or more

Activity:
Part A: 30 minutes
Part B: 30 minutes

OBJECTIVES

Students will

- Describe how leaf shapes, sizes, and other characteristics vary from plant to plant.
- Identify several trees using various physical characteristics.

BACKGROUND

Identifying trees is not only fun and interesting, it can also help people

- Choose the most suitable tree species to plant on a certain site.
- Determine the best care for trees.
- Diagnose pest issues.
- Recognize whether the trees are invasive.
- Determine whether the trees can provide lumber, paper, medicine, food, or other products.

Here are some characteristics that people use to identify trees:

NEEDLES OR BROAD LEAVES

There are two basic kinds of trees in the world: **conifers** or coniferous trees, and **broadleafed** or **deciduous** trees. Conifers have seeds that develop inside cones. Pines, spruces, hemlocks, and firs are all conifers. Most conifers also have needle-shaped **leaves** and are evergreen, which means they don't lose all their leaves each year but instead stay green year-round. Deciduous trees, such as oaks, maples, beeches, and aspens, have broad, flat leaves. They generally lose all of their leaves each year. They produce their seeds from pollinated flowers rather than from cones.

Some trees, however, aren't typical conifers or deciduous trees. For example, larches are conifers that have cones and needles but lose their leaves every year, and are thus "deciduous." Yew trees are conifers that have needle-shaped leaves and are evergreen but have berries rather than cones, and hollies are broadleafed trees that are evergreen.

THE SHAPE OF LEAVES

The overall shape of a leaf gives clues to the tree's identity. For example, willows have long, slender leaves; cherry trees and swamp magnolias have oval leaves; and cottonwoods have triangular or spade-shaped leaves. Fir needles tend to be flat, pine

Forests of the Blue Ridge Mountains, part of the Appalachian Mountain region, span seven states in the mid-Atlantic and contain more than 158 tree species. This region features some of the greatest floral diversity of any North American forest. Two of the dominant forest types are deciduous upland oak and coniferous spruce-fir, found at higher elevations.

needles are rounded, and sprucc needles are square-shaped. The shapes of leaves differ in many ways. For example, the tips of leaves may be notched, pointed, rounded, tapered, and so on, while their bases may be squared, rounded, heart-shaped, and so on.

MARGINS OF LEAVES
The edges or margins of leaves can also provide clues to the tree's identity. For example, some leaves are serrated, with teeth along their margins; some leaves have lobes, like oak leaves; and some leaf margins are smooth (entire). See *Margins of Leaves* diagram.

TEXTURES OF LEAVES
Some leaves are completely hairy, others have hairs on only one side, and others are completely smooth. Leaves may also be thick, thin, rough, or waxy.

SIMPLE VS. COMPOUND LEAVES
When most people think of leaves, they think of simple leaves. Simple leaves exist individually. Maple, oak, aspen, sycamore, and many other trees have simple leaves. Compound leaves, on the other hand, are made up of several leaflets, organized in a predictable pattern. (See *Simple vs. Compound Leaves* diagram). Ash, walnut, and sumac trees all have compound leaves.

LEAF ARRANGEMENTS
Another characteristic that can help you identify a tree is the way its leaves are arranged on the twigs. Many trees have alternate leaves that are staggered along the twig. Other trees have opposite leaves that grow in pairs along the twig (see *Leaf Arrangements* diagram). And some leaves grow in whorls, or circular patterns around the twig. The leaves on pines, spruces, firs, and other needle-leaved trees also grow in patterns. For example, leaves on pines commonly grow in clusters of two, three, or five, depending on the species.

TWIGGY CLUES
If you know what to look for, even leafless twigs on a winter tree can tell you the tree's identity. By looking at where the leaf scars or **buds** are on the twig, you can tell if the leaves grow in an alternate, opposite, or whorled pattern. (Leaf scars are the places on the twigs where leaves used to be attached.) The size, color, and shape of buds, as well as spines and thorns on twigs, can also help identify a tree.

MARGINS OF LEAVES

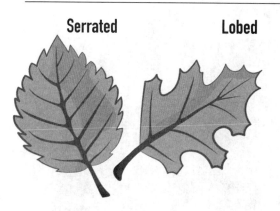

Serrated   Lobed

SIMPLE VS. COMPOUND LEAVES

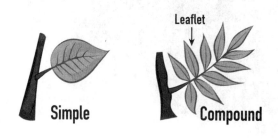

Leaflet

Simple   Compound

LEAF ARRANGEMENTS

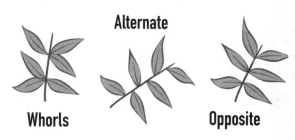

Alternate

Whorls   Opposite

FRUIT AND FLOWERS

Different trees produce different kinds of fruit, such as berries, winged seeds, nuts, or pods. Different conifers produce different kinds of cones. Different trees also have different flowers. The shape, color, texture, size, and other characteristics of the fruit, cones, and flowers can be used to identify trees.

BARK BASICS

Many people can identify trees just by looking at the color and texture of tree bark. For instance, bark may be shaggy, smooth, or rough; it may have deep furrows or markings. Paper birch is easily identified by its white, paper-like bark. It's best to look at bark growing on the trunk rather than on branches and twigs, because the bark on a branch is thinner and newer, and it may look quite different from the trunk). Bark also looks different as a tree ages.

SHAPING UP

Many trees have characteristic shapes or forms that can be used to identify them. In fact, just by glancing at the shape of a distant tree and the color of its leaves, some people can tell what kind of tree it is. For example, the American elm is vase- or fountain-shaped, with a trunk that is divided into large branches that spread further apart toward the top of the tree, while the Colorado blue spruce is shaped like a pyramid with branches that appear layered.

GETTING READY

PART A:

- Locate an area where the students can collect leaves (from the ground, if possible) from several different kinds of trees. You may also want to collect a sample. Try to include some needle-shaped ones from coniferous trees, collecting the entire cluster in which they grow. In temperate climates, this is easiest to do in the fall.

- As an alternative to real leaves, you may print and cut apart leaf drawings or photos, and then laminate them.

 SAFETY CHECK! Make sure you have the landowner's permission to collect leaves. Also, be aware that some students may be allergic to tree pollen. If so, adjust the activity as necessary to avoid contact.

PART B:

- Identify 7–10 trees on or near your site. If you don't have trees where you are, you can use shrubs or digital images from the internet instead. To identify the trees, you may use field guides or a tree identification app; ask a groundskeeper or fellow educator; or enlist the help of a forester, naturalist, arborist, or other tree specialist. Number each tree using an index card on string, landscape flags, or other identifiers.

- Create a tree identification sheet with a block of clues for each tree you have identified. Clues may include drawings or photos of the leaves, descriptions of the tree's bark or shape (such as "I have a pointy top"), or other information. Clues should not include phrases that tell the students where to look for the tree. Under each set of clues, write the name of the tree and place a square or circle for students to write in the tree number. See the *Sample Tree ID Sheet* on page 189 for an example.

SAMPLE TREE ID SHEET

My bark is gray, with long ridges.
My leaves are shaped like tulip flowers.

I am a tulip poplar.   TREE NUMBER

My branches look like spokes on a wheel.
My leaves grow in bundles of five needles.

I am a white pine.   TREE NUMBER

I have a broad, white trunk.
My leaves quiver in the breeze.

I am a cottonwood.   TREE NUMBER

My flowers grow like tassels.
I am shaped like a pyramid.

I am a pin oak.   REE NUMBER

My bark is orangey-brown.
My leaves have a sweet, fruity smell.

I am a sassafras.   TREE NUMBER

I am one of the straightest trees around.
I grow round, spiny seed pods.

I am a sweet gum.   TREE NUMBER

PART A: SORTING LEAVES

1 Ask each student to collect 3–5 different kinds of leaves. Encourage them to pick leaves off the ground rather than pulling them off trees.

 SAFETY CHECK! Establish clear rules of behavior, including respect for all living things.

2 **HANDS-ON LEARNING** Have teams of two or three students examine their leaves and sort them into groups according to criteria that they determine.

3 Have teams share some of the ways they sorted the leaves. Ask:

- What are some differences?
- What do the leaves have in common?
- Do any leaves have teeth (jagged edges)?
- Do any have hairs? Where?
- What do the leaves feel like?
- Who found the biggest leaf? The narrowest leaf? The smallest leaf?
- Have any leaves been eaten by insects? How can you tell?
- Can you trace the veins on your leaves with your fingers?

4 **HANDS-ON LEARNING** Optional: For students with visual impairment, cover the leaf veins with waxed yarn to better show the vein arrangement.

5 You may also want to point out leaf characteristics (from Background information), leaf bases and tips, leaf margins (edges), simple and compound leaves, and alternate and opposite branching patterns.

PART B: MYSTERY TREES

1 **MULTIPLE SOLUTION PATHWAYS** Ask students what characteristics they might use to identify trees. List their ideas where all can see and ask how they could use these characteristics to identify trees.

2 Give teams of two or three students copies of the identification sheet you made (see Getting Ready). Tell teams to use the sheets to identify trees on or near the site. Explain that they must find the tree that matches all the clues in a clue block.

3 Call the teams back together and go over the sheets as a group. Which team made the most correct identifications?

TAKE IT OUTSIDE

Take the students to an open area for a relay race. Place three leaves from each tree from Part B in a pile in front of each team. (You may wish to laminate the leaves between two pieces of clear contact paper.) Call out the name of a tree or hold up a leaf and say, "Go." The first student in each team should run, walk, or roll to the pile of leaves, find the leaf that comes from the tree you named, and hold it up. Each team gets one point for each leaf correctly identified. After each round, put the leaves back in the piles, and ask players to go to the end of their team's line. Continue the relay with the next student in line. The team with the most points wins.

ACADEMIC STANDARDS

SCIENCE

Practices
- Constructing explanations and designing solutions

Concepts
- Variation of traits
- Patterns

ENGLISH LANGUAGE ARTS

Practices
- Speaking and listening: comprehension and collaboration
- Language: vocabulary acquisition and use

ASSESSMENT

Ask students to

- Use a Venn diagram (or graphic organizer software) to compare two different leaves, either real or digital images. They may include characteristics such as leaf texture, color, shape, size, margins, smell, and vein or needle arrangement. Students then answer the question: Are these leaves more alike or more different? Have them support their answer with observations from their Venn diagram.

- Create their own field guides or riddle books for the trees they studied. Explain that they should design their books so that other students can use them to identify the trees. Their books should include the characteristics they learned about, such as leaf shape, bark color and texture, and the branching pattern of leaves. They might want to include tree drawings, bark rubbings, or leaf prints in their guides. Students might scan the leaves and use word processing or presentation software to create their books.

ENRICHMENT

Have students use one of the following methods to make prints of the leaves they collected in the activity. You can also make leaf print cards for playing "Memory" or for creating their own identification guides.

LEAF CRAYON RUBBINGS

Materials: Dark-colored crayons, plain drawing paper.

Directions: Set the leaf on a smooth surface, preferably vein-side up, then cover it with a plain piece of paper. Rub a crayon sideways back and forth across the paper above the leaf. The margin of the leaf and its veins should begin to show on the paper as you rub gently.

LEAF PRINTS

Materials: Tempera, paintbrush, paper.

Directions: Brush a thin layer of paint on the back of a leaf and lay it onto a piece of paper. Afterward, you can wash the leaves in a bucket to reuse them.

SPATTER PRINTS

Materials: 9" x 12" (23 cm x 30 cm) wire, plastic, or nylon net screen; toothbrush; straight pins; tempera paint; paper.

Directions: Place a leaf on a sheet of paper and secure it with pins. Then place the screen over the leaf and paint across the screen using a toothbrush. Afterward, lift off the screen, unpin the leaf, and carefully lift the leaf away.

PRESSED LEAVES

Materials: Iron, towel, wax paper.

Directions: Place a leaf between two layers of wax paper and then cover with a towel. Press the towel with a warm iron, being sure to iron over the entire area of wax paper. (This will seal the leaf between the two layers of wax paper.) Afterward, you can cut out each leaf, leaving a narrow margin of wax paper around the entire edge of the leaf. Then you can punch holes through the wax paper at the top margin of the leaf and hang the pressed leaf. Use several leaves to make a hanging leaf mobile or unique bookmarks.

LEAF PRINT T-SHIRTS

Materials: Clean, poly–cotton blend T-shirt; acrylic paints; paintbrush; piece of cardboard; wax paper; paper towels

Directions: Place the shirt on a clean, flat surface; then slide the cardboard between the front and back of the shirt to keep paint from soaking through. Place a leaf on a sheet of wax paper and coat it with a thin layer of paint. Make sure your fingers are clean, then carefully lift the painted leaf up and place it (painted side down) on the shirt. Cover the leaf with a paper towel and press it down. Lift the leaf straight off the shirt. Make as many more leaf prints on the shirt as you would like; then hang the shirt to dry. (Note: Do not use fabric softeners to clean or dry your shirt before you start printing. Also, to make the prints last longer, rinse the finished shirt in a mild water and vinegar solution before washing it for the first time.)

Once Upon a Time..

By reading a story such as *The Lorax* by Dr. Seuss, students can examine the importance of conserving natural resources.

TREES FOR MANY REASONS

SUBJECTS
Science, English Language Arts, Social Studies

PLT CONCEPTS
2.10, 3.9, 5.10

STEM SKILLS
Collaboration, Communication, Creativity

DIFFERENTIATED INSTRUCTION
Cooperative Learning, Literacy Skills, Personal Connections, Student Voice

MATERIALS
The Lorax by Dr. Seuss, or another suitable story; index card.

Variation: *The Man Who Planted Trees* by Jean Giono.

TIME CONSIDERATIONS
Preparation: 15 minutes
Activity: 50-minute period

OBJECTIVES
Students will

- Discuss and analyze fictional stories related to natural resources.
- Determine whether the main ideas of the stories build a case for the sustainable use of natural resources.

BACKGROUND

A quick look around the home, school, or office reveals many items made from wood and other forest resources. Trees are important to us, whether they are used for products or left in their natural environment, where they provide oxygen, soil protection, carbon storage, water filtration, beauty, and habitat for plants and animals. Well-managed forests can provide these benefits while continuing to generate products that people use.

Humans depend on trees for firewood, shelter, tools, paper, and many other needs. Consumer demand for these fiber-based products helps to keep forests as forests. Without that demand, some forest landowners will find another use for their land, which may lead to deforestation. Harvesting forest trees without planting new trees or encouraging natural regeneration can also contribute to deforestation and can have severe environmental consequences on a regional and a global scale.

Sustainable forest management aims to maintain the economic, social, and environmental benefits of forests for present and future generations. Forester managers practice sustainable forestry by planting seedlings and helping trees

FOREST FACT

did you know

In well-managed forests, harvested areas are reforested or planted with seedlings to keep the forest healthy. **Forest certification** is a process in which a professional certifier confirms that the forest is being managed sustainably. Products that come from these forests are labeled to indicate that they are certified, so consumers can find them easily.

grow well. They also work to protect the many other **ecosystem services** that forests provide, including maintaining soil, air, and water quality; storing carbon; supporting biological diversity; providing wildlife and aquatic life habitats; and providing recreational opportunities.

GETTING READY

- Obtain a copy of *The Lorax* to read aloud to your students. (For the Variation, you may choose to use *The Man Who Planted Trees*.) Videos of both *The Lorax* and *The Man Who Planted Trees* are also available, and *The Lorax* is readily available in Spanish, Mandarin, and other languages. Note that the 2012 film version of *The Lorax* is not a good fit for the activity.

- Alternatively, you may use another book that is suitable for your students (see suggestions on plt.org/myk8guide).

- Write discussion questions or statements related to *The Lorax* or the other book you have chosen (see Step 3 of Doing the Activity) on index cards (six cards total, with different questions on each card).

DOING THE ACTIVITY

1 **PERSONAL CONNECTIONS** Ask students to name things from nature (natural resources) that they use in their lives. Examples include trees, water, air, minerals, and so on. Ask students what might happen if one or more of these resources were "used up."

2 Read aloud the story you've selected or show the video. Ask students to list the major ideas of the story. Discuss with the group:

- Why do you think each character did what they did?

- What changes in the environment are noticeable throughout the story?

- What is the author's message about the difference one person can make?

3 **LITERACY SKILLS** Divide the group into six teams. Give each team an index card with a set of questions related to the story. Each team should discuss the questions, write down their answers, and be prepared to read them to the entire group. Questions for *The Lorax*:

- What could the Once-ler have done differently to not run out of trees for making "Thneeds"? Do you think people should conserve all trees "from axes that hack"? Why or why not?

- What did the Once-ler mean by "UNLESS"? What can people do to make sure that trees will be available for lots of different uses in the future?

- Compare the Once-ler's attitude toward the environment at the beginning of the story with his attitude at the end.

- In a video version of the story, the Once-ler explains his actions by saying, "If I didn't do it, someone else would." Do you think that is a good excuse for doing what he did? Why or why not?

- The Lorax says he speaks for the trees. What does this mean to you? What is the Lorax's attitude at the end of the story?

- What seems to be Dr. Seuss's reason for writing this fable? (A fable is a made-up story that teaches a lesson.)

4  **STUDENT VOICE** After teams have had time for discussion, invite each team to read their card and responses to the group. Other students can agree, disagree, or add their ideas to the team's answers.

VARIATION: GRADES 6–8

1 Have students read *The Man Who Planted Trees* or another story.

2  **COOPERATIVE LEARNING** Give each team an index card with one of the following six statements on it. Each team should decide whether team members agree or disagree with the statement. If they agree, they should give three reasons why and an example from real life showing that this statement is true. If they disagree, they should state why and modify it into a statement with which they agree.

- The balance of nature is important to all life on Earth and it can easily be destroyed.

- Humans cannot place themselves apart from nature when they make decisions about natural resources.

- Actions taken without thought or planning can have disastrous consequences.

- Natural resources are not limitless and can be used up if they are not managed carefully for the long run.

- Each person has a responsibility to help conserve resources and protect the environment.

- Consumers should demand that manufacturers produce products in an environmentally responsible manner.

TAKE IT OUTSIDE

Invite students to sit outside—under a tree, if possible—as you read the story aloud. To help them connect to the story more deeply, encourage them to imagine that area without a tree and to describe, draw, or write about how that would look or feel.

ACADEMIC STANDARDS

SCIENCE

Practices
- Obtaining, evaluating, and communicating information

Concepts
- Human impacts on Earth systems
- Cause and effect
- Systems and system models

ENGLISH LANGUAGE ARTS

Practices
- Reading informational text: key ideas and details
- Speaking and listening comprehension and collaboration

SOCIAL STUDIES

Practices
- Applying disciplinary concepts

Concepts
- Economics: exchange and markets
- Geography: human–environment interactions

ASSESSMENT

Ask students to

- Create a graphic organizer showing the main ideas presented in the story.

- Write their personal responses to one of the sets of questions from the activity.

ENRICHMENT

- Have students prepare a sequence of the key events in the story they examined. Then, have them draw a diagram or flowchart showing the connections between characters in the story and the natural resources.

- Either alone or in small teams, students can write and illustrate a sequel to the story. For *The Lorax*, for example, the sequel might explain how the Truffula tree made a come-back through replanting and proper care, or how new managers of the Truffula Tree Company are going to maintain environmental quality while making Thneeds.

- After the sequels are finished, ask older students to consider the following questions:

  » In what ways will your sequel lead to a more sustainable outcome than the original?

  » What are the environmental, social, and economic implications of your sequel? How does your sequel compare to the original in these three areas?

  » What other solutions to the problems presented in the original story can you imagine?

- Plan and carry out a tree-planting project on your site or in another suitable location. See the activity Plant a Tree (in Grades 6-8) for more information.

- Explore forest certification as a way to help ensure sustainable forest management. See the activity What's in a Label? (in Grades 6-8).

Students examine trees for signs of damage or poor health and investigate conditions that may cause trees and other plants to become unhealthy.

TREES IN TROUBLE

SUBJECTS
Science, English Language Arts, Math, Social Studies

PLT CONCEPTS
5.1, 5.3

STEM SKILLS
Data Analysis, Investigation, Problem Solving

DIFFERENTIATED INSTRUCTION
Hands-on Learning, Personal Connections

MATERIALS
Part A: Optional: Camera.

Part B: Materials needed for student investigations (see Getting Ready).

TIME CONSIDERATIONS
Preparation:
Part A: 15 minutes
Part B: 45 minutes

Activity:
Part A: One to two 50-minute periods

Part B: Two 50-minute periods over several weeks and 10 minutes daily to record observations

OBJECTIVES

Students will

- Recognize symptoms of unhealthy trees and describe possible causes of their poor health.

- Perform investigations to determine the effects of crowding and fertilizers on plant growth.

BACKGROUND

Trees require some of the same things that people and other animals need to grow and thrive. For example, they need plenty of water, nutrients, and room to grow. If these requirements are not met, a tree may grow slowly or even die.

When a person is ill, we look for symptoms to help us identify what is wrong. Distressed trees also exhibit symptoms that can help determine the problem. Loss of vigor, discolored or misshapen **leaves**, insect bore holes, and weeping wounds are all signs that something is wrong. The Tree-tective Trouble Guide and Learning Leaf-Reading student pages provide specific information about potential signs and what they might suggest about tree health.

The growth rings on a cross-section of a tree also reveal how well the tree's requirements have been met over the course of many years, providing a record of a tree's health over its lifetime. (For more information, see Background for the activities Tree Factory, Tree Cookies, and Every Tree for Itself.)

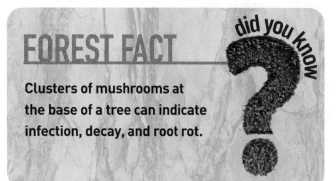

FOREST FACT _____ did you know

Clusters of mushrooms at the base of a tree can indicate infection, decay, and root rot.

GETTING READY

PART A:

- Plan a field trip onsite or to a nearby park, woods, or tree-lined street to observe different trees at a time when they have their leaves.

- Make copies of the Tree-tective Trouble Guide student page.

PART B:

- Gather the materials for student investigations. If you use the examples provided, collect planting pots (these can be half-gallon milk cartons with the tops cut off and drain holes punched in the bottom), trays or coated paper plates to catch water, potting soil, radish seeds or other seeds, white vinegar, fertilizer (liquid or granular), and rulers or measuring tapes.

- Check the estimated seed germination time(s) so you can plan appropriately.

DOING THE ACTIVITY

PART A: NEIGHBORHOOD CHECKUP

1  **PERSONAL CONNECTIONS** As a group, discuss what causes a person to get sick. Responses might include poor nutrition, contaminated water, a lack of food or water, viruses, toxic substances like smoke or drugs, disease, and physical injury. Students should also think of ways to prevent or treat these things, like proper diet, regular exercise, and safe behavior.

2 Ask students to consider what keeps trees healthy. How are those things like or unlike the things that keep humans healthy? Explain to students that they will act as "tree-tectives" (tree detectives) and search their neighborhood for healthy and unhealthy trees.

3 **HANDS-ON LEARNING** Take students outdoors to observe a variety of trees onsite or nearby. Provide students with copies of the Tree-tective Trouble Guide student page to identify symptoms of unhealthy trees. Encourage them to take additional notes and make sketches of their findings, such as broken branches; unusual leaf colors or shapes; holes; trunks damaged from scratches, carvings, or graffiti; or uprooted, fallen trees that still appear to be alive.

4 Have students explain what they think caused the damage they found, supporting their claims with evidence they observed.

PART B: PLANTS IN PERIL

1 **HANDS-ON LEARNING** Ask students how they might investigate the conditions that cause plants to become unhealthy.

2 Divide students into investigation teams of two or three students to plan and carry out an investigation. Teams may use one or both of the following investigations or another that they devise. The example investigations explore the effects of crowding and fertilizer on plant growth. Additional tests for light, water, and soil conditions can be found in the activity Here We Grow Again (in Grades K-2).

TAKE IT OUTSIDE

Bring paper and drawing materials outside to create a map that marks the location of unhealthy trees. Work as a group to identify the top three trees that need attention from a tree professional. Invite a certified arborist to inspect your trees in person, sharing your map as a point of reference.

PROJECT LEARNING TREE
An Initiative of SFI

EXAMPLE INVESTIGATIONS

CROWDING

Trees need space to grow so they can spread their branches to collect sunlight and their roots to collect water. Discover what happens when plants grow too close together.

a. Have students predict what will happen to plants that grow under crowded conditions. Their prediction can be stated in an "if–then" form, such as: "If plants grow too close together, then _____."

b. Provide each team with a planting pot on a tray (or coated paper plate) that will catch water as it drains. Fill the pots with potting soil.

c. Have half the teams plant two or three radish seeds in separate holes in their pots, while the other teams plant a dozen or so seeds in a single hole. All the pots should have the same light and water conditions, so that the only variable is the number of seeds per pot.

d. See how long it takes for the seeds to sprout. Measure the height of the plants above the soil level and record at daily intervals for several weeks.

e. After a specified time, students can dig up the plants and observe differences in the size of the radish bulbs. Cut the radishes in half; measure and record the diameters. Discuss the findings. Which radishes appear to be healthier?

FERTILIZER

Like people, plants need vitamins, minerals, and other nutrients in their diet to maintain good health. While most of these are supplied by the soil in which the plants grow, fertilizer can boost the amount of helpful nutrients available. But too much fertilizer can harm plants and can wash into waterways and cause environmental damage. Find out what happens if too much fertilizer is applied.

a. Ask students to predict the effects of too much fertilizer on plant growth. Their prediction can be stated in an "if–then" form, such as: "If plants receive too much fertilizer, then _____."

b. Help students plan an investigation to find out, using the same setup as in the crowding investigation. Guide students in keeping all variables constant except the amount of fertilizer added to the soil on a periodic basis. Following proper application instructions, ensure that one pot receives no fertilizer while another receives at least double the recommended amount.

c. Check plants periodically, record observations, and discuss changes in health and growth.

VARIATION: GRADES 6–8

1 Read aloud the following story attributed to the ancient Chinese philosopher Chuang Tzu.

> *A wise man saw an extraordinarily large tree. It was so big that a thousand chariots could shelter under it, and its shade would cover them all! He said, "What a tree this is! It must contain an extraordinary amount of timber!"*
>
> *When he looked up, however, he saw that its small branches were so twisted and crooked that they could not be made into rafters and beams. When he looked down, he saw that its trunk was divided into so many rounded portions that neither coffin nor boat could be made from them. He licked one of its leaves, and the taste was bitter. The smell of the tree made him feel ill. "Indeed," said he, "this is a tree good for nothing, and it is for this reason that it has reached such a great age."*
>
> *The cinnamon tree can be eaten, and therefore it is cut down. The varnish tree is useful, and therefore incisions are made in it. Everyone knows the advantage of being useful, but no one knows the advantage of being useless.*

2 Lead a discussion about the value of trees in the community and what the story might say about even those that are imperfect or unhealthy. Ask students how they might be able to assess the health of trees at your site or in the neighborhood.

3 Explain that one way to assess a tree's health is to look at its leaves, which can show symptoms of disease, insects, or physical damage. Invite students to assess trees on or near your site using the Learning Leaf-Reading student page.

4 If your students find any unhealthy trees, challenge them to identify the likely cause of the trees' poor health, using evidence from their observations. Encourage them to research possible actions that could be taken to help the trees and to develop an implementation plan.

5 Invite students to think back to the story from Step 1 and write their own stories about the value of both healthy and unhealthy trees, perhaps from the point of view of one of the trees they identified as unhealthy.

ACADEMIC STANDARDS

SCIENCE

Practices
- Constructing explanations and designing solutions
- Planning and carrying out investigations

Concepts
- Ecosystem dynamics, functioning, and resilience
- Cause and effect

ENGLISH LANGUAGE ARTS

Practices
- Speaking and listening: comprehension and collaboration

MATH

Practices
- Reason abstractly and quantitatively

Concepts
- Measurement and data

SOCIAL STUDIES

Practices
- Developing questions and planning inquiries
- Communicating conclusions and taking informed action

Concepts
- Geography: human–environment interactions

ASSESSMENT

Ask students to

- Draw pictures of a healthy tree and an unhealthy one. Using the group's collected drawings, students can list the qualities of healthy trees and some causes of poor tree health.

- Report on their investigation from Part B, describing the results and explaining the findings. Explanations should include a claim, evidence to support the claim from students' data, and reasoning that involves a rule or scientific principle describing why the evidence supports the claim (see Appendix K: Making a Scientific Argument for an example format).

ENRICHMENT

- Locate a dead or partially dead tree nearby and monitor its changes over time. Is there evidence of decomposition? Are there signs of woodpeckers or other living things using the dead tree? Are fungi growing on the tree? Did the city have to trim or cut down the tree for safety reasons?

- "Read" annual tree rings from a tree cross-section or a cut stump along a city sidewalk. These rings tell interesting stories about the health, life, and history of the tree (see the activity Tree Cookies). Look at the rings for evidence of drought and damage from lightning, fire, insects or disease.

- Conduct research to investigate **acid rain**, including its causes and effects on trees and other plants.

STUDENT PAGE
Tree-tective Trouble Guide

NAME _____ DATE_____

Check trees for the trouble signs below, circling any that you find. Be sure to note the location of any troubled tree and document any evidence that indicates the possible cause.

BROKEN BRANCHES
(possible cause: weak structure, damaged by truck driving under tree, storms)

Location: _____

Evidence for the cause: _____

TRUNK DAMAGE
(possible cause: hit by car or lawnmower)

Location: _____

Evidence for the cause: _____

TRUNK CRACKED OR SPLIT
(possible cause: weakened by lightning or frost)

Location: _____

Evidence for the cause: _____

ROTTEN SPOTS
(possible cause: dying section of tree)

Location: _____

Evidence for the cause: _____

TREE LEANING
(possible cause: root damage)

Location: _____

Evidence for the cause: _____

NAME _____ DATE_____

DEAD TREE
(possible cause: disease)

Location: _____

Evidence for the cause: _____

LEAVES FULL OF HOLES
(possible cause: insects feeding on leaves)

Location: _____

Evidence for the cause: _____

CURLED OR FUNNY-SHAPED LEAVES
(possible cause: fungus or other infection)

Location: _____

Evidence for the cause: _____

BALD SPOTS ON BARK
(possible cause: dead section of tree)

Location: _____

Evidence for the cause: _____

MUSHROOMS GROWING ON TRUNK NEAR GROUND
(possible cause: rot or decay)

Location: _____

Evidence for the cause: _____

CAREER CORNER

I LOVE MY GREEN JOB!

URBAN FORESTERS plant and protect the trees in a city. They monitor the trees to make sure they are healthy and develop long-term plans for the urban forest.

NAME _____ DATE_____

Trees can't tell us when they are sick. Instead, we must interpret the signs of illness that trees show to determine what and how serious their health problems are.

Tree leaves usually show the first symptoms of disease, insect infestation, or damage from impacts. By learning leaf-reading, you can diagnose your tree's condition. Here are some common leaf symptoms and likely causes.

1. **Symptom: Ragged leaves with holes.**
   Likely causes: Insect feeding, especially if it is summer and the leaves were not showing damage earlier. But if it is spring and the leaves never developed properly, the damage may be due to either low temperature during the bud stage or being torn by high winds when they were small leaves.

2. **Symptom: Leaves suddenly turn brown or black.**
   Likely causes: If a frost occurred a day or two earlier, that's probably the cause. Sudden high temperatures in spring also cause problems. If there were no recent temperature extremes, it might be a leaf or a stem disease. If the symptoms show up on a branch or two at a time, trunk or branch invasion or injury is probably the cause.

3. **Symptom: Spots on the leaves.**
   Likely causes: Leaf spots are usually the result of disease or insect activity. Chemicals, such as sulfur dioxide from nearby coal-burning plants, or improperly applied fertilizer or pesticides, can cause leaf blotches, too.

4. **Symptom: Bumps on the leaves.**
   Likely causes: Leaf galls, or growths, are often the result of insects that have fed or laid eggs on the leaves. Bumps on leaves may also be a response to infections by fungi, bacteria, or viruses. Sometimes, an imbalance between the tree's water intake and loss can cause leaf bumps.

5. **Symptom: Margins (edges) of leaves turning brown**.
   Likely causes: Moisture deficiencies or high-temperature stresses are usually to blame. Sometimes root or trunk damage, including injury from road salt, is the reason.

6. **Symptom: Sudden leaf drop, not during autumn.**
   Likely causes: If inner leaves are dropping during a dry spell, or if a few leaves fall from throughout the tree, it's probably not serious. Drought or squirrels may be to blame. But if leaves are dropping heavily from multiple branches, there is a problem somewhere with the water-conducting system of the tree. The root cause may be disease or boring insects.

NAME _____ DATE_____

7. **Symptom: Light green or yellow leaves.**
Likely causes: Probably a "micronutrient" disorder, such as iron or manganese deficiency. Curiously, trees rarely show deficiencies of the major plant nutrients, such as nitrogen and potassium.

8. **Symptom: Twisted or malformed leaves.**
Likely causes: This could be caused by stray herbicide drift, but insects, mites, occasionally a disease, and sometime low-temperature injury can all produce this symptom.

9. **Symptom: Leaves turn autumn colors prematurely.**
Likely causes: This is a serious symptom suggesting trunk or root damage of some kind. Leaves can withstand a certain amount of abuse, but when heavy losses occur two or more years in a row, early-season loss causes a new flush of leaves, the tree is only marginally hardy to the area, or the tree is under some form of stress (such as recent transplanting), the problem is serious. Your county extension agent has a number of publications to help in diagnosis and treatment of tree problems, or you may need to call an arborist who is competent in tree health diagnosis.

Source: Adapted from Gayle Worf, UW-Extension plant pathologist. Reprinted by permission of UW-Extension.

CAREER CORNER

I LOVE MY GREEN JOB!

PLANT PATHOLOGISTS (path-AWL-uh-gists) **study the health of plants. They work to identify diseases, pests, and other health problems that plants may experience.**

The water cycle is the system by which Earth's water is collected, purified, and distributed from the environment to living things and then returned to the environment. Through modeling and an experiment, students explore the various steps of the water cycle and make connections between the water cycle and all living things.

WATER WONDERS

SUBJECTS
Science, English Language Arts, Social Studies

PLT CONCEPTS
3.1, 3.7, 4.1

STEM SKILLS
Data Analysis, Investigation, Organization

DIFFERENTIATED INSTRUCTION
Hands-on Learning, Higher-order Thinking, Literacy Skills, Personal Connections

MATERIALS
Part A: Seven dice, labels for seven stations, watch or stopwatch.

Part B: Two sloped areas or stream tables (see Getting Ready), watering can or coffee can.

TIME CONSIDERATIONS
Preparation: 30–60 minutes

Activity: Part A: 50 minutes
Part B: 50 minutes

OBJECTIVES

Students will

- Describe the various components of the water cycle and the path that a water molecule might take on its way through this cycle.

- Explain why the water cycle is important to living things.

- Describe how plants affect the movement of water in a watershed.

BACKGROUND

Water covers 71% of Earth's surface. It can exist in liquid, vapor, or solid (ice) forms. It consists of two parts hydrogen to one part oxygen. Its unique physical properties enable life to exist on Earth. Those properties include water's ability to remain liquid in a wide range of normal Earth temperatures and its ability to dissolve and transport other substances. It constitutes 50–70% of the weight of all plants and animals, including humans.

Water is constantly moving. In general, it evaporates from oceans and lakes into the atmosphere (as water vapor), condenses into clouds, falls as rain or snow, and eventually returns to oceans through a drainage system of streams and rivers. This journey is called the **water cycle**. The cycle is powered by energy from the sun, which promotes evaporation, and by gravity.

In the coldest regions of Earth, water is stored for a long time as ice and hard-packed snow. But even ice and snow are in motion. Glaciers are essentially rivers of ice, always changing shape and sometimes melting as they move inch by inch. Icebergs break away from glaciers and float in the ocean, slowly melting as they move into more temperate climates and warmer waters.

The movement of water is greatly influenced by the contours of land and by geographic features such as mountains, valleys, and hills. A watershed is the area of land that collects water and guides it into a particular stream or river system; it may be large, as in the Mississippi River watershed, or small, as in the watershed for a local creek. Water's movement in the watershed, in turn, creates the contours of the land through erosion and sedimentation.

In addition to clouds, oceans, rivers, and land, living organisms are part of the water cycle. All living things need water to live because it is essential to their bodily functions. Plants and animals take in water and return it to the atmosphere as vapor (by breathing or transpiring) or to the soil as liquid (by excreting).

PROJECT LEARNING TREE
An initiative of SFI

FOREST FACT

Urban forests and neighborhood trees help to prevent runoff and erosion, thus maintaining water quality. For example, 1 inch of rainfall on a 10,000-square-foot area with no trees will generate 639 cubic feet of runoff, but if 30% of the area is covered by tree canopy, it will generate just 3.9 cubic feet of runoff.

Forests greatly affect watersheds. When rain falls on the forest, it drips down through the forest canopy to the forest floor. Trees, other plants, and layers of plant litter muffle the impact of precipitation and absorb water, reducing erosion and runoff. Tree roots also help to hold soil in place so that it doesn't wash away. But when rain falls on bare ground, the full force of raindrops can wash soil into streams, making them muddy, and reducing the quality of that water for human use and aquatic life.

Forests help improve water quality by helping to regulate flow, and by filtering out impurities that could be potentially harmful in streams or groundwater (water found in the cracks and spaces in soil). Through the process of transpiration, water that is absorbed by tree roots is released as vapor through the leaves, and impurities (many of which are good for a tree) remain in the tree.

Although the gradual wearing down and erosion of soil is a natural process, human activities such as clearing vegetation for development, engaging in unsustainable logging practices, farming, and draining wetlands will increase the rate of erosion in watersheds and reduce water quality. But practices such as reforesting areas, engaging in sustainable forestry, practicing conservation agriculture, and restoring wetlands can limit erosion and help to maintain water quality.

Changes in the Earth's climate due to the increase of greenhouse gases also affect the water cycle. Rising temperatures may cause increases in water evaporation, the rate at which sea ice melts, runoff, distribution and growth rates of forests, and other effects.

ESTIMATE OF GLOBAL WATER DISTRIBUTION

Water source	Water volume (cubic miles)	Water volume (cubic kilometers)	Percent of total water*
Oceans	321,000,000	1,338,000,000	96.54
Icecaps, glaciers	5,844,970	24,364,000	1.762
Groundwater	5,614,000	23,400,000	1.69
Lakes	42,320	176,400	0.013
Soil moisture	3,959	16,500	0.001
Atmosphere	3,095	12,900	0.001
Swamps	2,752	11,470	0.0008
Rivers	3,261	2,120	0.0002
Biological water (water in living things)	269	1,120	0.0001

Source: U.S. Geological Survey. "Where Is Earth's Water?" https://www.usgs.gov/special-topic/water-science-school/science/where-earths-water

*Note: Percents do not add to 100 due to rounding.

 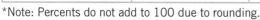

GETTING READY

PART A:

- Make copies of the Go to the Head of the Cloud student page and cut the station instructions apart. Also make copies of the Water Cycle Data Sheet student page.

- Using paper and marking pens, make a large label for each of seven stations: Cloud, Glacier, Stream, Groundwater, Ocean, Plant, and Animal. You may want to draw or download pictures that you attach to each label.

- Set up seven stations around the room with the labels. At each station, put a die and the relevant directions from the Go to the Head of the Cloud student page. If you have a large group, use two or more dice at each station.

PART B:

- On or near your site, find two sloped areas with about the same angle of slope. One should have little or no vegetation on the soil (a roadway cut bank or steep bare slope works well), and one should be covered with grass, shrubs, or trees.

- As an alternative to the sloped areas, make two stream table boxes about 16" long x 12" wide x 4" deep (40.6 cm x 30.5 cm x 10.2 cm). You may use planter boxes, cake pans, or aluminum foil roasting pans with the approximate dimensions. Make them water-tight by lining them with plastic material or aluminum foil. At one end of each box, cut a v-shaped notch about 1.5" (3.8 cm) deep and fit it with a spout of stiff paper that it directs water off the table into a container, as in the diagram *Stream Tables* below. Put a piece of sod (cut from a pasture, field, fence row, or lawn) in one box and place an equivalent amount of bare soil (preferably from the same location) in the other. Set both boxes on a table so the spouts extend over the edge; place boards under the opposite ends to give both boxes the same slope. Place jars on stools underneath the spouts to collect the water that runs off.

- Another alternative is to use two five-gallon buckets with a hole cut in the bottom of each. Partially fill each bucket with equal amounts of soil. In one bucket, add a layer of leaf litter from a nearby forest area on top of the soil. Place the buckets in a sink or on the ground outside.

STREAM TABLES

PROJECT LEARNING TREE
An initiative of SFI

DOING THE ACTIVITY

PART A: GO TO THE HEAD OF THE CLOUD

1 Divide the group into pairs and ask the pairs to write down words that describe what they know about the water cycle. Then ask them to write a description or create a drawing of the water cycle. Ask volunteers to share their description or drawing with the whole group.

2 **LITERACY SKILLS** Optional: Share a diagram of the water cycle like the one shown below. As needed, review sequencing words like "next," "after," "before," "while," "during," etc. Help students understand the terms evaporation, groundwater, etc. (see the Glossary at plt.org/glossary).

3 Explain that the water cycle is really a simplified model for looking at the "journey" of a water molecule. Ask students whether they think water always follows the same path in the water cycle. Challenge them to think of times that water may follow a different path.

THE WATER CYCLE

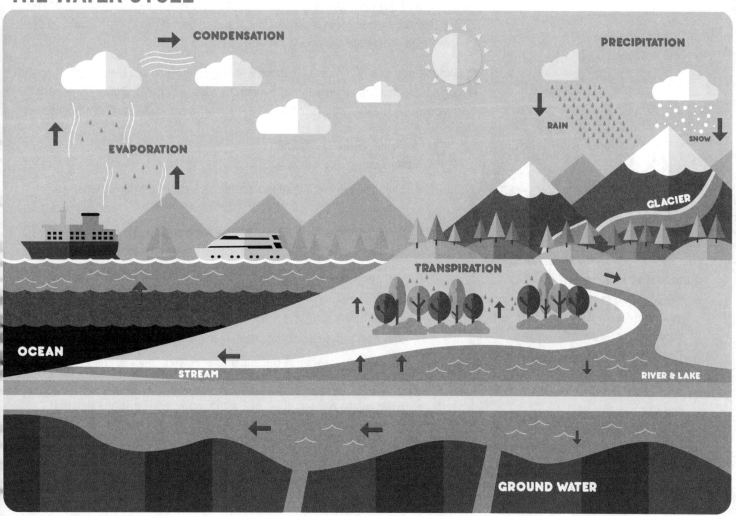

4 Ask students how they might model the water cycle to learn more about it. Suggest that they can follow the different paths a water molecule might take. Explain that you have set up a sample model where they can do just that. Distribute the Water Cycle Data Sheet student page to record the path they follow in the model. Later, they will compare data.

5 Divide students into seven groups and have each group begin at one of the stations. Explain that each student will be a water molecule in the model. Have students roll the die and read the statement for their station corresponding to the number on the die. On their Water Cycle Data Sheet student page, they should write their current station, what happens to them according to the die roll, and their next destination. Call out "cycle," to have students go to the next station as directed by the station statements.

6 Repeat Step 5 about 10 times or until most students have cycled through the Cloud station a couple of times.

7 Ask students to write a brief story from a water molecule's point of view that describes the journey they took through the water cycle in the activity. For example, a student whose journey was Glacier > Stream > Ocean > Cloud > Stream > Animal > Cloud > Glacier > Ocean might start their story like this: "I was a lonely water molecule frozen in a glacier on top of a mountain. When the spring came and the ice thawed, I melted into a stream. The stream roared down the mountain, going over large boulders. After a long journey, I reached the ocean."

8 Write the names of the seven stations where everyone can see them. Beginning with Cloud, ask students to share all the different ways they got to Cloud. Show each response by drawing arrows to the word Cloud. Repeat with the other stations.

9 **HIGHER-ORDER THINKING**
Discuss the following questions:

- Even though individual molecules took different paths, what was similar about the journeys they took?

- Which stations were visited by the most water molecules, regardless of their particular journeys? What can we infer from this?

- Can you think of other parts of the water cycle that were not included in the model? (e.g., lakes, rivers, wells) Where might they be added?

- Do you think simple diagrams of the water cycle are useful, even if they don't include all the paths water might take? Why or why not?

- What would happen if the sun's energy were blocked from reaching Earth?

- What might happen if all of Earth's water stayed in the oceans? In the clouds?

- How is the water cycle important to plants and animals?

TAKE IT OUTSIDE

Take students outdoors to look for evidence of the water cycle. Challenge them to find evidence of:
- **Evaporation (such as a dried-up mud puddle, low water levels in a pond, or a dried leaf)**
- **Condensation (such as clouds, dew on grass, or fog)**
- **Precipitation (such as rain, hail, or snow)**
- **Other elements of the water cycle**
Ask them whether the amount of sunlight affects the water cycle and, if so, how.

PART B: ON A SLOPE

1  **PERSONAL CONNECTIONS** Ask students to name some ways that people try to control the water cycle directly (e.g., building dams, making snow at ski resorts). Ask them how humans' activities affect the water cycle indirectly (e.g., climate change from rising levels of greenhouse gases increases glacier melt and evaporation).

2 Ask students what effect plants might have on the water cycle. Ask how they could find out more about this.

3 Suggest that one way would be to compare how water acts on two sloped surfaces, one with and one without plants. Take them to the two sites or use two stream tables (see Getting Ready). Describe the experiment to students (see Step 4). Then have them predict whether there will be any difference in what occurs on the two slopes.

4 **HANDS-ON LEARNING** Fill the watering can or coffee can with water. Help students hold the can at the same height so they can pour or sprinkle water at the same rate over the same point of each slope. Have students look for the following:

- The plants' effect on the water's speed

- The amount of run-off from each slope

- The appearance of the run-off water

- The water's effect on the contour (shape of the surface) of each slope

5 As you lead a discussion about what students observed, ask questions such as these:

- What happened to the water on the bare slope? What do you think will be the water's next stop in the water cycle? (probably entering a stream)

- What happened to the water on the planted slope? What do you think will be the water's next stop in the water cycle? (absorbed by plants, entering groundwater, or entering a stream)

- In what ways do plants affect the movement of both water and sediment (soil carried in water) through the water cycle? (For example, they slow down the water so that more of it soaks into the ground rather than running off, and they hold soil with their roots so it doesn't wash away.)

- What effect did the two slopes have on the quality of the water? Why?

- How are forests important for maintaining the balance of water in a watershed? How are forests important for maintaining quality of life for people? Aquatic animals?

ACADEMIC STANDARDS

SCIENCE

Practices
- Developing and using models

Concepts
- Earth materials and systems
- Systems and system models
- Cause and effect

ENGLISH LANGUAGE ARTS

Practices
- Speaking and listening: presentation of knowledge and ideas

SOCIAL STUDIES

Practices
- Applying disciplinary concepts

Concepts
- Geography: geographic representations
- Geography: human–environment interactions

ASSESSMENT

Ask students to

- Write a story describing the journey of a water molecule (as in Part A). The story should:
  - » Include all stops of their water molecule's journey, in chronological order.
  - » Include details about the journey, explaining accurately how and why the water molecule went where it did.
  - » Convey the importance and cyclical nature of the water cycle.
- Create a diagram of the water cycle based on the model they simulated in Part A.
- Write individually or in groups a response to the following prompt: Imagine two pieces of land that are exactly alike, except one is bare and the other is covered by a forest. Now imagine a stream running through each area. What differences might you see between the two streams? Think about how the water might move and how clear the water would be in each.

ENRICHMENT

- Use terrariums to observe the water cycle in action. Build two identical terrariums with a layer of soil, small plants in the soil, and a small cup of water to simulate a pond. Cover one tightly with plastic wrap and the other with aluminum foil. Lightly moisten the soil and plants of each terrarium and place them both in indirect sunlight. Invite students to observe what happens in each terrarium as time passes. What causes the changes? Based on what you see in the two terrariums, what role does the sun's energy have in the water cycle?
- Explore the quantity and distribution of water on Earth. Toss an inflatable globe to a student. When the student catches the globe, ask them if their right thumb is on water or land. Have that student toss the globe to another student and ask the same question. Continue tossing the ball, tallying student responses after each catch. With enough tosses, about three-fourths of the time the students' thumbs should land on water, and one-fourth of the time on land. Ask students what they learned from this exercise.

NAME _____ DATE _____

CLOUD Station

If you roll a …

1: You fall as rain onto an ocean. Go to Ocean.
2: You fall as rain onto an ocean. Go to Ocean.
3: You fall as rain onto a stream. Go to Stream.
4: You fall as snow onto a Glacier. Go to Glacier.
5: You fall as snow onto the ground. Go to Groundwater.
6: You fall as rain into a forest. Go to Stream.

GLACIER Station

If you roll a …

1: You evaporate into the air. Go to Cloud.
2: You stay frozen in ice. Stay at Glacier.
3: You stay frozen in ice. Stay at Glacier.
4: You stay frozen in ice. Stay at Glacier.
5: You melt and become part of a stream. Go to Stream.
6: You break off from the glacier and fall into the ocean. Go to Ocean.

OCEAN Station

If you roll a …

1: You are one of countless water molecules in an ocean and you stay there. Stay at Ocean.
2: You are one of countless water molecules in an ocean and you stay there. Stay at Ocean.
3: You are one of countless water molecules in an ocean and you stay there. Stay at Ocean.
4: You are one of countless water molecules in an ocean and you stay there. Stay at Ocean.
5: You evaporate into the air. Go to Cloud.
6: You evaporate into the air. Go to Cloud.

STREAM Station

If you roll a …

1: You evaporate into the air. Go to Cloud.
2: You evaporate into the air. Go to Cloud.
3: An animal comes to the stream and drinks you. Go to Animal.
4: You continue rolling downhill and become part of an ocean. Go to Ocean.
5: You continue rolling downhill and become part of an ocean. Go to Ocean.
6: A human purifies water from the stream and then drinks it. Go to Animal.

NAME _____ DATE_____

GROUNDWATER Station

If you roll a …
1: You move slowly downward and become part of an aquifer (an underground layer of rock containing water). Stay at Groundwater.
2: You move slowly downward and become part of an aquifer (an underground layer of rock containing water). Stay at Groundwater.
3: You move slowly underground between grains of sediment and eventually flow into a wetland and from there into a stream. Go to Stream.
4: You move slowly underground between grains of sediment and eventually flow into a wetland and from there into a stream. Go to Stream.
5: A plant absorbs you through its roots. Go to Plant.
6: You are pumped out of the ground from a well to irrigate a farm. Go to Plant.

ANIMAL Station

If you roll a …
1: After using you to process food, the animal urinates and you end up in the ground. Go to Groundwater.
2: After using you to process food, the animal urinates and you end up in the ground. Go to Groundwater.
3: You are exhaled from the animal's lungs into the air as vapor. Go to Cloud.
4: You are exhaled from the animal's lungs into the air as vapor. Go to Cloud.
5: A human uses you for brushing their teeth and spits you out; you travel from the sink down into the pipes, then through a sewage treatment plant and into a stream. Go to Stream.
6: A human drinks you. When they urinate, you travel from the toilet down into the pipes, then through a sewage treatment plant and into a stream. Go to Stream.

PLANT Station

If you roll a …
1: The plant transpires you through its leaves and you evaporate into the air. Go to Cloud.
2: A tree transpires you through its leaves and you evaporate into the air. Go to Cloud.
3: The plant transpires you through its leaves and you evaporate into the air. Go to Cloud.
4: The plant uses you to grow. Stay at Plant.
5: A tree stores you in its edible fruit and you are eaten by an animal. Go to Animal.
6: The plant stores you in its edible leaves and you are eaten by an animal. Go to Animal.

NAME _____ DATE _____

ROUND	STATION STOP	WHAT HAPPENS TO THE WATER MOLECULE?	NEXT STOP
Example	*Cloud*	*Falls as rain*	*Ocean*
1			
2			
3			
4			
5			
6			
7			
8			
9			
10			

CAREER CORNER

HYDROLOGISTS (hye-**DRAW**-luh-jists) investigate water in forests by studying how it travels through the forest, into the soil, and eventually to a stream. In addition to learning about the water cycle, hydrologists may try to solve questions such as how streamflow affects forests or how climate change impacts watersheds.

By conducting research and modeling a food web, students take a close look at a forest ecosystem and discover ways that plants and animals are connected to one another. Although this activity focuses on forests, you can also use it to study other ecosystems, such as oceans, deserts, marshes, or prairies, by substituting the appropriate information.

WEB OF LIFE

SUBJECTS
Science, English Language Arts, Visual Arts

PLT CONCEPTS
3.2, 3.4

STEM SKILLS
Collaboration, Organization, Problem Solving, Technology Use

DIFFERENTIATED INSTRUCTION
Nonlinguistic Representations, Student Voice

MATERIALS
Resource materials about forest plants and animals; paper, string, or safety pins for nametags; 200 feet of string or yarn.

TIME CONSIDERATIONS
Preparation: 30 minutes

Activity: Two 50-minute periods

OBJECTIVES

Students will

- Conduct research to learn how one organism is connected to other organisms in an ecosystem.

- Use a model to understand the interdependence of organisms in an ecosystem.

BACKGROUND

A forest is a complex living system. In addition to trees, a forest ecosystem is composed of many other plants and animals that interact with and depend on one another.

One way that forest plants and animals are connected is through energy from food. All life depends on **photosynthesis**, the ability of plants and a few other organisms to capture the sun's energy and use it to synthesize simple sugars from carbon dioxide and water. Through photosynthesis, organisms make the sun's energy available to animals. Plant eaters, or herbivores, eat plants directly; in turn, animal eaters, or carnivores, eat herbivores or other carnivores. This flow of energy is called a **food chain**.

A food chain is a simplified way of showing energy relationships between plants and animals in an ecosystem. For example, one food chain might be sun ➡ plant ➡ mouse ➡ owl: a plant is eaten by a mouse, which in turn is eaten by an owl.

It is rare for an animal to eat only one type of food. A **food web** describes the complex interconnection of all the food chains and cycles in an ecosystem and gives a clearer picture of how plants and animals in an ecosystem are related to one another. No matter how unrelated organisms may seem, they are, in fact, connected. For example, when plants and animals throughout the food chain die, they become food for **decomposers**, which break down the dead matter and release nutrients to the soil, thus continuing the cycle.

Plants and animals are interdependent in other ways besides food. For example, plants may depend on insects and other animals to pollinate their flowers, disperse their seeds, and keep insect populations in check. And animals may depend on plants for shelter and to help modulate the amount of moisture and sunlight in their environment. For more information about what plants need, see the activity Here We Grow Again (in Grades K-2).

did you know

FOREST FACT

Forests are home to 80% of the world's terrestrial biodiversity, so it's important to conserve them and practice sustainable forestry. A healthy forest ecosystem includes a variety of plants and animals. One way to assess this diversity is to determine whether there is a mix of plant species of different sizes, ages, and functions, thus creating diverse conditions that provide habitat for many species.

SIMPLIFIED FOOD WEB

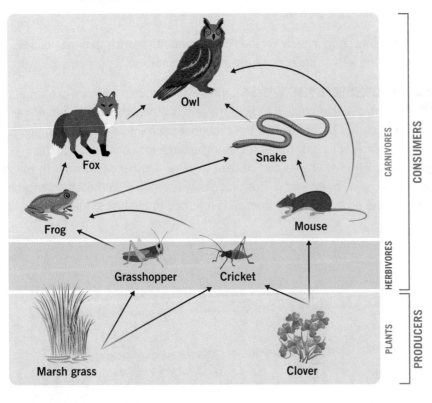

A food web describes the complex interconnection of organisms in an ecosystem. Each arrow points to the eater and shows the transfer of energy. This diagram of a food web is simplified, as many more species would actually be involved.

GETTING READY

- Create a list of forest animals and plants that students might research. Aim to include at least two of each type: mammal, arthropod (insect or spider), bird, reptile, amphibian, tree, and other plant.

  » Animal possibilities: bark beetle, bat, beaver, bear, box turtle, butterfly, chipmunk, deer, earthworm, field mouse, red fox, tree frog, grasshopper, king snake, lizard, mosquito, hawk moth, opossum, barred owl, rabbit, raccoon, skunk, snail, squirrel, tick, or woodpecker.

  » Plant possibilities: azalea, clover, columbine, cottonwood, honeysuckle, maple tree, Douglas fir, paintbrush, pine tree, poison ivy, or violet.

- Students will need access to resource materials or the internet. Arrange time in the library or media center, as needed.

- Optional: For nonformal audiences or English language learners, you might plan to provide students with the nametags used in Steps 4–9 instead of having them research and make their own. See plt.org/myk8guide for sample nametags for a variety of locales.

1 Ask students to work in pairs or teams to brainstorm components of a healthy forest ecosystem. Invite them to share their ideas with the rest of the group.

2 Have each student choose a forest organism to study. Make sure the group selects a variety of plants and animals, including mammals, insects, birds, reptiles, trees, and other plants.

3 Instruct students to collect the information about their chosen organism, using the Web of Life Research student page as a guide. After students have completed their research, have them make a nametag for their forest plant or animal, including a picture.

4 Have students sit in a circle on the floor or ground, wearing their nametags. Introduce the web of life concept (see Background).

5  **NONLINGUISTIC REPRESENTATIONS** Starting with a student who has chosen a plant, ask that student to hold the end of a ball of string and to name another organism in the circle with which that plant interacts (for example, is eaten by or depends on). Unroll the string enough to pass the ball to this second student. Ask the second student to name another organism with which his or her organism interacts. This process will continue until each organism is linked in the ecosystem, and the ball is returned to the first student.

TAKE IT OUTSIDE

Create an outdoor "web of life" to show connections in the immediate environment. Start by tying one end of a string to a tree or other plant. Connect it to other plants, animal signs (chewed leaves, scratched bark, etc.), and nonliving things around it. Ask students what this outdoor web of life tells them about ecosystems.

 SAFETY CHECK! Be careful not to harm any plants or animals. Pick up the string when you're done.

PROJECT LEARNING TREE
An initiative of SFI

6 Now have students slide back, making a larger circle, until the string is taut. Tell students to keep still. But if they feel a tug, they should tug in response. When everyone is still, tell the student holding the original end of the string to gently begin tugging. Keep reminding everyone that if they feel a tug, they should tug in response. Vibrations will spread through the food web until everyone is tugging and the whole web is shaking.

7 Ask students how the tugging demonstration might illustrate what happens when one of the links in an ecosystem is damaged by natural or human-made stress. (The rest of the ecosystem feels the effects.)

8 Ask students to pick one organism and have it drop out of the web. Ask if any other organisms should drop out because they depended on that organism. After one or more have dropped out, ask the students again to identify an organism to drop out, and repeat the procedure.

9 **STUDENT VOICE** Continue modeling for a few more rounds, then ask the following questions:

- What happens when we remove a link in the forest ecosystem? (Organisms that depend on it are affected. The web itself changes shape.)

- Can another species take the role of one that was dropped? (Sometimes, when a species is removed from an ecosystem, another species may fill that role. For example, if a prey animal disappears, predators might be able to switch to a different type of prey.)

- Were the changes more dramatic when the system was composed of many parts or when it had fewer parts? (They're usually more dramatic when there are fewer parts.)

- What can we say about the relationship between the number of parts in a system and its stability? (In general, the more complex or diverse a system is, the more stable it is.)

- How might humans be connected to this web? (Students may have different ideas, depending on the ecosystem. They might suggest that people are connected to forests through forest products or recreation, or by the fact that forests filter water and air.)

ACADEMIC STANDARDS

SCIENCE

Practices
- Obtaining, evaluating, and communicating information
- Developing and using models

Concepts
- Interdependent relationships in ecosystems
- Systems and system models

ENGLISH LANGUAGE ARTS

Practices
- Writing: research to build and present knowledge

Concepts
- Reading informational text: key ideas and details

ASSESSMENT

Ask students to

- Illustrate the web of life modeled in the activity, using concept mapping or a graphics software program.

- Select a local bird, fish, reptile, amphibian, or mammal, and write about the organisms it depends on and organisms that depend on it.

- Create a web of life illustration showing the impact of one species on other organisms. You might provide students with information or a link to an article about a non-native invasive species (plant or animal) that is causing a negative impact on the local environment.

ENRICHMENT

- Help students create a forest mural showing the "web of life." Have them draw hills, valleys, streams, and other features on sheets of cardboard or poster paper and then add photos or drawings of the organisms they studied in the activity. Place a push pin next to each plant or animal. Then use yarn to connect organisms to other animals and plants with which the organisms directly interact.

- Make food web mobiles. Have each student select a plant or animal that is part of the forest ecosystem or another ecosystem. Students should research their organism's place in the food web, cut out shapes representing this organism and others in its food web from construction paper, and decorate them with colored markers. Using a clothes hanger and thread to hang cutouts in the proper arrangement, students can construct mobiles that represents their food webs.

NAME _____ DATE_____

ORGANISM: _____

Research to find the following information about your organism.

1. Where in the forest does it live?

2. What does it eat?

3. What eats it?

4. What other organisms live in the forest with it?

5. In what ways does it depend on other organisms?

6. How does it influence its environment?

CAREER CORNER

I LOVE MY GREEN JOB!

WILDLIFE BIOLOGISTS (buy-ALL-uh-jists) study wildlife and their habitats to understand what these animals need to thrive. They look at the relationships of birds, mammals, fish, reptiles, or amphibians to the forest and to each other.

ACTIVITY	6-8	3-5
Decisions, Decisions	◉	⇕
Environmental Justice for All	◉	
Exploration Energy!	◉	⇕
Field, Forest, and Stream	◉	⇕
Forest in the City	◉	
Global Goods	◉	
If You Were the Boss	◉	
Improve Your Place	◉	⇕
Invasive Species	◉	
Life on the Edge	◉	⇕
Living with Fire	◉	
Nature's Skyscrapers	◉	⇕
Nothing Succeeds Like Succession	◉	⇕
Our Federal Forests	◉	⇕
Plant a Tree	◉	⇕
Reduce, Reuse, Recycle	◉	⇕
Renewable or Not?	◉	
The Global Climate	◉	
What's in a Label?	◉	

◉ = Core Activity   ⇕ = Grade-Level Variation

For more details, see Grade Level in the At-a-Glance Index.

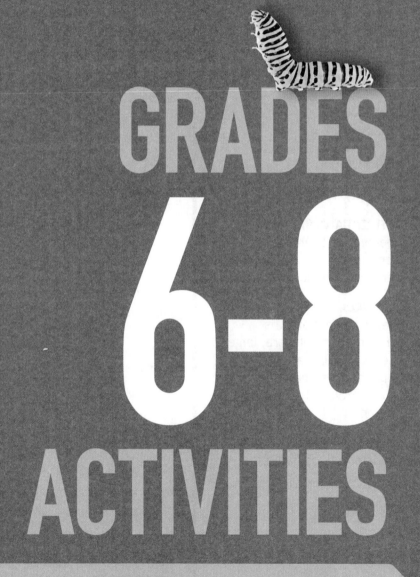

GRADES
6-8
ACTIVITIES

explore your environment

Decisions about community land use are complex and often involve many people in many ways. In this simulation, students use trees as a backdrop to develop a land-use plan.

DECISIONS, DECISIONS

SUBJECTS
Science, English Language Arts, Social Studies, Visual Arts

PLT CONCEPTS
3.9, 3.10, 4.9

STEM SKILLS
Collaboration, Communication, Creativity, Problem Solving

DIFFERENTIATED INSTRUCTION
Cooperative Learning, Nonlinguistic Representations, Personal Connections

MATERIALS
Presentation materials (presentation software, large sheets of paper and marking pens, or other materials), watch or clock that displays seconds.

TIME CONSIDERATIONS
Preparation: 15 minutes

Activity: One or two 50-minute periods

OBJECTIVES
Students will

- Compare options for using a piece of land.
- Make a land use decision and explore its consequences.
- Develop an understanding of how communities solve problems and make decisions.

BACKGROUND

Land is a precious commodity. Land-use decisions affect people in many ways, including where they can live, what kind of work they do, the transportation that is available to them, and even the environmental integrity of their local region.

Land-use planning is the process of figuring out how to use a community's land for various purposes. Decisions must accommodate the community's current and long-term needs, while considering landowner rights, future development, and population growth.

Most communities have a planning process that includes a city plan, zoning regulations, and city ordinances. A city plan describes the community's goals, objectives, and policies regarding growth and development. Zoning regulations outline the community's decisions about location, intensity, and development of public facilities and private land use. Ordinances permit or prohibit certain activities in specific areas of the community.

This activity presents two land-use conflict scenarios, representing some of the complex legal, political, ecological, economic, and social results of land-use decisions. In controversial situations like these, the people on opposing sides are not "good" or "bad," but merely have different needs, perspectives, and beliefs. Every stakeholder has an interest in the outcome and should be heard and respected. While this activity focuses on land use, it can be adapted to examine other community issues.

One of the scenarios involves urban trees, known collectively as the **urban forest**. Urban forests provide many community benefits, including cleaner air, protection from flooding and water pollution, cooler summer temperatures, calmer traffic, and more. Many communities promote urban forests through street tree ordinances that regulate the planting, maintenance, liability, and responsibility for long-term care of urban trees, as well as any requirements for replacement or removal.

FOREST FACT

Urban Forest Master Plans are developed by city governments and nonprofit organizations to establish long-term management goals and strategies that improve the health and longevity of urban forests.

The other scenario centers on a natural forest. It highlights the **open space** versus development debate that many communities face as populations grow. Open space includes all undeveloped land, such as forestland, farmland, and grasslands. According to the U.S. Forest Service, an estimated 6,000 acres of open space in the United States are converted to other uses every day. This loss is significant and concerning, as open space provides many **ecosystem services**, including clean water, natural flood control, wildlife habitat, biodiversity, and recreation opportunities.

GETTING READY

Decide which student page scenario students will examine: The Heritage Oak (an urban forest scenario focusing on a particular tree) or The Forest of Morris Woods (a natural forest scenario presenting an open space vs. development decision). As an alternative, half the group may focus on one scenario, while the other half explores the other scenario. Make copies of the student pages or make them available electronically.

DOING THE ACTIVITY

1 **PERSONAL CONNECTIONS** Ask students: "Imagine that you and your friends have three hours to spend together, and each of you wants to do something different. How might you decide what to do as a group?" Invite students to brainstorm the options that groups have for making decisions. Examples might include voting, choosing a leader who will always decide, taking turns deciding, having everyone decide together, compromising, or having an outsider listen and make the decision for the group.

2 To experience the wide range of opinions that people have on environmental topics, share the Viewpoints on the Line student page. Have students rank how much they agree or disagree with each statement. Then, read one of the statements aloud and have students stand in a line that represents their answers on a scale of 1 to 10. Point out how the line reflects the range of opinions among the group. Repeat this exercise for several other opinion statements.

3 Explain that students will simulate how communities make decisions. In this simulation, teams of students representing communities will present multiple solutions to a "town council" that will vote on what to do.

4 Share the student page for the selected scenario and read it as a group.

5 To prompt solution-oriented thinking, ask:

- What stakeholders (interested parties) are involved in this conflict?
- What does each of them need or want? (Create a list of the stakeholders' goals so that all can see.)
- In what specific ways do the stakeholders disagree?
- In what ways do they agree?
- What possible solutions can you think of that would satisfy two or more stakeholders?

Students may use the Stakeholder Solutions student page to record their ideas.

6 Divide the group into teams of four. Explain that each team must come up with a proposal to resolve the community dilemma. Each proposal should include a map or other illustration of the area in question, a statement of the issue, and details about the proposed solution. Provide paper and drawing materials or have students use a presentation program for communicating the main elements of their proposal. Explain that a town council will determine the final action.

7  **COOPERATIVE LEARNING** Give students 30 minutes to develop a proposal. Explain that teams will then make a two-minute presentation to the town council, and more than one person must help present.

8 After 20 minutes of proposal planning, choose one person from each team to be on the town council. Have town council members meet in a separate area of the room. Explain that their job is to listen to the proposals and vote on a final action. Ask them to decide what criteria they will use to judge the proposal. For example, they might prioritize creativity, environmental impact, public appeal, etc.

9 When time is up, seat town council members in front of the group. Ask for a volunteer timekeeper to limit each presentation to two minutes. After all teams present, the town council should meet privately for 5–10 minutes to make a final decision. While the council meets, each team can identify pros and cons of the other teams' proposals.

10 When the council has reached a decision, ask the members to return, announce the results, and explain the basis of their decision. Lead a group discussion covering these topics:

- Do you agree with the town council? Why or why not?
- What criteria did the town council use to decide? Do you agree with those criteria?
- Did your team or the town council take into consideration the future needs of the community, or just the current needs? How might different perspectives produce a different result?
- Was it difficult or easy to decide what to do? Explain.
- What else would you want to know to make a final decision?
- What changes would you make to the decision process?
- How is this process like what happens in real life? How is it different?
- Why do you think cities have zoning laws and land-use plans? What would happen if they didn't?

TAKE IT OUTSIDE

Locate two areas near your site that students can compare: one with street trees and one without.

- **What effect do trees have on a street?**
- **How do trees affect the temperature, shade, or feel of an area?**
- **What benefits do street trees provide? (They cool and clean the air, muffle noise, and provide beauty.)**
- **What problems do trees cause? (Their fruits and leaves fall. They block signs and have a potential to damage power lines. Their roots can damage sidewalks. Their falling limbs could cause damage or injury.)**
- **Which area do more students prefer and why?**

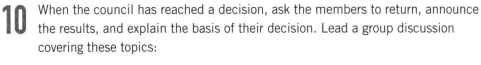

PROJECT LEARNING TREE
An initiative of SFI

VARIATION: GRADES 3–5

1 Using chalk, string, or tape, mark a line that is 10 yards or meters long on the ground or floor and number it from 1 to 10, placing the numbers one yard or meter apart. Tell students that the line represents a scale on which to rank their responses to opinion statements (with 10 being "strongly agree" and 1 being "strongly disagree").

2 Read one of the opinion statements on the Viewpoints on the Line student page or another of your choosing. Have students place themselves on the number that indicates their response for that statement.

3 When everyone is settled, make a group graph or diagram showing how students are distributed on the scale.

4 Break the line at its midpoint and have half the students stay in place, while the other half move to meet them so that each student has a partner.

5 Give one person in each pair 30 seconds to explain to their partner why they chose that ranking. Then allow partners to switch roles.

6 Have students reposition themselves on the scale, allowing them to change their ranking based on what they heard. Draw another graph or diagram showing their revised positions. Compare the graph or diagram and discuss the changes.

7 Repeat with additional statements, or ask the group to draft opinion statements to discuss.

ACADEMIC STANDARDS

SCIENCE

Practices
- Engaging in argument from evidence
- Obtaining, evaluating, and communicating information

Concepts
- Human impacts on Earth systems
- Systems and system models

ENGLISH LANGUAGE ARTS

Practices
- Speaking and listening: presentation of knowledge and ideas

Concepts
- Speaking and listening: comprehension and collaboration

SOCIAL STUDIES

Practices
- Applying disciplinary concepts

Concepts
- Civics: participation and deliberation
- Civics: processes, rules, and laws

ASSESSMENT

Ask students to

- Submit their team proposals for evaluation. How well does each proposal resolve the conflict? Does it consider the needs and rights of all stakeholders? How clear was its position? Was there cooperation and consensus within each group?

- Answer questions about a local environmental issue. Have students determine which community groups are involved in resolving the issue. What are the varying points of view? Encourage students to generate creative solutions.

ENRICHMENT

- Contact your local land-use planning office to find out what policies or ordinances your community has involving trees. Discuss whether students agree with those policies, and whether they think the policies are enough. Students may make recommendations about the policies to the appropriate governing body.

- Identify a local environmental issue and learn about the various positions on it. Encourage students to ask a local forester or check local news sites to identify a local issue. Explore ways to minimize the human impacts on the environment with regard to this issue.

- **NONLINGUISTIC REPRESENTATIONS** Challenge students to create an e-newsletter, video, or podcast that features a controversy from the activity, or from their own community. Students can write a supporting news story, opinion article, political cartoon, photo essay, or other content piece.

- Invite a local land-use planner to talk with the group about zoning, restrictions for different areas of the community, and how zoning disputes are revolved. To find a planner, search for your town's land-use planning office or planning commission.

NAME _____ DATE _____

Circle the number showing how much you disagree or agree with each statement.
A "1" indicates that you strongly disagree, and a "10" indicates that you strongly agree.

1 It is important for people to preserve wilderness areas. 1 2 3 4 5 6 7 8 9 10

2 The world's natural resources exist for people to use. 1 2 3 4 5 6 7 8 9 10

3 Damage to the environment is the biggest problem facing humanity today. 1 2 3 4 5 6 7 8 9 10

4 People will eventually develop new technologies to cope with environmental problems. 1 2 3 4 5 6 7 8 9 10

5 People have a responsibility to protect all forms of life on Earth. 1 2 3 4 5 6 7 8 9 10

6 Protecting a country's natural resources and natural heritage is primarily the government's responsibility. 1 2 3 4 5 6 7 8 9 10

7 The government is doing a good job of protecting our country's natural environment. 1 2 3 4 5 6 7 8 9 10

8 Recycling is the most important thing people can do to help improve the environment. 1 2 3 4 5 6 7 8 9 10

9 People should be able to use their own land in whatever way they see fit (for farming, housing, wildlife habitat, and so on). 1 2 3 4 5 6 7 8 9 10

10 All people have a right to clean air and water. 1 2 3 4 5 6 7 8 9 10

11 People using up natural resources is the greatest factor contributing to Earth's environmental problems. 1 2 3 4 5 6 7 8 9 10

12 Use of energy-saving light bulbs should be required in all public buildings. 1 2 3 4 5 6 7 8 9 10

13 International treaties are needed to address Earth's changing climate. 1 2 3 4 5 6 7 8 9 10

14 New energy production on the planet should be limited to carbon-free energy sources. 1 2 3 4 5 6 7 8 9 10

15 There should be laws restricting development on farmland or forestland outside cities or towns. 1 2 3 4 5 6 7 8 9 10

16 Zoning laws should prevent people from living in places that have a history of major forest fires. 1 2 3 4 5 6 7 8 9 10

CAREER CORNER

I LOVE MY GREEN JOB!

MEDIA COORDINATORS create content for a variety of media platforms. They may research, write, and edit information about an environmental topic, and plan and carry out outreach campaigns.

STUDENT PAGE

The Heritage Oak

NAME _____ DATE _____

The town council of Center City is facing a dilemma. Ms. Keesha Thomas owns a vacant lot downtown. She wants to build a car dealership on the lot to sell low-emission and electric cars. But she wants to remove the huge, 150-year-old oak tree, known as the Heritage Oak, that grows in the middle of the lot.

The town's plan does not prohibit developing a car dealership downtown, but it does require that people obtain special permission to remove trees. The plan also requires that all lots have at least one street tree for every 20 feet (6.1 m) of sidewalk frontage. Since the vacant lot is about 120 feet (36.6 m) long, it will require six trees.

The town council has heard from the following stakeholders in this case:

MS. THOMAS: My downtown lot is perfectly situated to attract customers to my new business. I plan to build a small sales office and pave the rest of the area for parking cars. I would like to remove the Heritage Oak because I need the space for cars and because the tree would damage the cars with falling branches, acorns, leaves, and bird droppings. I do not want to plant any street trees for the same reason; they would create a mess that could damage the cars.

NEIGHBORS: We live in an apartment complex behind the lot and are strongly against the car dealership. We currently enjoy a beautiful view of the Heritage Oak from our windows and do not want to look out onto a sea of cars. We also worry that the business would create lots of traffic and make a lot of noise.

CLEAN CENTER CITY: As a local civic group, we support the sale of environmentally friendly cars, as they help reduce carbon emissions and pollution. We believe that forward-thinking businesses like Ms. Thomas's will help Center City in the long run. We urge the town council to do all it can to help Ms. Thomas's business thrive—including removing one tree, if need be.

TOWN PLANNING DEPARTMENT: Our department oversees the long-term planning and development of Center City. We believe that trees are important for the town, as they provide beauty, shade, and habitat for birds and wildlife. Large trees like the Heritage Oak are especially valuable because they clean pollution from the air and absorb lots of carbon, storing it in the wood. Even if the tree is allowed to remain in the lot, paving over its roots could harm it and threaten its health. We also stand behind our town's street tree plan, which ensures that all lots have street trees.

What should the town council do?

I LOVE MY GREEN JOB!

CAREER CORNER

COMMUNITY PLANNERS develop land-use plans to help meet the changing needs of cities, towns, and counties. They also recommend whether new proposals should be approved or denied.

NAME_____ DATE_____

The Morrisville town council has an important decision to make. A citizen recently donated 250 acres (101 hectares) of nearby land called Morris Woods to the town. There are no zoning restrictions on Morris Woods, and the town council has to decide what to do with it. Morris Woods is completely covered with forest, including about 100 acres of large trees that are over 150 years old. A stream flows through the forest and it has good places for swimming. Deer, raccoons, frogs, salamanders, foxes, many different birds, and other animals live in the forest.

Morrisville is a medium-sized town. Many of the residents work for a local forest products company, but a lot of people also work at a computer-parts plant in a neighboring town. Others work at the schools, the library, and all sorts of small businesses.

The council is faced with three different options, supported by three different citizen groups:

Option 1: Keep Morris Woods Natural
Save Our Woods: We are concerned about the long-term health of our forestland. We want the town to keep Morris Woods as a nature park, with hiking and biking trails for people to enjoy. This option would preserve the forest for the future and provide residents with a wilderness area close to home.

Option 2: Sell Morris Woods to Simpson Tree Farm
Jump for Jobs: We are interested in increasing job prospects in Morrisville. We want the town to sell Morris Woods to Simpson Tree Farm, the local forest products company. Simpson Tree Farm has agreed to sustainably manage Morris Woods as a working forest to provide local jobs and lumber for local construction, while caring for the land and protecting animal habitats.

Option 3: Sell Morris Woods to Build Homes
More for Morrisville: We believe that Morrisville needs to grow in order to thrive. We want the town to sell the Morris Woods to the Morrisville Development Company to build new homes. More houses would mean more property taxes to help pay for schools, the library, and other services.

What should the town council do?

CAREER CORNER I LOVE MY GREEN JOB!

FORESTERS manage forests for public and private use. They may develop short- and long-term plans for the forest. Their plans may include planting, growing, and monitoring trees for healthy growth and making sure forest practices meet environmental regulations.

NAME _____ DATE_____

Use the chart below to identify stakeholders and detail their viewpoints as they relate to your community issue. Finally, propose solutions that will satisfy the needs of two or more stakeholder groups.

Stakeholder	What does the stakeholder need or want?	In what ways does the stakeholder agree with the others?	In what ways does the stakeholder disagree with others?
What solutions would you propose?			

CAREER CORNER

I LOVE MY GREEN JOB!

Conflicts like the Morris Woods debate may be addressed with the help of <u>ENVIRONMENTAL LAWYERS</u>, who specialize in legal matters concerning the environment. They represent different stakeholders, ensure that environmental laws are respected, and lobby for balanced environmental regulations.

Everyone has an equal right to a healthy environment—but does everyone *have* a healthy environment? In this activity, students propose actions to resolve various scenarios and then research issues related to environmental justice in their own state.

ENVIRONMENTAL JUSTICE FOR ALL

SUBJECTS
Science, English Language Arts, Social Studies, Health

PLT CONCEPTS
1.9, 2.10, 3.11

STEM SKILLS
Data Analysis, Investigation, Problem Solving, Technology Use

DIFFERENTIATED INSTRUCTION
Hands-on Learning, Multiple Solution Pathways, Student Voice

MATERIALS
Chart paper, tablets, or laptops; internet access

TIME CONSIDERATIONS
Preparation: 45 minutes
Activity: Two 50-minute periods, plus time for research

OBJECTIVES

Students will

- Examine the principle of environmental justice by looking at case studies involving different communities.
- Explore environmental justice in their state.
- Propose actions to address local environmental justice issues.

BACKGROUND

What characteristics describe the areas where you work, live, and play? Is your neighborhood exposed to environmental hazards such as a congested freeway, a hazardous waste incinerator, or heavy industry manufacturing? Do some people in your community have less access to clean air, clean water, or green spaces than others?

According to the National Institute for Environmental Health Science, certain groups of people are disproportionately exposed to environmental conditions that can harm their health. In the United States, people of color, low-income communities, and tribal populations are at greater risk of exposure to lead, air pollutants, and other hazardous substances. Extended and repeated exposure to these substances can shorten life expectancies; raise cancer rates; cause birth defects and greater infant mortality; and lead to higher incidence of asthma, diabetes, and cardiovascular disease.

Many systemic inequalities contribute to this problem, but here are the primary causes:

- Market dynamics drive both businesses and residents to low-cost real estate.
- Toxic facilities are often placed in low-population areas, which means that they also are more likely to be in areas with high poverty rates.
- Low-income communities often wield less political power than other communities and are thus less able to oppose the siting of problem facilities or advocate for improved conditions.
- Regulations, policies, and government or corporate decisions often empower existing social systems that do not protect low-income communities, or people of color in low-income communities, equally.

- Low-income areas often are subjected to less environmental enforcement than more affluent areas. Regulators detect violations in vulnerable communities at a slower rate and impose lighter penalties on polluters there.

The U.S. Environmental Protection Agency (EPA) defines **environmental justice** as "the fair treatment and meaningful involvement of all people regardless of race, color, national origin or income with respect to the development, implementation and enforcement of environmental laws, regulations and policies." Environmental justice means that everyone has a fair say in environmental decisions that may affect them.

The EPA's Office of Environmental Justice was created in 1992 to help identify affected communities and the adverse health or environmental effects they face. The National Environmental Policy Act requires that any proposed actions consider the impact and cumulative effects on the people in the affected area. Environmental justice efforts seek to:

- Protect minority, low-income, tribal, and other vulnerable communities from disproportionate levels of environmental pollution and other environmental risks, and from exposure to hazardous substances at work.

- Ensure that everyone has access to adequate public services such as sewage and water treatment and to parks and green spaces.

- Improve situations in which people are already suffering from disproportionate exposure to environmental hazards.

- Help communities to become meaningfully involved in resolving environmental issues that affect them.

Many community-based organizations have made progress reducing the number and degree of noxious industrial sites in their areas and in addressing other equity issues related to the environment. In addition, many communities are developing "Good Neighbor" agreements with the industries within their borders, which aim to address issues of concern in a collaborative way. Through these efforts, communities are working to improve the health, environment, and quality of life of their residents.

Be aware that some of your students may be experiencing poverty or may live in an area that makes them more vulnerable to environmental hazards. Tailor this activity to ensure that these students do not feel stigmatized or overly fearful, and help those who have not experienced poverty first-hand develop compassion for those who have been less fortunate.

Help students frame any issues they uncover in terms of societal decision-making rather than individual shortcomings. Also help students understand that the statistics they may encounter are indicators of potential problems, not predictors of outcomes. You might also identify people who are working to address these issues in your community, and invite them to speak to your students about their work.

USING EJSCREEN

The U.S. EPA's Environmental Justice Screening and Mapping Tool or EJSCREEN (available at epa.gov/ejscreen) is a powerful and easy-to-use tool for exploring and mapping environmental justice issues in communities.

To find county-level information, enter the county name and state (such as Fulton County, GA) under "Select Location" and hit "Go." See the CDC Report that pops up under "Chart or Report" for a summary report showing population data, environmental indicators, and health statistics for the selected location.

The tool also allows you to draw shapes or a round "buffer" around a location. Students might try identifying your site by drawing a buffer and exploring what's inside it. Or, if your neighborhood has very specific boundaries, such as a freeway, you can use EJSCREEN to draw the shape and explore what's within it.

Users can also investigate multiple map overlays (by selecting "EJSCREEN Maps" under "Add Maps") that detail:

- Cancer risk
- Lead paint indicator
- Superfund proximity (a Superfund site is land that has been contaminated by hazardous waste and identified by the U.S. EPA as a candidate for cleanup because it poses a risk to human health and/or the environment)
- Hazardous waste proximity
- Wastewater discharge indicator (where pollutants have been discharged into bodies of water)
- Other variables such as education level of residents and location of parks and schools

Note: Some of the summary reports use the term **percentile** in presenting the data. A percentile is a value on a scale of 100 that indicates the percent of a distribution that is equal to or below it. For example, if a community is in the 80th percentile in terms of cancer risk, this community may experience a greater cancer risk than 80 percent of other communities measured. In the summary reports of environmental indicators, a higher percentile indicates a greater potential risk.

POTENTIAL ENVIRONMENTAL JUSTICE ISSUES

Using the EJSCREEN tool, students may be able to identify environmental justice issues in their community related to:

- Air quality (particulate matter)
- Cancer risk
- Asthma
- Hazardous waste
- Lead-based paint
- Ozone
- Traffic proximity
- Wastewater
- Other topics

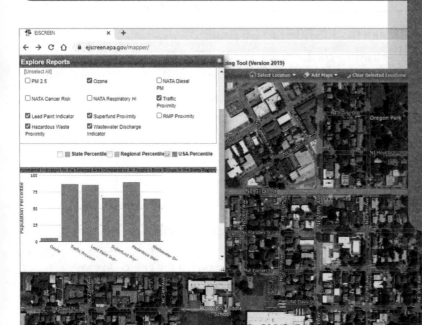

This activity was adapted from "Environmental Justice for All" in *WET in the City Curriculum and Activity Guide*.

GETTING READY

PART A:

- Make copies of the Community Case Study and The Rest of the Story… student pages or plan to share them with students digitally.

PART B:

- Make copies of the Seeking Environmental Justice student page.

- Familiarize yourself with the EJSCREEN tool for exploring environmental justice issues in communities, which may be found at epa.gov/ejscreen. This interactive mapping tool has overlays showing Superfund sites, brownfields, toxic release sites, park locations, public housing sites, population density, census data, and more. See the *Using EJSCREEN* box on page 235 for more information.

- To learn more about potential toxin sources in your community, dig deeper into the EJSCREEN tool. Under "Add Maps > Additional Maps," click on "Sites Reporting to EPA." A box titled "Select Map Contents" will appear. If you click on any of the categories listed in the box (Superfund, Toxic releases, Water dischargers, Air pollution, or Brownfields), relevant sites will appear on your map. Click one of the sites to see the facility name and address. You can also copy the URL provided and paste it into your search engine to see a report on releases and clean-up activities for that site.

- Optional: Explore other possible tools, depending on the students' interest. See Resources for suggestions. Determine the best to way to share and use the selected tools with students.

DOING THE ACTIVITY

PART A: ENVIRONMENTAL JUSTICE CASE STUDIES

1 Introduce the activity by conducting a brief survey. Take students to an open space and invite them to form a line representing a scale of 1 to 10, with the "1" end of the line representing "strongly disagree" and the "10" end of the line indicating "strongly agree." Read one of the following statements and have students position themselves in line according to how they rank their response:

- Access to clean air and water is the most important human right.

- Some people are exposed to more pollution than others.

- Some people have better access to parks and green spaces than others.

- It's fair that some people have healthier living conditions than others.

2 **STUDENT VOICE** Point out the range of opinions in the group. To give students a chance to discuss their opinions, break the line at its midpoint and have half the students stay in place while the other half moves down so that each student has a partner. Give each person in each pair 30 seconds to explain the ranking they chose.

3 Repeat Steps 1 and 2 with the other statements. As a group, discuss what people could do to make living conditions fairer.

4  **MULTIPLE SOLUTION PATHWAYS** Divide the group into teams of three to five students each. Give each team one of the Community Case Study student pages, pointing out that these scenarios are based on real-life, documented case studies from across the United States and internationally. Have teams review their case, identifying the problem and any challenges that might make it difficult to address the problem. Next, teams should propose solutions to the problem.

5 Once teams have finished, bring everyone together to discuss the scenarios, challenges, and proposed solutions, using their notes on the student page.

6 Share the information in The Rest of the Story… student page (or hand out copies) and have teams compare their ideas with what the community in each case actually did.

7 Ask students whether they have heard the term environmental justice before and ask them what they think it means. Reflecting on the scenarios and students' proposed solutions, discuss:

- Which, if any, of these case studies involve environmental justice issues? Support your answer with facts from each case.

- In addition to coming up with fair solutions, environmental justice also means recognizing that some people are disproportionately impacted by a situation or may be more vulnerable than others. In each of the cases, who is most impacted? How might your solution help to make things better for them? How could they be involved in a meaningful way?

- What else would you need to know to develop a more comprehensive solution or to make your proposed solution work better?

- What challenges might you encounter with your proposed solution(s)?

- What would you do to build on the actions taken by the real communities?

- Which neighborhoods or communities in our local area might be similar to those described in any of the scenarios? Why?

TAKE IT OUTSIDE

Invite students to select a site or feature they explored using EJSCREEN, and go to that location to "ground truth" their findings. What do they notice at the site using their senses or previous experiences? How does that compare with, contrast with, or add to what they learned from EJSCREEN? What might they learn from the experience of others with that place? How has that place changed or how might it change in the future?

PART B: ENVIRONMENTAL JUSTICE AND YOU

1 Ask students whether they think there are any environmental justice issues in their community. What are they, and what evidence supports the students' opinions?

2 Challenge students to investigate one or more of these issues by gathering and analyzing data on their community compared with other communities in your state. Assign each team of three to five students a specific county in your state to study, and then distribute copies of the Seeking Environmental Justice student page.

3  **HANDS-ON LEARNING** Share the EJSCREEN tool (see Getting Ready) with students and walk them through some of the features. You might refer students to the terms and definitions presented in the Using EJSCREEN box on page 235. In addition to the information listed on the student page, each team should choose one other variable to investigate using this tool.

4 Allow time for students to conduct their research and analyze their results. Each team should create a poster or other visual representation for their assigned county.

5 Have each team present their findings. Discuss:

- What do the numbers in your presentations tell us about the people living there? Do any of these numbers represent their quality of life or health? What could we infer from those numbers?

- Why should we care about environmental justice?

- If environmental justice issues exist, what could we do to make the situation more equitable?

- How might we find out what people in the community are already doing about the issue?

- How might we alert community members to these potential hazards?

ACADEMIC STANDARDS

SCIENCE

Practices
- Analyzing and interpreting data
- Obtaining, evaluating, and communicating information

Concepts
- Human impacts on Earth systems
- Patterns

ENGLISH LANGUAGE ARTS

Practices
- Writing: research to build and present knowledge
- Speaking and listening: presentation of knowledge and ideas

SOCIAL STUDIES

Practices
- Developing questions and planning inquiries
- Communicating conclusions and taking informed action

Concepts
- Civics: processes, rules, and laws
- Geography: spatial patterns and movement of human population

ASSESSMENT

Ask students to

- Describe an environmental justice issue from the activity, including their claim, the evidence that supports it, and their reasoning for why the evidence supports the claim. Have them also propose an action that would help the situation.

- Use the information they collected about their own community to create an educational social media message, web page, video, or other presentation to inform the community about an environmental justice issue. If appropriate, post it to PLT's social media at facebook.com/projectlearningtree and twitter.com/PLT.

ENRICHMENT

- Help students find out what other communities have done to address environmental justice issues such as those described in the case studies or one they have identified in their own community.

- Encourage students to research success stories and write a profile of a group that addressed an environmental justice problem or a person who did so. The profile could include the problem, the strategy, and the results.

- Take students to visit one of the locations from their research and interview local residents about whether they think environmental justice issues exist in the community. Help students develop a short, objective survey with questions specific to their community. Find ways to share the results with community members. See plt.org/myk8guide for an example.

- Invite students to write a letter to the editor or to their local lawmaker about what they learned in the activity, including their proposed solutions.

- Get your students involved in a local or national community science project, such as World Water Monitoring Day.

NAME _____ DATE _____

The following description is based on a real community that faced an environmental justice issue. As you read through the scenario, identify the problem and the challenges that might make it difficult to address the problem. Then, write the solutions you would propose.

Norma and her family are tribal members in the Pacific Northwest of the United States. Salmon have sustained her tribe for thousands of years. Members of the tribe value salmon as an important gift from the Creator. The tribe depends on salmon economically, culturally, and spiritually.

Norma's tribe and 11 other tribes once lived in a large area that is now eastern Washington State and parts of Oregon, Idaho, and British Columbia. In the 1800s, they gave up most of their land in exchange for the right to continue fishing and living the way they always have. Today, the tribes' reservation covers a much smaller area.

Across the border from the reservation, a Canadian company processes lead and zinc. Lead, which is highly toxic, is used in car, truck, and cell phone batteries. Zinc is used to coat steel and iron and for sunscreen, fertilizers, and other products. High levels of zinc can be toxic to people.

According to tribe members, the company's operations discharged more than 400,000 tons of zinc, lead, and other toxic metals into the river over many years. They claim that this toxic waste has turned some of the shoreline black and has threatened the tribes' livelihood. The U.S. Environmental Protection Agency says this toxic waste is poisonous to animals and plants—especially to ones living at the river bottom. When salmon swallow the toxic metals, they are passed along the food chain to people.

The company claims that its waste was not aimed at the reservation on purpose and that other companies contributed to the pollution too. It also says that U.S. laws and courts have no authority over Canadian companies.

Problem: _____

_____

Challenges: _____

_____

Proposed Solutions: _____

_____

CAREER CORNER

I LOVE MY GREEN JOB!

STUDENT PAGE

STUDENT PAGE

NAME _____ DATE_____

The following description is based on a real community that faced an environmental justice issue. As you read through the scenario, identify the problem and the challenges that might make it difficult to address the problem. Then, write the solutions you would propose.

Angel's family lives in a large city in the southern United States. Angel's neighborhood doesn't have as many trees as other parts of the city. On hot summer days, the lack of shade means that people have little relief from the sweltering sun.

In addition to shade, city trees provide lots of other benefits, including:

- Lowering city temperatures by as much as 15 degrees on hot days
- Improving air quality
- Reducing noise levels
- Increasing a city's sense of community
- Creating a nicer-looking city
- Reducing stress in city residents

The lack of trees in Angel's neighborhood has created health problems for the residents. For example, because it is hotter there than in the surrounding areas, Angel's neighbors tend to stay indoors rather than being active outdoors. That means that there are more cases of asthma, diabetes, and heart conditions than in other neighborhoods in the city.

Studies show that an uneven distribution of urban trees is often related to wealth and class. Angel's family and neighbors experience poverty at a higher rate than the city as a whole. They do not have extra money to pay for trees around their homes or for maintaining them, as other neighborhoods in the city do.

Problem: _____

_____

_____

Challenges: _____

_____

_____

Proposed Solutions: _____

_____

_____

I LOVE MY GREEN JOB !

CAREER CORNER

LANDSCAPE ARCHITECTS plan and design land areas for cities, parks, campuses, recreational facilities, and businesses. They work in urban and rural landscapes to create outdoor spaces that contribute to thriving communities.

NAME _____ DATE _____

The following description is based on a real community that faced an environmental justice issue. As you read through the scenario, identify the problem and the challenges that might make it difficult to address the problem. Then, write the solutions you would propose.

Dani lives in a tropical coastal village in a country made up of numerous small islands. Like many other communities in the country, Dani's village relies on shrimp farming as a source of income. Most of the shrimp is exported to other countries, like the United States, where shrimp is the most popular seafood. The average U.S. resident eats 4.1 pounds of shrimp per year.

Although shrimp farming makes lots of money for the country, the industry also has negative effects. Shrimp are raised in ponds near the ocean, which can spill harmful waste into the sea and spread diseases to ocean sea creatures. In order to build the ponds, farmers remove mangrove trees, destroying the mangrove forests.

Mangrove forests grow at the water's edge along ocean coastlines. Their tangled roots and thick canopies shield villages from storms and floods, and they prevent soil from washing away. Mangroves also help protect villages from the effects of sea-level rise due to the changing climate. They also provide habitats for beneficial animals and improve air quality.

Dani's village used to be surrounded by mangrove forests. However, as shrimp farming has expanded in recent decades, most of the mangroves have been cut down. Worldwide, more than one-third of the world's mangroves have been removed to create shrimp ponds. Shrimp farming makes villages more vulnerable to storms, flooding, and sea-level rise. It also puts residents in the difficult position of choosing between having a good income to support their families and protecting their local environment.

Problem: _____
_____
_____

Challenges: _____
_____
_____

Proposed Solutions: _____
_____
_____

CAREER CORNER

I LOVE MY GREEN JOB!

<u>WATER QUALITY SPECIALISTS</u> assess the water in rivers, lakes, and water systems to make sure it is safe for people and the environment. They may analyze water samples for pH or other chemical properties and to determine the level of pollution.

NAME_____ DATE_____

The following description is based on a real community that faced an environmental justice issue. As you read through the scenario, identify the problem and the challenges that might make it difficult to address the problem. Then, write the solutions you would propose.

Harper lives in a rural, mountainous region of the United States, where most of the residents are white and experience poverty. It is hard to make a living in the area, as there aren't many jobs. For decades, coal mining has been the biggest industry and the biggest employer in the region. Both of Harper's parents are coal miners.

In recent years, mountaintop removal mining has become more and more common in the region. With this type of mining, coal companies use dynamite to blast off the tops of mountains to access thin layers of coal beneath. The process creates many environmental problems: destroying trees, burying streams and waterways, polluting drinking water, and damaging natural habitats. The process also causes health problems for people who live nearby, including cancer, kidney disease, birth defects, heart disease, and lung disease.

Although mountaintop removal mining provides jobs for many of Harper's neighbors, the jobs don't pay very much, so the residents of the region remain in poverty. Also, working in this industry doesn't require an education, so kids don't have much incentive to stay in school. Harper's region has lower graduation rates and higher drop-out rates than the rest of the country.

Still, many of Harper's neighbors support mountaintop removal mining because it provides jobs. For them, having an income for their families is a more immediate need than protecting the environment.

Problem:_____

_____

_____

Challenges:_____

_____

_____

Proposed Solutions:_____

_____

_____

CAREER CORNER

ENVIRONMENTAL COMPLIANCE INSPECTORS conduct routine investigations of job sites to ensure that all projects comply with environmental laws. They protect the health of workers, the general public, and the land.

NAME _____ DATE _____

The following description is based on a real community that faced an environmental justice issue. As you read through the scenario, identify the problem and the challenges that might make it difficult to address the problem. Then, write the solutions you would propose.

Kim's family recently moved to a new neighborhood in a large city. Kim enjoys playing basketball, but the closest park with a basketball court is nearly a mile away. To get there, Kim must walk past several vacant lots enclosed by chain-link fences with signs reading, "Caution: Toxic Waste." These lots once held factories and are still contaminated by chemicals that leaked into the soil.

The park is located near a solid waste facility that processes one-third of the city's garbage. All day, every day, diesel trucks carrying garbage to and from this facility pass by houses, exposing Kim's neighbors to fumes from burning diesel. As a result, asthma rates are three times higher in this neighborhood than elsewhere in the city.

Kim's neighborhood is one of the poorest in the country, with nearly one-third of the residents living in poverty. One-quarter of the residents are unemployed. Because of the pollution and lack of parks, people in the neighborhood tend to stay inside and not exercise, which increases the level of asthma, obesity, and diabetes.

Despite these challenges, many neighbors worry that closing the solid waste facility would take jobs away from the neighborhood. They also worry that adding parks or other improvements will hurt them because it would drive up property values. They've seen how in other areas of the city, redevelopment has driven up prices and forced people to move out.

Problem: _____

_____

_____

Challenges: _____

_____

_____

Proposed Solutions: _____

_____

_____

CAREER CORNER

I LOVE MY GREEN JOB!

SAFETY INSPECTORS ensure that the workplace is a safe and healthy place for workers. They provide information, advice, and guidance to both employees and employers to help them meet safety policies and regulations.

NAME _____ DATE _____

The five case studies you've explored are based on real communities that faced environmental justice issues. Here's how these communities worked to address these issues. What additional solutions would you suggest?

SALMON PEOPLE

This scenario is based on a real situation on the Columbia River in northern Washington State, the home of the Confederated Tribes of the Colville Reservation. The 12 bands of the Confederated Tribes of the Colville Reservation joined with the State of Washington to sue a Canadian company for polluting the river and threatening the livelihood of tribe members. They asserted that the company had been polluting the river for nearly 100 years.

After pursuing this lawsuit for more than 15 years, the Confederated Tribes of the Colville Reservation finally won it. As a result of the lawsuit:

- The company will reimburse the Colville Tribes $8.6 million for attorney fees and the cost to investigate the river pollution.
- The company will work with the U.S. EPA to clean up some of the toxic waste.
- The EPA will be responsible for enforcing any additional cleanup of the river with the company.
- Further court proceedings will determine damages from the pollution and decide whether the company owes Colville Tribes more money.

What additional solutions do you suggest? _____

_____

TREES, PLEASE

This scenario is based on a real situation in the Oak Cliff neighborhood of Dallas, Texas. An organization called Cool and Connected Oak Cliff used GIS technology to discover that the neighborhood would benefit from more trees. They worked to solve the problem by:

- Recruiting volunteers to plant more than 500 trees, with a goal of planting 1,000.
- Asking residents for feedback about where to plant the trees.
- Creating "green teams" in the community to water and tend the young trees.
- Hiring interns from local high schools to help care for the trees and monitor their growth.

What additional solutions do you suggest? _____

_____

THE SHRIMP CONNECTION

This scenario is based on a real situation in a village called Mangunharjo in Indonesia. After facing devastating erosion as the result of mangrove removal, villagers worked to reverse some of the damage by:

- Volunteering to replant mangroves to restore the area. Birds and wild shrimp have already returned.
- Looking for ways to reduce ecological impacts of shrimp farms, including using mangrove trees as natural filters.
- Protecting the local fishing industry by making sure that all shrimp pond water entering the sea is filtered first.

What additional solutions do you suggest? _____

The Rest of the Story... (cont.)   STUDENT PAGE

NAME _____ DATE _____

MOUNTAINTOP REMOVAL

This scenario is based on a real situation in the Appalachian region of the United States. Although many residents still support mountaintop removal mining and the practice continues, some local community groups have fought against it by petitioning the federal government. These groups have been:

- Raising awareness of the effects of mountaintop removal mining through a bi-monthly newspaper (The Appalachian Voice) in affected communities of North Carolina, Virginia, and Tennessee.

- Urging lawmakers to close six power plants in North Carolina that burn coal.

- Creating a partnership of nonprofit organizations working to end mountaintop removal mining across the region.

- Working politically to challenge mountaintop removal mining. In 2016, the federal government ruled to restrict coal companies and require that they monitor the impact on streams and restore damaged waterways.

What additional solutions do you suggest? _____

_____

TRACED TO WASTE

This scenario is based on a real situation in the South Bronx neighborhood of New York City. Through an organization called Sustainable South Bronx, residents are working to promote green jobs and create more green spaces to make their community a healthier place. Some of their efforts include:

- Planning a network of waterfront and on-street bike paths that also supports local businesses.

- Starting a job training program that teaches skills to restore the environment, like safe clean-up of contaminated land, caring for urban trees, and green-roof installation.

- Developing an eco-industrial center for businesses that process and use recyclable materials as raw materials.

- Educating people about the connection between the industrial facilities in the neighborhood and the health issues that residents face.

- Working to reduce the amount of garbage the city produces.

What additional solutions do you suggest? _____

_____

CAREER CORNER

I LOVE MY GREEN JOB!

ENVIRONMENTAL JOURNALISTS collect and analyze facts about topics related to the environment. They dig for information from documents, conduct interviews, and write fact-based stories for podcasts, e-journals, newspapers, radio, or television.

NAME _____ DATE_____

Use the EJSCREEN tool or other online tools to collect data for your assigned county. Create a visual display with the following information.

> **To find information about your assigned county with EJSCREEN:**
> - **Under "Select Location" enter in the name of the county and state (such as Washington County, OR) and hit "Go."**
> - **A pop-up window titled "Chart or Report" will appear.**
> - **Select "CDC Report" to find population data, environmental indicators, and health statistics for your county.**
> - **Go to "Add Maps" and then "EJSCREEN Maps" to add and explore other variables with the mapping tool.**

County: _____

1. Average Income: _____

2. Percentage of residents living below the poverty line: _____

3. Races of residents (by percentage): _____

4. Concentration of particulate matter in the air: _____

5. Percentage of residents living within one-half mile of a park: _____

6. Percentage of residents living close to a major highway: _____

7. Another variable of your choice, including its description and value: _____

8. Did you find an environmental justice issue in this county? Explain your answer using the evidence you found. _____

   _____

   _____

9. If you found an environmental justice issue, how would you propose addressing it? _____

   _____

   _____

10. If you did not find an environmental justice issue, what additional data would you recommend collecting to be sure there isn't an issue? _____

    _____

    _____

CAREER CORNER

COMMUNITY ENGAGEMENT MANAGERS build relationships with groups of people to identify and address issues affecting their well-being. The work often involves partnerships that help mobilize resources and drive changes in policies, programs, and practices.

The energy we use at home, school, or work enhances our lives, but it also often contributes to air and water pollution, wildlife and habitat loss, and climate change. Students learn about different sources of energy, conduct an audit of the electricity they use in their own homes, and create an action plan to use energy wisely.

EXPLORATION ENERGY!

SUBJECTS
Science, English Language Arts, Math, Social Studies

PLT CONCEPTS
2.10, 4.6, 4.7

STEM SKILLS
Creativity, Data Analysis, Leadership, Technology Use

DIFFERENTIATED INSTRUCTION
Cooperative Learning, Hands-on Learning, Higher-order Thinking, Personal Connections

MATERIALS
Thermometers, art supplies, calculators, access to internet. Optional: Digital or print version of *Reading an Electric Meter*

TIME CONSIDERATIONS
Preparation: 30-45 minutes

Activity: Several 50-minute periods over a week, plus time at home for energy audit

OBJECTIVES

Students will

- Describe different energy sources and some of the positive and negative effects of using them.

- Identify ways to use less electricity in their daily lives.

- Explain how using energy more wisely can reduce the negative effects of energy sources on people and the environment.

BACKGROUND

When you turn on a heater or air conditioner, take a shower, or use a computer, you're using electricity, the most common form of energy used in residences and workplaces.

Electricity is a **secondary energy source**, which means that we get it by converting a **primary energy source** that is mined or captured in the environment. Primary sources include coal, oil, natural gas (methane), uranium, hydropower, **biomass**, wind power, and solar energy.

Every energy source has advantages and disadvantages, which may include cost, available supply in the short- and long-term, and the environmental and social impacts of its use. (See *The Pros and Cons of Primary Energy Sources* at plt.org/myk8guide for specific information on different sources.)

To produce electricity, a primary energy source is used either to operate an electric generator or to make electricity directly via an electrochemical process. The most

FOREST FACT

did you know

Forests provide a source of renewable energy from woody biomass, which consists of forest residues (such as fallen limbs and leaves) and sawdust and wood scraps from sawmills. Using forest residues as fuel supports sustainable forest management by reducing the risk of insect infestations, disease, or fire and by enhancing wildlife habitat.

HOW WE USE ENERGY

Energy use is typically divided among different sectors.

- **Residential and Commercial.** We use energy at home and at work in similar ways: lighting spaces; keeping rooms at a comfortable temperature; heating water for cleaning and washing; and using computers, appliances, and other technologies. Electricity and, to a lesser extent, natural gas and heating oil, are the most significant energy sources in residential and commercial spaces.

- **Transportation.** It takes energy to move people and goods from one place to another. Personal vehicles use energy, as do public transportation vehicles (buses and trains), trucks, airplanes, freight trains, ships, and barges. Liquid fossil fuels, primarily diesel oil and gasoline, are the major sources of energy used in transportation.

- **Industry.** We use energy to manufacture or grow all the things we consume and own. Every product we rely on—including food, cars and gasoline, electronics, paper, appliances, and buildings—takes energy to produce. Industry heavily depends on natural gas, petroleum and other liquid fuels, and electricity.

This activity focuses on residential energy use, with an emphasis on electricity. You may choose to expand the activity by encouraging students to explore other ways they depend on energy, including for transportation and for the goods they use.

common way that electricity is made is with a generator: the primary energy source is used to turn a turbine connected to a generator. Fossil fuels or fuels from renewable resources may be burned to make hot gases or steam that turn the turbine, or wind or hydropower may be used to turn it directly. The turbine is connected to a generator that uses bundles of copper wire to create a magnetic field, which causes electrons to move from atom to atom, forming an electric current.

An increasing percentage of electricity generation comes from electrochemical processes. Solar energy is one example: energy from sunlight is absorbed by manufactured photovoltaic cells, which causes electrons to move and an electric current to form. Electricity can also be produced electrochemically in fuel cells and batteries. Fuel cells convert a fuel (often hydrogen) into electricity through an electrochemical process, without combustion. Batteries can also convert electricity into chemical energy that can be easily converted back to electricity at a later time.

HOW CLEAN IS IT?

While electricity itself is a clean, nonpolluting form of energy, the primary sources used to generate electricity vary in terms of how clean they are. Much of the electricity in the United States is generated in power plants that burn coal, oil, or natural gas. They emit large amounts of carbon dioxide, carbon monoxide, nitrogen oxides, sulfur dioxide, and other pollutants that affect air and water quality and contribute to the greenhouse gas effect and climate change.

Other sources, such as hydropower, wind, and solar, do not involve combustion and are relatively clean. Nuclear power plants generate electricity without pollution but create dangerous waste that is radioactive and must be carefully managed and stored. For information about carbon dioxide and its relation to global climate change, see the Background for the activity The Global Climate.

NONRENEWABLE VS. RENEWABLE

In addition to how clean they are, energy sources may be classified as renewable or nonrenewable. **Nonrenewable energy** sources exist in fixed amounts: once they're used up, they're gone. Fossil fuels, including coal, oil, and natural gas, are nonrenewable because they are formed through natural processes that take millions of years and cannot be restored. **Renewable energy** sources, on the other hand, can be replenished through natural processes or resource management practices. Solar, wind, and hydropower are examples of renewable sources of energy that are perpetually being renewed or restored. Wood and other forms of biomass are also renewable sources of energy when the trees or plants are sustainably managed to assure regrowth.

Some renewable energy sources are intermittent in nature. For example, solar energy can only be produced during the day, and wind energy can only be produced when it is windy. Since electricity cannot be directly stored, **energy storage** systems such as large-scale batteries are an important complement to these resources, particularly if there is a policy goal to increase renewable energy use. Energy storage helps balance the output of intermittent resources with the demand for electricity, which is also variable.

Biofuels, such as ethanol and biodiesel, are primarily made from corn, soy, sugarcane, wheat, and related crop wastes. Biogas (or renewable natural gas) is another form of biofuel that is typically made from the anaerobic digestion of farm and crop wastes. Although biofuels are considered renewable resources, they may require fossil fuels in the thermal or chemical process used to create them.

USING ENERGY WISELY

The least expensive way to reduce the harmful impacts of energy consumption is to use less energy. But saving energy doesn't mean putting on a thick sweater and sitting in the dark. Wise energy use means using energy when you need it, not using it when you don't, and using the least amount needed to get the job done. It also means choosing clean and renewable energy sources, when possible.

Energy efficiency refers to technologies or measures that use less energy to provide the same result. Energy-efficient electric devices reduce the amount of primary energy consumption, which usually reduces fossil fuel consumption and emission of carbon dioxide and pollutants. Higher-efficiency electric devices also make small-scale distributed energy systems more feasible (see *Making It Local* box).

There are many simple ways that people can use energy more wisely, including using energy-efficient light bulbs, caulking doors and windows to minimize drafts, lowering the temperature setting of the water heater, turning off lights and appliances that are not in use, and adjusting the heating or air conditioning thermostat when no one is home.

MAKING IT LOCAL

Some energy sources can be used to produce electricity locally. Solar energy, for example, can be produced on the rooftop of the building where it is consumed. Small, localized sources of energy are known as distributed generation and are a fast-growing component of modern power systems. Solar, fuel cells, and battery storage systems are the most common types of distributed generation.

WHAT'S A WATT?

Electricity is measured in a unit of power called a watt (W). The amount of electricity we use over a period of time is measured in kilowatt-hours (kWh), or the energy of 1000 watts for one hour. For example, if you use a 9-watt LED light bulb for five hours, you will use 45 watt-hours of electricity, or 0.045 kWh.

GETTING READY

PART A:

- Choose which energy sources students will research. See the table below for possibilities. For details about each source listed in the table, see *Pros and Cons of Primary Energy Resources* at plt.org/myk8guide.

PRIMARY ENERGY SOURCES	
Renewable Sources	**Nonrenewable Sources**
Biofuels (ethanol, biodiesel, biogas)	Coal
Geothermal	Natural Gas (methane)
Hydropower	Nuclear Power (uranium fission)
Solar	Petroleum (oil)
Wind	Waste (refuse-derived fuel)
Wood (biomass)	

PART B:

- Make copies of the Home Energy Audit student page.

- Find out what types of electric meters are common in your area—digital or analog (dial) meters, or both. Plan to share information from Reading an Electric Meter under Doing the Activity, Part B, as needed. If you have any questions about the types of meters in your area or how to read them, check with your local power supplier.

- Find out how the electricity in your area is generated. Check with your local power supplier or see the U.S. Environmental Protection Agency's Power Profiler website at epa.gov/energy/power-profiler.

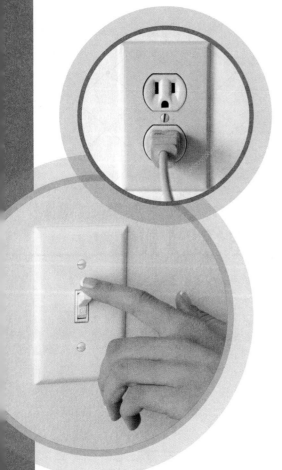

 SAFETY CHECK! Electricity can be dangerous and even fatal. Electric meters are very safe, but be sure to follow some basic safety precautions around them:

- Do not allow children to climb or play on an electric meter.

- Never attempt to fix, alter, or tamper an electric meter. If you notice damage to a meter, call your power supplier immediately.

- Do not store anything around your electric meter. Do not cover the meter with insulation or another obstacle. Keep the meter free from snow and ice.

- Do not tie pets to a meter.

DOING THE ACTIVITY

PART A: ENERGY SLEUTHS

1 ⊙ **PERSONAL CONNECTIONS** Ask students if the power has ever gone out in their home. What happened? Why? How did they feel about it? Ask students if they know where electricity comes from. Explain that they will be learning about sources of energy in this activity.

2 Invite students to list as many different sources of energy as they can, posting the list where everyone can see it. Add to the list to fill any gaps or to clarify between primary and secondary energy sources. If students don't know, you may want to use information from the Background to describe how electricity is generated from a primary source.

3 Divide the group into small teams and assign one primary energy source from the list to each team.

4 ⊙ **COOPERATIVE LEARNING** Give the teams time to research their energy source. Have them create a report that explains:

- How and where people get it
- Whether it is used in your area
- How clean it is
- Whether it is renewable or nonrenewable
- Other pros and cons of using it
- Recommendations for its use in the future

5 Have the expert teams present their reports to the entire group. Students should take notes on the other teams' reports.

PART B: WASTE WATCHERS

1 Ask students to brainstorm a list of ways they use energy in a typical week. Discuss: Which uses take the most energy? Which uses involve electricity? Why is it a problem if we waste electricity? Help students understand the relationship between electricity generation and environmental impacts.

2 Pass out copies of the Home Energy Audit student page. Explain that students will do an energy audit of their homes to help determine how much electricity they use in a week and to look for ways they might save energy.

3 Explain that students will read their electric meter at the beginning and the end of the week to determine the number of kWh of electricity their family used during the week (one kWh is the amount of energy expended by one kilowatt in one hour).

TAKE IT OUTSIDE

Look for solar energy systems in your neighborhood. Take students on a walk around your site or in the surrounding area and invite them to check rooftops for solar panels. Discuss the best conditions for these small systems. For example, rooftop solar works best on south- or west-facing roofs and where the panels aren't shaded by tall trees or other obstructions.

4 Share the information in the Reading an Electric Meter box below to explain how students can read their electric meter and to give them practice. For students who live in apartment buildings, suggest that they ask the building manager for access to the meters.

HANDS-ON LEARNING Encourage students to write down or take pictures of the numbers in each display or dial of their meter. They can then bring this information to class and work with a partner to determine the kilowatt hours.

5 Throughout the week, students should complete the other items on the Home Energy Audit student page. If necessary, they should get help from an adult at home to complete their energy audits.

6 At the end of the week, remind students to read their meter again and calculate the amount of electricity their household used. Tally all the results and post the group total where everyone can see it.

7 **HIGHER-ORDER THINKING** Help students analyze the results. What were the total and average electricity uses in a week? Can students think of anything else they could do use less energy? For example, they might open the refrigerator door as few times as possible, ride their bike or take public transportation, encourage their parents to buy energy-efficient appliances when they need new ones, and so on.

8 Have the students work with their families to develop an action plan for using less energy or using energy more wisely.

VARIATION: GRADES 3–5

1 Introduce the topic of energy by asking students to draw a picture of a superhero—one from their imagination or one they know from TV, books, computer games, or movies—showing how they get their power to do superhuman things. Invite students to share their pictures and to describe the sources of power.

2 Ask students where they get their power to do human things. Help the group make a list of energy sources people use (such as the sun, wind, wood, etc.).

3 Divide the group into small teams, with each team assigned to one of the energy sources they listed. Students may conduct their own research or glean the information from *Pros and Cons of Primary Energy Resources* available at plt.org/myk8guide.

4 Invite teams to create a poster or other presentation about their energy source. Their presentations should include:

- A description of the energy source
- How people use this source
- Pros and cons of using this source

5 Have teams share their presentations with the group.

READING AN ELECTRIC METER

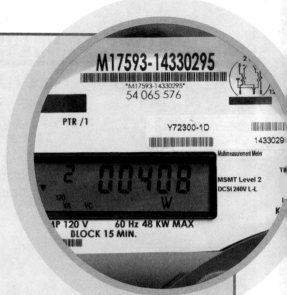

DIGITAL OR "SMART" METERS

Most electric meters in the United States have digital readouts. Many are "smart" meters that can be read remotely and have additional features.

There are many different types of digital meters. They typically have one readout display that shows different values in a cycle that repeats. The values may include:

- A "display check" or test (often looking like "88888888")
- Date
- Time of day (usually in 24-hour format)
- Power: current or instantaneous demand, in kW or possibly shown in amps
- Energy: cumulative consumption, in kWh

Note: The last two values (power and energy) may repeat themselves for specific time-of-use periods.

You may have to wait for the digital meter to cycle through different displays before you get to kWh. One strategy for reading a digital meter is to write down or take a picture of each value that cycles through. When you return to the meter later, it should be easy to compare and figure out which values represent date, time, power, and electric energy.

ANALOG OR "DIAL" METERS

Many nondigital electric meters consist of four or more round dials. To determine the kWh used, start by reading the dial on the right.

- If the pointer lies between two numbers, record the smaller number.
- If the pointer is between 9 and 0, record 9.
- If the pointer is exactly on a number, record one number less than that number, unless the pointer to the right is between 0 and 1. Then, you would record the number that the pointer is on.

In the first example below, the dial on the right is between 1 and 2. Record 1. Moving to the left, the next dial is between 3 and 4. Record the 3. Repeat this process for the remaining dials.

For the second meter, work through each of the four dials to figure out the reading.

Answer to second meter reading: 2049

ACADEMIC STANDARDS

SCIENCE

Practices
- Obtaining, evaluating, and communicating information
- Using mathematics and computational thinking

Concepts
- Human impacts on Earth systems
- Energy and matter: flows, cycles, and conservation
- Cause and effect

ENGLISH LANGUAGE ARTS

Practices
- Writing: research to build and present knowledge
- Speaking and listening: presentation of knowledge and ideas

MATH

Practices
- Reason abstractly and quantitatively
- Number and operations in base ten

Concepts
- Measurement and data

SOCIAL STUDIES

Practices
- Evaluating sources and using evidence
- Communicating conclusions and taking informed action

Concepts
- Economics: economic decision-making
- Geography: human–environment interactions

ASSESSMENT

Ask students to

- For Part A, summarize the key points in their team's report.

- For Part B, draft a webpage that outlines energy-saving actions people can take and explains why it is important to use energy wisely. Students might use a web-creating app and camera to create their webpage.

ENRICHMENT

- Conduct a classroom or school-wide energy investigation to monitor the school's energy consumption using PLT's *GreenSchools Investigations.* Then design and carry out a plan for wiser energy use. Visit plt.org/greenschools to access PLT's five *GreenSchools Investigations,* which are focused on energy, environmental quality, the school site, waste and recycling, and water. Invite other students, administrators, or community members to take part in the resulting action project.

- Have students read their electric meter or look at their electric bill so they can keep track of the number of kWh of electricity they use over a longer period. (Electric bills specify the number of kWh used each month.) Students can analyze their usage by making a graph. Is the monthly usage fairly even through the year, or does it rise and fall? What might account for increases or decreases in energy use during the year?

- Challenge students to look for Energy Stars at your site or at home. Students may find them on lightbulbs, computer monitors, water heaters, furnaces, air conditioners, refrigerators, and more. Energy Star is a joint program of the U.S. Department of Energy and the U.S. Environmental Protection Agency that recognizes the most energy-efficient products. A product displaying the Energy Star rating has an energy performance among the top 25% of all products of its type and has been certified by an independent third party. Homes and commercial building can also earn an Energy Star rating by going through a certification process that demonstrates a specified level of energy efficiency.

- Have students research energy-efficient building designs such as LEED-certified (Leadership in Energy and Environmental Design) buildings, Green Globes–certified buildings, and net-zero energy homes, or examine other energy-saving technologies and report on them to the rest of the group.

- Ask a landscape architect, urban forester, or horticulture expert to recommend ways to save energy by planting trees, shrubs, and ground cover on your site. For example, the expert might recommend planting trees or shrubs to block winter winds, provide shade, or channel cooling breezes to the building. Then invite students to develop and carry out a plan to implement some of the recommendations. (See the activity Plant a Tree.)

NAME _____ DATE _____

AUDIT START

Date: _____ Electric Meter Reading: _____ kilowatt-hours (kWh)

ONE WEEK LATER

Date: _____ Electric Meter Reading: _____ kilowatt-hours (kWh)

How much electricity was used during the week? (Subtract the second reading from the first.) _____ kilowatt-hours (kWh)

Check your home to see what your household is doing to save energy.

1. Staying Warm

☐ Heater temperature is set for 68°F (20°C) or lower[1] when someone is home.

☐ Heater temperature is set for 62°F (17°C) or lower when no one is home or everyone is asleep.

☐ Heater thermostat is on a timer or "smart" control that automatically changes it at night or during the day when no one is home.

☐ Furnace filter is changed regularly.

2. Keeping Cool

☐ Air conditioner temperature is set for 78°F (25°C) or higher[2] when someone is home.

☐ Air conditioner temperature is set for 88°F (31°C) degrees or higher when people will be out of the house for four hours or more.

☐ Air conditioner thermostat is on a timer or "smart" control that automatically changes it at night or during the day when no one is home.

3. Lights

☐ Some or all the light fixtures have LED or compact fluorescent (CFL) bulbs.

☐ Lights are turned off when there is no one in the room.

☐ Lights have labels on the switches to remind people to turn them off or have motion-based, timer, or "smart" controls.

4. Electronics

☐ Televisions are turned off when no one is watching them.

☐ Computers, radios, and other electronics are powered off when no one is using them.

☐ Electronics are plugged into a power strip to turn them off, reducing "phantom" loads from standby power.

☐ One or more electronic devices shows an Energy Star rating.

1, 2 These temperatures are recommended by Energy Star, a joint program of U.S. Department of Energy and the Environmental Protection Agency.

NAME _____ DATE_____

5. Out the Window

☐ Some or all windows are made of double-paned glass or have storm windows installed over them.

☐ Windows are well sealed so that there are no drafts around the frames. (Move a piece of ribbon around the frame to see if it flutters anywhere.)

☐ Doors are well sealed so that there are no drafts around the frames. (Move a piece of ribbon around the frame to see if it flutters anywhere.)

6. Down the Drain

☐ Water heater is set at 120°F (49°C). If your water heater doesn't have a temperature setting, measure the temperature of the water coming out of a faucet. (Just run the water until it's hot, then use a cooking thermometer.)

☐ Water heater shows an Energy Star rating.

☐ Showers have low-flow shower heads.

☐ Sink faucets have low-flow aerators on them.

☐ There are no leaky faucets or pipes.

☐ Clothes are usually washed in cold water.

☐ When possible, clothes are hung up to dry.

☐ The lint trap on the dryer is always cleaned out before drying a load of clothes.

☐ Dishes are allowed to air dry. (If you have a dishwasher, that means using the "eco" mode or opening the door rather than running the drying cycle.)

CAREER CORNER

ENERGY MANAGERS monitor the energy use of a facility or organization and recommend ways to reduce energy. They may redesign processes, retrofit buildings and equipment, plan energy-related systems for new projects, or contract with new renewable energy resources.

Students conduct a field study of three different environments as they focus on sunlight, soil moisture, temperature, wind, water flow, plants, and animals in each environment. By comparing different environments, students will learn how nonliving elements influence living elements in an ecosystem.

FIELD, FOREST, AND STREAM

SUBJECTS
Science, English Language Arts, Math

PLT CONCEPTS
3.1, 3.2, 3.4

STEM SKILLS
Collaboration, Investigation, Organization

DIFFERENTIATED INSTRUCTION
Cooperative Learning, Literacy Skills, Personal Connections

MATERIALS
Chart paper, marking pens, paper for recording observations, trowel or stick for digging, phones with light meter app, thermometer, small strip of paper, compass or smartphones with compass app, bottle of tap water. Optional: Topographical map of area.

TIME CONSIDERATIONS
Preparation: 60 minutes

Activity: One or more 50-minute periods

OBJECTIVES
Students will

- Describe similarities and differences they observe in the nonliving (abiotic) and living (biotic) components of three ecosystems.

- Identify ways that abiotic components of an ecosystem affect the biotic components.

BACKGROUND

An **ecosystem** is a community of different species interacting with each other, and with chemical and physical factors that compose its nonliving environment. It is a system of interrelationships among organisms and between organisms and the physical environment.

FOREST FACT

did you know

The leaf shape of any tree species can vary with elevation and temperature. At cooler temperatures and higher elevation, red maple leaves tend to have more teeth and dissected lobes, which allow for more photosynthesis to occur along the leaf margins.

Plants and animals in an environment interact with each other in various ways. For example, plants may depend on insects or birds to pollinate flowers and on earthworms to aerate the soil; animals may depend on plants for food or shelter.

Plants and animals also interact with the nonliving elements of their environment. Physical factors such as sunlight, moisture, temperature, wind, and water flow influence the suitability of a local area for particular organisms. Those factors determine the kinds of plants and animals that live there.

Physical attributes of the environment are determined by factors such as topography, proximity to water, elevation, or geological features. In addition, the resident organisms (particularly plants) may affect the sunlight, moisture, temperature, and wind of the area. For example, the tall trees of a redwood forest tend to block sunlight and thus create a dark, moist environment, or microclimate, on the forest floor that is suitable for shade-loving plants but is too shady for other kinds of plants. **Microclimate** refers to special conditions of light, moisture, and temperature that occur in a narrowly restricted area within an ecosystem, such as under a bush or in a small woodland opening.

HOW TO MEASURE WIND DIRECTION

The amount and direction of wind in an ecosystem can affect soil moisture levels and the ability of organisms to grow and thrive.

Wind direction tells you where the wind is coming from. A northerly wind blows from the north to the south. To measure wind direction using a compass or smartphone compass app:

- Turn your body so that you are facing into the wind.

- Hold the compass or smartphone in the palm of your hand, at waist level, so that the white pointer is facing away from your body. The white pointer and the bearing below indicate the direction from which the wind is coming.

To measure direction of water flow, follow the same procedure so that you face in the same direction the water is flowing.

GETTING READY

- Find three study sites that are somewhat different from each other in terms of sunlight, air temperature, soil moisture, wind, topography, and number and types of plants and animals living there. If possible, select one site that is open, like a field or lawn; one that has trees; and one that contains water. Possible study sites include a lawn; a park, playground, or other area with many trees; a flowerbed or vegetable garden; a vacant lot; a pond, stream, or marsh; an open field; and a forest.

- Plan to visit the sites on the same day or on different days (at about the same time each day). Obtain any necessary permission to take students to visit the sites you have chosen.

 SAFETY CHECK! Check the sites beforehand to identify any safety hazards such as deep holes, sharp objects, or poisonous or irritating plants.

- Arrange to have at least one parent volunteer, aide, or older student help supervise students during outdoor investigations. This person will help the activity go more smoothly, ensure students' safety, and prevent damage to the sites.

- Make copies of the student page for each team to record their observations. Using chart paper and marking pens, prepare a large chart for compiling team data, or plan to use spreadsheet software.

- Have students practice using equipment like thermometers and light meter and compass apps (see the box *How to Measure Wind Direction* for information on reading a compass).

DOING THE ACTIVITY

1 ➤ **PERSONAL CONNECTION** Ask students to think of a place they enjoy visiting. It might be a park, a grandparent's house, or the library. Invite them to consider:

- What do you particularly enjoy about the place? Is it the people? The physical space?
- What living things make the place enjoyable?
- What nonliving things make the place enjoyable?

2 Help students see that any place has both living and nonliving parts that work together to make an ecosystem. Explain that students will investigate ecosystems at three different study sites to find out how living and nonliving elements affect each other. Ask students what they might look for and what tools they might use to investigate.

3 ➤ **COOPERATIVE LEARNING** Divide your group into teams. Explain that each team will investigate and record observations of a different component at three different study sites. (If you have a large group, have two teams study each component and then average their data.) Be sure to discuss appropriate outdoor behavior with students. All living things, including plants, are to be respected and not injured in any way. Talk with students about following the rule: look, learn, leave alone. (See Appendix B: Tips for Teaching Outdoors.)

4 Give students instructions, a copy of the student page, and materials as described below, or have them plan their own investigations.

TEAM 1: SOIL

This team will determine the soil moisture and soil characteristics at each study site. Students can use a trowel or stick to scrape the surface of the ground and obtain a small sample of soil from underneath the surface. By feeling the soil, they should be able to tell whether it is wet, moist, or dry. (Moist soil will stick together.) They should examine the soil for other characteristics, such as texture, color, and smell. They should also note plant material or organisms in the soil. (See the activity Soil Builders [in Grades 3–5] for more information.)

TEAM 2: WIND AND SUN

This team will determine wind movement and measure how much sunlight reaches the ground at each study site. To assess the amount of wind, one student can hold a small strip of paper away from the body, while the others observe whether it hangs straight down or blows at an angle. They can use the compass or compass app to determine the direction from which the wind seems to be blowing. To determine sunlight intensity, students may use a photographic light meter or photosensitive paper. If these items are not available, they can describe the site in relative terms, such as shady, dark, medium light, or bright, or they can note "Site 1 is brighter than site 2, and site 2 is brighter than site 3."

TEAM 3: TEMPERATURE

This team will measure each site's temperature at ground level, 1" (2.5 cm) deep in the soil, and 1 yard (.9 m) above ground. If one site is a pond, stream, or lake, have the team measure the temperature at just above the water, at 1" (2.5 cm) deep, and at 1 yard (.9 m) above the surface of the water.

TEAM 4: LAY OF THE LAND

This team will determine whether each site is flat or sloped and will record any other land features that affect the study site (such as tall buildings or cliffs adjacent to it). The team will also determine which direction water flows from the site. They can do so by slowly pouring water onto the ground and observing where it goes. They can use the compass to determine the direction of flow. If possible, also have them study a topographic map to locate the site and determine the body of water into which the site drains.

TEAM 5: PLANT LIFE

This team will observe the various kinds of plants at each site (large trees, small trees, shrubs, small plants, grasses—no need to identify species). Students should record the most common kinds of plants found in each location and note especially where each grows relative to the others.

TEAM 6: ANIMAL LIFE

This team will record the various kinds of animals at each site (insects, birds, reptiles, fish, frogs, or tadpoles). Students should include evidence of animals such as scat, tracks, burrows, or leaves that have been chewed.

5 After teams have had sufficient time to investigate each location, have them all come together to present their findings and share what they have learned.

6 Each team should listen to the reports of the other teams and use the information to complete their team chart.

7 Ask teams to enter their data on the large chart you prepared or into a spreadsheet. Use this chart or spreadsheet as a basis for discussing differences between the locations and any interactions students observed among the elements. Discuss:

- Which ecosystem has the greatest number of plants? Animals? Which has the least number of each? How do you explain this difference?
- What plants and animals are found at more than one site? How are the plants and animals the same and how are they different at different sites?
- Which site had the highest air temperature? The lowest? The most wind? The least?
- What has the wettest soil? The driest?
- How are the number and type of plants in an area affected by light intensity, air temperature, and soil temperature?
- How does water influence the soil temperature, air temperature, and soil moisture?
- What relationship does light have with air temperature? With soil moisture? With plants?
- How might water flow affect soil moisture and plants?
- Which of the elements we studied seems most important for determining the diversity or number of plants and animals at each site? What makes you say so?

TAKE IT OUTSIDE

Take a hike! Invite students to join you on a walk near your site. On the way, encourage them to look for places where moisture, temperature, sunlight, wind, and other factors are higher or lower, and to note differences in vegetation. You might use an app such as AllTrails, which can help you find places to hike, bike, fish, and more.

VARIATION: GRADES 3–5

1 Using index cards attached to sticks or stakes, prepare two markers for each pair of students. Write one of the following labels on each marker with suggested symbols:

- Most Sunlight [sun]
- Least Sunlight [sun covered by cloud]
- Highest Temperature [thermometer with high mercury]
- Lowest Temperature [thermometer with low mercury]
- Most Wind [fluttering flag]
- Least Wind [limp flag]
- Most Soil Moisture [faucet gushing]
- Least Soil Moisture [faucet dripping]
- Most Plants [several plants]
- Least Plants [one plant]
- Most Animals [several insects]
- Least Animals [one insect]

2 After choosing a study area such as a vacant lot, mark it off with string or rocks. Divide the group into pairs, and give each pair the "most" and "least" markers for one factor.

3 **LITERACY SKILLS** Invite teams to explore the study area and determine which location has the most and the least of each factor. For example, a team studying plants should decide which site has the most plants and which has the least. Students will indicate their choice by placing their markers in the ground.

4 After all students have marked their choices, examine the entire area to see where the markers of each type are located. According to the markers, which spot had the most or least sunlight? Heat? Moisture? At which spot did you find the most animals? Why might animals prefer that spot? Did that spot have the most or least of any other factors? At which spot did you find the most plants? Why might plants grow well at that spot?

ACADEMIC STANDARDS

SCIENCE

Practices
- Planning and carrying out investigations
- Analyzing and interpreting data

Concepts
- Interdependent relationships in ecosystems
- Patterns

ENGLISH LANGUAGE ARTS

Practices
- Speaking and listening: comprehension and collaboration
- Speaking and listening: presentation of knowledge and ideas

MATH

Practices
- Reason abstractly and quantitatively
- Use appropriate tools strategically

Concepts
- Measurement and data

ASSESSMENT

Ask students to

- Design a graphic organizer drawing connections between the elements they studied and their observations. Have students place the names of each of the elements (sunlight, soil moisture, wind, temperature, water flow, plants, animals) in large circles around the edge of the page. They should draw lines between elements that they observed to be connected. On each line, they should briefly describe the relationship. For example, students might draw a line between sunlight and soil and then write, "More sunlight = drier soil."

ENRICHMENT

- Visit each site again at a different time of year and repeat your investigations. Compare your results. How has the soil changed? The temperature? The wind? The plants and animals? What factors influenced each change?

- Bring the outdoors inside by creating a terrarium of a local ecosystem. See the box *Building a Terrarium* for tips. Discuss: what differences are there between our terrarium and the real ecosystem it represents? What can we learn about natural ecosystems from a terrarium?

BUILDING A TERRARIUM

To build a terrarium, start with a clear, uncolored glass or plastic container and cover the bottom with about ¾ inch (1.8 cm) of gravel or pebbles. Then, spread a piece of cheesecloth on the gravel and layer 2–3 inches (5–7.5 cm) of the appropriate planting mixture on top of that (see "Ecosystem Models" chart). Dig small holes for the plants and add them. Water, cover, and place the terrarium in the appropriate location, as described below.

ECOSYSTEM MODELS			
Materials	**Desert**	**Woodland**	**Tropical**
Planting mixture	Commercial cactus plant mix or mixture of equal parts potting soil, perlite, and sand	Garden or potting soil	Garden or potting soil
Plants	Desert plants	Woodland plants	Tropical plants
Cover	Do not cover	Cover with a piece of glass or plastic	Cover with a piece of glass or plastic
Water	Spray with water until moist	Water until moist, approximately once a week	Water until moist, approximately once a week
Location and light	Location that gets about 3–4 hours of direct sunlight	Cool location with indirect light	Warm location with bright light, not too hot

NAME _____ DATE _____

For each site, record observations of each ecosystem component.

Ecosystem Component	Site 1: _____	Site 2: _____	Site 3: _____
Soil • Moisture: wet, moist, or dry • Texture • Color • Smell • Animals or plant material			
Wind and Sun • Amount of wind • Direction from which wind is blowing • Amount of sunlight: shady, medium light, or bright			
Temperature • At ground level • At 1" (2.5 cm) deep into soil • At 1 yard (0.9 m) above ground			
Lay of the Land • Flat or sloped • Other land features (buildings, trees, cliffs) • Direction of water flow • Body of water into which site drains			
Plant Life • Most common kinds of plants • Where each kind grows			
Animal Life • Animals seen • Animal evidence seen (such as droppings, tracks, burrows, chewed twigs or leaves) • Where each animal or animal sign was found			

I LOVE MY GREEN JOB!

CAREER CORNER

FORESTERS manage public or private forestlands. They develop short- and long-term plans for planting, growing, and monitoring trees for healthy growth and make sure to use forest practices that comply with environmental regulations.

The trees in our communities provide many benefits: they improve air quality, store carbon, and conserve energy. Trees also enhance human health by reducing blood pressure, decreasing stress, and elevating attentiveness. Students conduct a survey to investigate the social and psychological effects of the urban forest.

FOREST IN THE CITY

SUBJECTS
Social Studies, Math, Science

PLT CONCEPTS
1.4, 1.7, 1.9, 1.10

STEM SKILLS
Collaboration, Data Analysis, Investigation

DIFFERENTIATED INSTRUCTION
Literacy Skills, Higher-Order Thinking

MATERIALS
Copies of student pages

TIME CONSIDERATIONS
Preparation: 25 minutes

Activity: Two 50-minute periods, plus time in between to conduct surveys

OBJECTIVES

Students will

- Survey an audience and analyze the results.
- Compare results from different audience subsets.
- Describe how urban forests affect communities, based on their results.

BACKGROUND

The trees around our homes, on our streets, in our parking lots, beside our schools, and throughout our parks are part of an **urban forest**, which includes all the vegetation within the built environment.

People receive a range of important benefits from the urban forest. These trees help to regulate air temperature and improve air quality by creating shade, absorbing UV rays, and trapping small particle pollution. They act as wind breaks to reduce the intensity of wind. They also release oxygen and store considerable amounts of carbon in their wood. They help to stabilize topsoil and to filter and absorb rainwater, which improves the water quality. In addition, they dampen sound and reduce noise pollution.

Trees satisfy a deep need in the human psyche and can affect our moods, our attitudes, and even our health. For example:

- The urban forest is associated with fewer deaths from cardiovascular illness, faster recovery from surgery, and cancer reduction.
- People who live in areas with more trees have lower stress levels and improved self-discipline.
- City dwellers with greater access to an urban forest tend to have more and deeper connections with others in the community than people without access.
- People with views of trees from their work environment are less frustrated, more patient, and have greater enthusiasm for their job than those who do not.
- Residents living in areas with trees use more constructive problem-solving methods to deal with conflict than residents living in areas without trees.

Livability may be defined as the sum of the factors that add up to a community's quality of life. Trees are just one element that affect a community's livability. Other factors include economic prosperity, social stability and equity, educational opportunity, and opportunities for recreation and culture.

FOREST FACT

While many major U.S. cities are planning for a future tree canopy cover of 30-40%, most hold averages between 27-33%. By some estimates, Tampa, Florida and New York City exhibit the most tree canopy cover.

GETTING READY

- Decide whether students will develop their own surveys or use the example provided. If using the example, make color copies of the Community Survey – Questions student page or make digital copies available.

- Make copies of the Community Survey – Responses student page. Create a large chart for compiling the whole group's survey results.

DOING THE ACTIVITY

1 Introduce the activity by asking students whether they noticed any trees today. Ask, "What role do trees play in our community? What benefits do they provide? What problems do they cause?" Point out that all the trees in a town or city make up the urban forest. Ask, "How is the urban forest like or different from other forests? Do you think people in our community feel positive or negative about trees in the urban forest? How might we find out?"

2 If students create their own surveys, help them determine appropriate questions for learning whether or how trees affect members of the community. You might have them look at the Community Survey – Questions student page and decide what they would keep, change, or add for their own survey. Questions should be quantifiable and yield an understanding of how trees are perceived in their community.

3 If students are using the survey provided, share the Community Survey – Questions student page. Ask students what differences they notice between the A pictures and the B pictures.

4 **HIGHER-ORDER THINKING:** Discuss whether there is anything students would want to know about the people taking the survey. For example, they might want to examine whether age, gender, ethnicity, or location influences respondents' choices. Help students compose an appropriate question to add it to the survey (see Question 12 on the example survey).

5 Direct students to first practice administering their own survey before using it with others. Ask them to take turns with a partner to practice giving and taking the survey and recording responses.

6 LITERACY SKILLS: Suggest that students think about their own family or community to determine whether it would be helpful to have the survey translated into other languages. If so, invite volunteers to create a translation sheet for each language. Students may want to use a translating app to help them.

7 Collectively determine who students will survey and how many responses to collect. Recommend asking family members, other youth, or neighbors. For safety reasons, require that students conduct the survey in pairs, except when surveying immediate family members.

8 Allow students time to conduct their surveys over the next two to three days. This would be an appropriate homework assignment.

9 With surveys complete, have student teams tally their data and add it to the group chart (see Getting Ready). For the example survey, teams should tally all A responses and B responses and then, as a group, sum the totals. If they added an additional variable for Question 12, they should also tally their results by the responses to that question. Direct students to graph the group results, as in the *Sample Graph of Survey Results* below. (For the example, students added a Question 12 asking about gender.)

TAKE IT OUTSIDE

Take students to two different nearby locations—one with a tree or trees and one without. In each location, invite the students to sit or stand as still as possible. Ask them to record things they hear, see, and smell. Afterward, discuss differences they observed between the two locations and how each location made them feel.

Sample Graph of Survey Results

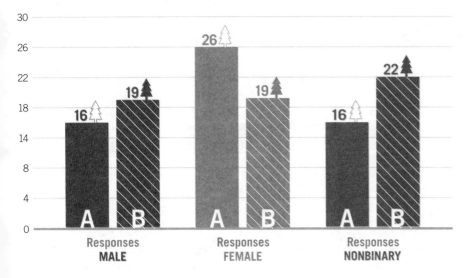

10 Lead a discussion to interpret the results:

- What were some of the most interesting findings from our study? Was there anything that surprised you?

- (If students included a question about respondents) What differences, if any, do you observe between the different groups of respondents?

- Do you think people prefer having trees in the community? What evidence from our study supports your view?

- What do you think the term livability means? Research suggests that the urban forest can help make a place more livable, with social and psychological benefits. Do our results support that? Why or why not?

- Might the urban forest have other benefits to human health or the local ecosystems? What else could we test to explore this idea?

ACADEMIC STANDARDS

SCIENCE

Practices
- Planning and carrying out investigations
- Analyzing and interpreting data

Concepts
- Biodiversity and humans
- Patterns

ENGLISH LANGUAGE ARTS

Practices
- Writing: text types and purpose
- Speaking and listening: presentation of knowledge and ideas

MATH

Practices
- Reason abstractly and quantitatively
- Model with mathematics

Concepts
- Statistics and probability

SOCIAL STUDIES

Practices
- Developing questions and planning inquiries
- Evaluating sources and using evidence

Concepts
- Geography: human-environment interactions

ASSESSMENT

Ask students to

- Write a paragraph detailing the raw data collected from the group survey and their interpretation of it.

- Identify a community forum to share their results, and have students prepare an appropriate presentation. In what ways might their audience influence positive change in the community?

See Appendix M. Assessment Rubric for a sample rubric.

ENRICHMENT

- **Biophilic design** stems from research that confirms humans feel better, learn better, and work better when they are connected to nature. Invite students to assess their current location for how well it integrates nature though access to the outdoors and use of natural building products (wood, stone, sand, etc.) How might they propose increasing these connections?

- Have students choose a wild animal that lives in an urban environment (such as a fox, skunk, or robin) and write a story from its perspective about how it gets what its needs to survive and be happy there. Then ask students to think about how this differs from living in a larger forest, if it does.

- Help students hold a tree planting service day so that others can enjoy the social, health, and psychological benefits of trees.

- Assess urban trees in your area using i-Tree, an online tool used by urban foresters, comparing your results to the state's average. See Project Learning Tree's *Teaching with i-Tree* curriculum for more ideas (plt.org/i-tree).

STUDENT PAGE

NAME_____ DATE_____

A　　　　　　**B**

For Questions 1-6, choose one picture – either A or B.

1. Which apartment building do you find more inviting?

☐ **A**　　　☐ **B**

2. Which house's surroundings do you like better?

☐ **A**　　　☐ **B**

3. In which of these office buildings would you rather work?

☐ **A**　　　☐ **B**

4. Which shopping area is more appealing to you?

☐ **A**　　　☐ **B**

5. On which path would you prefer to walk or ride?

☐ **A**　　　☐ **B**

6. Which park is more inviting?

☐ **A**　　　☐ **B**

NAME _____ DATE_____

For Questions 7-11, choose one group of pictures, A or B.

7. In which group of places would you prefer to live, work, shop, or play?
   ☐ **Group A**   ☐ **Group B**

8. In which group of places would you feel more relaxed?
   ☐ **Group A**   ☐ **Group B**

9. In which group of places would you be more likely to spend time outside?
   ☐ **Group A**   ☐ **Group B**

10. Which group of places looks most welcoming?
    ☐ **Group A**   ☐ **Group B**

11. In which group of places would you prefer to hang out with your friends or family?
    ☐ **Group A**   ☐ **Group B**

12. Additional question (added by student):

    _____

    _____

    _____

NOTES:

_____

_____

_____

_____

_____

CAREER CORNER

URBAN FORESTERS plant, care for, and protect a city's tree population. Urban forests provide shade, improve air quality, reduce energy use, absorb carbon dioxide, and add beauty.

NAME _____ DATE _____

Tally the responses people give to the Community Survey – Questions.

	PERSON 1		PERSON 2		PERSON 3		PERSON 4		PERSON 5		PERSON 6		PERSON 7	
	A	B	A	B	A	B	A	B	A	B	A	B	A	B
1														
2														
3														
4														
5														
6														
7														
8														
9														
10														
11														
12														

Total A responses = _____

Total B responses = _____

CAREER CORNER

I LOVE MY GREEN JOB!

COMMUNITY PLANNERS help shape the physical, social, geographic, and economic elements of their community. They may survey community members to identify priorities, and work in teams to draft and carry out plans.

Students gain an appreciation for how many natural resources they depend on in their day-to-day lives. By tracing the resources that go into making one item, students learn how its manufacturing can have an impact on the environment.

GLOBAL GOODS

SUBJECTS
Science, English Language Arts, Social Studies, Visual Arts

PLT CONCEPTS
1.4, 2.4, 2.8

STEM SKILLS
Data Analysis, Investigation, Organization

DIFFERENTIATED INSTRUCTION
Hands-on Learning, Nonlinguistic Representations, Personal Connections

MATERIALS
Part A: Pencils, world map or globe, large pieces of paper, colored pens.

Part B: Paper and art supplies or access to computers or tablets for presentations. Optional: Collection of everyday objects made from different materials.

TIME CONSIDERATIONS
Preparation: 15 minutes

Activity: One to two 50-minute periods

OBJECTIVES

Students will

- Explain how all the different materials that go into making a product ultimately come from natural resources.

- Depict a product's life cycle, identifying the natural resources—and their sources—used to make the product.

- Describe some of the environmental effects of making or using a product.

BACKGROUND

Most of the products we use every day are composed of a variety of materials. For example, a pencil may be composed of resources from around the world, including incense cedar from California, pumice from Italy, rubber from Brazil, copper from Canada, and graphite from Sri Lanka (see the *Materials That Go into a Pencil* map).

MATERIALS THAT GO INTO A PENCIL

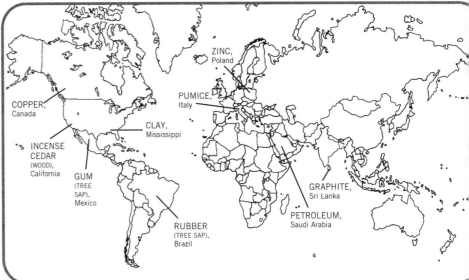

FOREST FACT

did you know

A product life cycle that involves a continuous loop is part of a **circular economy**, which aims to reuse, repair, and recycle products at the end of their life—as opposed to disposing of them.

The cycle of producing, distributing, and disposing of a product like a pencil requires natural resources and energy each step of the way. These steps can be thought of as a **life cycle**, that includes the processes and materials involved (see *A Pencil's Life Cycle* diagram).

A PENCIL'S LIFE CYCLE
This is one example of what may happen to a pencil.

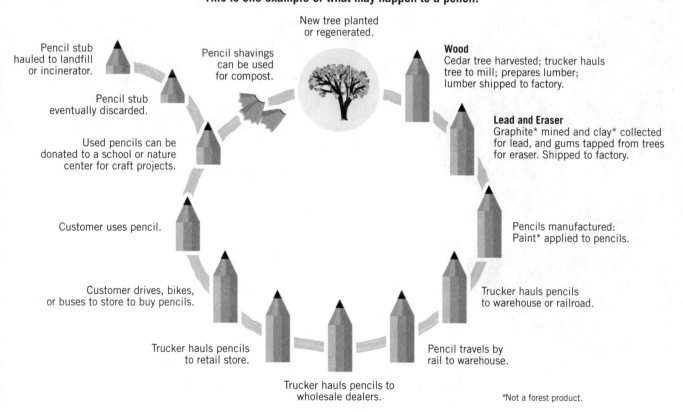

New tree planted or regenerated.

Pencil stub hauled to landfill or incinerator.

Pencil shavings can be used for compost.

Wood
Cedar tree harvested; trucker hauls tree to mill; prepares lumber; lumber shipped to factory.

Pencil stub eventually discarded.

Lead and Eraser
Graphite* mined and clay* collected for lead, and gums tapped from trees for eraser. Shipped to factory.

Used pencils can be donated to a school or nature center for craft projects.

Customer uses pencil.

Pencils manufactured: Paint* applied to pencils.

Customer drives, bikes, or buses to store to buy pencils.

Trucker hauls pencils to warehouse or railroad.

Trucker hauls pencils to retail store.

Pencil travels by rail to warehouse.

Trucker hauls pencils to wholesale dealers.

*Not a forest product.

Every material and the energy used to make a product comes from a renewable or nonrenewable resource. **Renewable resources**—like wood from trees—can be replenished through planting or natural reforestation. **Nonrenewable resources**—like graphite for pencils—are finite and cannot be replenished naturally. Once these materials are mined or taken from their points of origin, they cannot grow again naturally or replace themselves.

The energy needed to make and transport the products we use also comes from renewable or nonrenewable resources. Fossil fuels, like coal and oil, which are used to generate electricity or burned as gasoline in engines, are nonrenewable resources. On the other hand, the sun and wind are perpetual, renewable energy resources.

No matter where the materials for a given product come from, they are all a part of the Earth's resources and energy cycles. How wisely we choose and use the products determines the outcome of these cycles.

MAKING A PENCIL

To make a pencil, an incense cedar log is cut into slats 7 inches (19 cm) long. A machine cuts grooves into the slats and glues in a writing core, which is what we call the lead (it's actually a mixture of graphite and clay, not lead). A second grooved slat is glued on top of the core-filled slat, making a "sandwich." A machine shapes each side of the slat sandwich and then cuts it into individual pencils.

After being sanded smooth, each pencil is painted, and a shallow recess is cut into one end to accept the "ferrule," the metal ring that holds the eraser to the pencil. The eraser may be made from rubber, gum, or synthetic rubber (which comes from petroleum) and blended with pumice. Both the ferrule and the eraser are attached to the end.

Of the materials needed to make a pencil, the wood, rubber, and gum are renewable resources, while the others are all nonrenewable.

GETTING READY

Depending on your group, you may choose to do just Part A or both Parts A and B. Copy one or both student pages as needed.

PART A:
- Gather materials. Display the world map or globe.

PART B:
- Optional: Gather a collection of everyday objects that are made of different materials or invite students to bring in objects.

- As necessary, arrange time for online student research.

DOING THE ACTIVITY

PART A: THE LIFE CYCLE OF A PENCIL

1 **HANDS-ON LEARNING** Begin the activity by giving each student a pencil to handle and observe. Encourage students to identify all the materials that make up the pencil and the natural resources from which the materials are derived. Ask where these natural resources might have come from. Using the Background information, discuss possible origins of these resources and locate these areas on a world map or globe.

2 Have students describe a cycle that occurs in their lives. For example, the yearly seasonal cycle includes fall, winter, spring, and summer, repeating endlessly. Point out that a cycle is a series of events that are repeated in the same order and that continue without end.

3 Explain that objects also go through a cycle, starting with raw materials and including manufacture and use. A complete product life cycle includes the object's disposal or recycling back to nature or into a new product.

4 Divide the group into teams and give each team a large piece of paper and colored pens. Invite each team to create a large diagram showing the life cycle of a pencil, including all the materials and steps involved.

5 Ask teams to share their life cycle diagrams. As a group, consider how the diagrams are the same and whether anything has been left out.

6 Discuss the pathways that natural resources took to form the finished pencil. Where did the materials come from? How were the resources transported? What energy was needed to extract, process, manufacture, and distribute the resources?

PART B: MY FAVORITE THING

1 **PERSONAL CONNECTIONS** Divide the group into teams and have each team select a favorite product to examine and research. For example, they might choose a book, skateboard, toy, or shoe. Explain that teams will identify and present (a) the natural resources or raw materials used to make the product and (b) the steps necessary to produce it from its natural resources and to recycle it back to nature or into a new product.

2 **NONLINGUISTIC REPRESENTATIONS** You may have teams use the Your Product's Life Cycle student page to draw their product's life cycle and identify the sources of its raw materials. Alternatively, you might encourage them to use poster paper, a computer program, or other means to present the information.

3 Give teams time to research their product using the internet or other resources, and then to prepare and share their presentations.

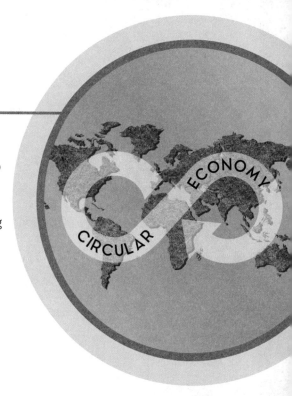

TAKE IT OUTSIDE

Challenge students to a scavenger hunt to look for examples of renewable and nonrenewable resources and energy at your site. Renewable resources may include trees, plants, sun, or wind. Nonrenewable resources may include rocks, metals, tar, and gasoline in cars.

4 Discuss:

- How many different natural resources make up your product?

- How many different countries were involved?

- What type of fuel or energy was used to make your object and to transport it to you? (Most transportation in our country uses petroleum, which is a fossil fuel. Manufacturing may use natural gas, which is also a fossil fuel, or electricity, which is generated using coal, natural gas, nuclear, hydropower, or solar.)

- Which of the natural resources and energy are renewable resources? Which are nonrenewable?

- What happens to the product when you are done using it? Where does it go?

- How does making or using this product affect Earth systems or ecosystems?

- What can people do to minimize any negative environmental effects of this product?

- What did you learn about natural resources from this activity?

ACADEMIC STANDARDS

SCIENCE

Practices
- Developing and using models
- Obtaining, evaluating, and communicating information

Concepts
- Natural resources
- Human impacts on Earth systems
- Systems and system models

ENGLISH LANGUAGE ARTS

Practices
- Writing: research to build and present knowledge
- Speaking and listening: presentation of knowledge and ideas

SOCIAL STUDIES

Practices
- Evaluating sources and using evidence

Concepts
- Economics: exchange and markets
- Geography: geographic representations

ASSESSMENT

Ask students to

- Use their team's diagram from Part A or presentation from Part B to describe:
  - » The raw materials needed to make the product.
  - » The steps of the product lifecycle in which energy is needed.
  - » Possible sources of energy and materials needed to make and transport the object.
  - » What happens to the product at the end of its useful life.

- Write a response to this prompt: What did you learn about natural resources from this activity?

ENRICHMENT

- Introduce the concept of **globalization** (the increasing interdependence of countries and greater movement of goods and people around the world), which has cultural, economic, social, and political impacts. Ask students to brainstorm potential pros and cons of globalization. Invite them to research and write a position paper, providing evidence to support their view on globalization.

- Have students find out what happens to manufactured items when people throw them away in your community. (They probably end up in a landfill or incinerator, as these products are often very difficult to recycle.) What alternatives to this type of disposal would students propose? Are some products compostable?

- Set up a group Swap Shop to encourage students to reuse objects rather than throwing them away. Have students bring useable items from home that their family no longer wants. Students can place them on a table and other students can see if there's anything they want. The group should discuss what rules should apply to the swap. One possibility is to have students sign out items on a first-come basis: If more than one person wants an item, students take turns, with each person having it for a certain time.

- Invite students to come up with new inventions or alternate uses for broken items, such as turning a broken aquarium into a planter. Have students bring an item from home that is broken and would normally be thrown out. Put all the items on a table and have students select something they would like to try to fix or find an alternate use for. Your class could have a Trashion Show in which students exhibit the new creations they have made from trash.

NAME _____ DATE _____

Draw the life cycle of your product.

CAREER CORNER

SUSTAINABILITY MANAGERS ensure that an organization, school, or company upholds environmental standards and minimizes environmental harm. For example, they might help an organization switch to using certified paper products that come from sustainably managed forests.

NAME_____ DATE_____

Indicate on the map where the materials for your product came from.
For each material, calculate or estimate how far it traveled to get to you and show it on the map.

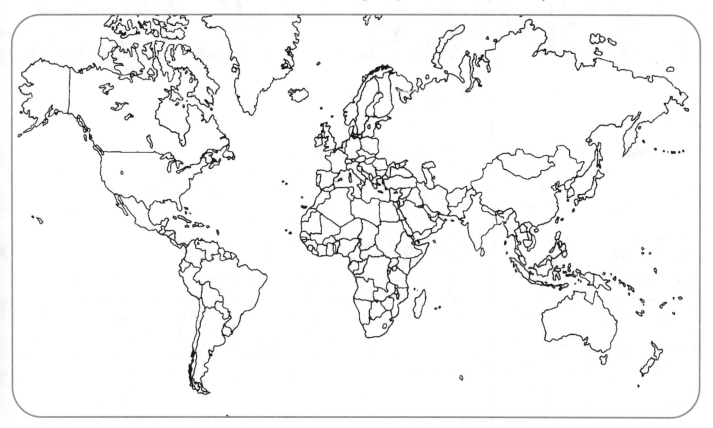

CAREER CORNER

I LOVE MY GREEN JOB!

<u>LOGISTICS SPECIALISTS</u> review and coordinate the shipping and handling of national and international forest products. They analyze data to find sustainable and cost-effective processes.

Students play the role of forest manager for a 400-acre (162-hectare) public forest, exploring the complex factors that influence management decisions about forest lands.

IF YOU WERE THE BOSS

SUBJECTS
Science, Math, Social Studies

PLT CONCEPTS
1.10, 3.6, 3.7

STEM SKILLS
Creativity, Leadership, Problem Solving

DIFFERENTIATED INSTRUCTION
Cooperative Learning, Higher-order Thinking, Multiple Solution Pathways

MATERIALS
Chart paper, colored markers, masking tape. Optional: Calculators and video to introduce forest management.

TIME CONSIDERATIONS
Preparation: 60 minutes

Activity: Two to three 50-minute sessions

OBJECTIVES

Students will

- Generate a plan for managing a forested area.

- Conduct a cost–benefit analysis on potential environmental, social, and economic effects of their proposed forest management plan.

- Experience some of the responsibilities and challenges of foresters.

BACKGROUND

Public and private forests cover nearly one-third of the United States and 40% of Canada. More than just trees, healthy forests are made up of a wide variety of species that interact to create a thriving ecosystem. They provide habitats for many species of plants and animals, as well as vital resources for people. Forests produce timber and provide places for camping, hiking, hunting, and fishing. They provide clean water by anchoring the soil, preventing soil erosion, and filtering pollutants out of water. Forests also absorb tremendous quantities of carbon dioxide from the atmosphere and are critical for slowing climate change and reducing its effects on people and other living things.

A forest manager, or forester, is a professional who works to maintain forest health and ensure the sustainability of forests and woodlands. Forest managers must consider the economic effects of the decisions they make about forest lands. But they must also consider elements such as recreation, water, soil, and wildlife values that are harder to evaluate. In addition, they must do all they can to safeguard cultural sites and other cultural values. Foresters also play an important role in bringing together members of the community to discuss the needs of the forest, including Indigenous communities, local citizens, and local governments. They must take into consideration all values of the forest based on these consultations.

An important tool for foresters is a forest management plan that is specific to the designated forest area. This plan describes the current forest condition and outlines a course of action to achieve management goals. A forest management plan is not just about the trees. It includes all the resources—roads, water sources, wildlife habitat, recreational sites, and anything else that is relevant to the goals. To be effective, these plans typically span 5–20 years. They provide the medium-term stability needed for sustainable forest management while

FOREST FACT

Partnerships between landowners and local organizations can render positive outcomes for local communities, including recreational opportunities and sustainable multiple-use forest management.

also considering long-term effects 100 years or more into the future. In addition, foresters may use an annual plan of operations that outlines specific activities for one year.

Management plans also take into consideration the objectives of the forestland owner. Forests may be managed for timber, recreation, wildlife habitat, or for other uses. Many forests are managed for multiple uses. For example, forests owned by a forest products company may be used for hiking, fishing, and camping, as well as timber production and **ecosystem** protection. As this learning activity demonstrates, **multiple use management** involves making choices about the types of activities that can take place in particular areas of the forest.

GETTING READY

- Make copies of the student pages.

- Make an enlarged map for each team to work on by projecting the 400-Acre Wood map onto a piece of chart paper and using a light-colored marker to trace the map. Alternatively, teams can use an electronic version of the map.

- Optional: Select a video to introduce the concept of forest management. Possibilities include:

  » *Forest Fact Break: Forest Management*, from the Oregon Forest Resources Institute (2 minutes; available at oregonforests.org)

  » *Starting Your Forest Management Plan: Introduction to Managing Your Forest*, from University of California Extension (7 minutes)

  » *STEM Career: Forestry Management*, from WOUB Public Media (5 minutes)

1 Optional: Share a video with students on forest management (see Getting Ready).

2 Ask students what they understand about the job of forest manager or forester. Introduce the activity by explaining that they will examine some of the complex issues that foresters must face as they oversee wooded lands.

3 Help students brainstorm a list of activities that take place in a forest. Encourage them to include a wide range of activities like hiking, visiting ancestral sites, fishing, hunting, meditating, taking pictures, birdwatching, camping, rock climbing, skiing, snowmobiling, logging, grazing, or mining. Ask the group to review the list and decide whether any activities would conflict with others if done on the same piece of land, or if they were done at the same time. Ask: How might foresters determine the best use of a forest? What criteria might they use to make their decisions?

4 **COOPERATIVE LEARNING** Explain that teams will decide the best uses for 400-Acre Wood, a fictitious forest that has been donated to the community. Have them read the You Decide student page, and then divide the group into teams of 4 to 5. Each team will develop a forest management plan to serve the best long-term interests of the community.

5 Optional: Point out that the activity involves a measure called an acre, which foresters typically use to determine area. Explain that an acre is a square with approximately 70 yards per side, with an area of 4,840 square yards. An acre can be any shape and is slightly smaller than an NFL football field, without the end zones.

6 Make sure students understand that their team can use the entire 400 acres for one use or divide it up for multiple uses. For example, they can devote 200 acres to hiking trails, 80 acres to a campground, and 120 acres to timber or hunting. No matter what uses they choose, they must keep the cultural site intact. If their plan includes timber activities, they must ensure that there is a "buffer" along the stream. This means that no timber areas on their map can touch the stream.

7 Before the teams begin, ask:

- Which forest uses in the You Decide student page are compatible with other uses? (For example, building a campground and hiking trail next to each other.)

- Which uses might be incompatible with each other? (For example, hunting near the cultural site.)

- In terms of wildlife, why are we only focusing on barred owls, wood rats, and salamanders? (Looking at three animals with different habitat requirements gives an idea of the general health of the forest ecosystem.)

- What could you learn by figuring out the costs, revenues, trees, wildlife populations, and number of visitors for each management plan? (You could learn how the plan affects different forest values.)

8 ⊙ **MULTIPLE SOLUTION PATHWAYS** Give each team an enlarged map of 400-Acre Wood (see Getting Ready). Each team should discuss strategies for managing the forest. When the team arrives at a consensus on how the land should be managed, direct students to illustrate their plan on their map, using colors, symbols, and a map key or legend to help viewers make sense of their plan.

9 Optional: Have teams use the What's the Score? student page to conduct a cost–benefit analysis of their plan. They should discuss the effects of their plan on five priority areas: 1) number of visitors, 2) wildlife conservation, 3) number of trees, 4) cultural site protection, and 5) costs and revenues.

10 Ask teams to present their plans to the entire group, making it clear how decisions were made, sharing findings from the What's the Score? student page (if used), and posting their maps for all to see.

11 ⊙ **HIGHER-ORDER THINKING** Lead a group discussion about the different plans. Ask:

- Which plan enables the most benefits for all? Which plans cost the most and the least? Which plan has the most effect on wildlife? Which has the least effect on the cultural site?

- Which do you think is most important: making the most money, having the most trees, supporting the most wildlife, having the most visitors, or safeguarding the cultural site? What makes you think so?

- Which plan provides the best balance of environmental factors (wildlife and trees), social factors (visitors and cultural site protection), and economic factors (costs and revenues)? Why do you think so? Should the goal be to balance all these things? Why or why not?

- What other criteria may be missing from the analysis?

- What will be the long-term effects of each plan? Which plan is the most sustainable over time? How are we measuring sustainability? Is that an adequate measure?

TAKE IT OUTSIDE

Invite students outdoors to make a map of your site or neighborhood. Students should include trees and other vegetation in their maps. Encourage them to be creative rather than worrying about scale or accuracy. Afterward, ask them what they learned from mapmaking. How has their perspective changed?

ACADEMIC STANDARDS

SCIENCE

Practices
- Using mathematics and computational thinking
- Obtaining, evaluating, and communicating information

Concepts
- Ecosystem dynamics, functioning, and resilience
- Developing possible solutions
- Systems and system models

MATH

Practices
- Reason abstractly and quantitatively
- Model with mathematics

Concepts
- Ratios and proportional relationships
- Statistics and probability

SOCIAL STUDIES

Practices
- Applying disciplinary concepts

Concepts
- Economics: exchange and markets
- Geography: human–environment interactions

ASSESSMENT

Ask students to

- Write a one-paragraph description of their team's plan, including the primary features of the design and why they were selected.

- Have teams present their plan to a "community council," composed of students from this group, external groups, parents, or community members. Give each team five minutes to explain why their plan should be accepted by the council. After all teams have presented their plans, direct council members to choose the best plan using parameters they devise. Presentations can be used to assess how well students understand the pros and cons of each proposal.

ENRICHMENT

- Repeat the activity with each team extending its plan into the next year. Have students calculate the effect on number of visitors, wildlife conservation, number of trees, cultural site protection, and costs and revenues for the second year.

- Invite a forester to talk to your group about how their organization makes land-use decisions. Encourage students to ask questions based on what they experienced in the activity. For example, how do foresters weigh environmental, social, and economic impacts?

- Challenge students to use mapping applications to produce supporting visuals for their presentations. For example, ArcGIS is professional mapping software that also has a free student-friendly version. See "Teaching with GIS: Introduction to Using GIS in the Classroom," a free 5-hour web course available from ESRI.com.

- Consider the health and wellness benefits that forests provide and how these might affect the forest plans the group developed. For example, mental health is improved when people recreate outdoors, lowering the societal cost of health care. What other benefits and costs can students identify? Explore associated forest careers focusing on outdoor recreation and tourism.

NAME _____ DATE_____

A magnificent forest, 400-Acre Wood, has just been donated to your community. You and your team have the job of deciding what to do with this forest. An acre is an area of land equal to a square that is 209 feet or 70 yards on each side, so 400 acres is approximately 0.6 square miles.

400-Acre Wood is made up of pine forest, with about 150 mature pine trees per acre. Because the forest has no roads or trails, few people visit it. A small stream containing trout runs through it. In addition, lots of wildlife live in the forest, including owls, deer, bears, woodpeckers, turkeys, quails, wood rats, and woodland salamanders.

Wildlife biologists focus on **management indicator species** to evaluate the positive and negative effects of people's actions on the environment. The impacts of changes on these species carry over to other species as well. For 400-Acre Wood, the indicator species are barred owls, wood rats, and woodland salamanders. Biologists estimate that eight owls, 400 wood rats, and 10,000 salamanders live in 400-Acre Wood.

In the northwest corner of the wood is a rock outcropping with three petroglyphs on it. These images were chiseled into the rock surface by Indigenous ancestors and are believed to be 600 to 1,000 years old. Your plan should safeguard this cultural site, keeping trails, camping, and exhaust from cars (which can erode the rock) a safe distance away.

You and your team will develop a management plan for 400-Acre Wood and make a map of it. You may decide to do one thing with the entire forest, such as create a campground. Or you may want to divide the forest and do different things in different areas, such as devoting some portion to wildlife management or hiking, some to a campground, and some to timber or hunting. Your goal is to find what your group thinks is the best balance among five priority interests: 1) number of visitors, 2) wildlife conservation, 3) number of trees, 4) cultural site protection, and 5) costs and revenue.

Using a landscape in various ways can have either positive or negative effects. The effects of forest uses described in the box on the following page are specific to this learning activity. Actual forest uses may have very different effects, depending on the geography, species of trees, types of animals, and people involved, as well as other local conditions.

The What's the Score? student page will help you evaluate your plan's total effect on the five priority interests (visitors, wildlife, trees, cultural site, and costs and revenue).

HOW BIG IS AN ACRE?

An acre is a measure of land that is exactly **4840 square yards**. It can be any shape, but it is approximately the size of an American football field without the end zones.

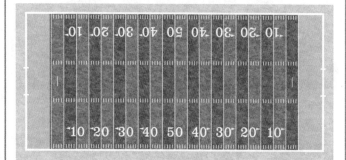

1 acre = about the area of a football field

Metric unit conversion:
1 acre = 0.4047 hectare
1 hectare = 1 square kilometer

NAME _____ DATE_____

Forest Use	Effects
Wildlife Management Area	
The purpose of a wildlife management area is to allow wildlife to thrive by preserving important ecosystem features that are critical to maintaining wildlife populations. Typically, areas that are managed for wildlife have few or no roads, timber operations, graded trails, or campsites.	Wildlife management areas will bring some visitors to the forest. The numbers of trees and amount of wildlife will remain the same. This type of management is compatible with protection of the cultural site. It will cost money to monitor the area.
Timber	
Timber harvest and regeneration involves cutting trees and planting new trees. Part of sustainably managing a forest includes determining which areas of the forest to harvest and regenerate. Using sustainable practices based on research, trees are removed in a way that minimizes effects on wildlife and people, while also producing valuable products over the long term. Pine trees take 35 years to reach maturity, but some trees may be removed periodically through "thinnings" to maximize growth and generate products. Trees must also be removed to build the road.	To protect the stream's water quality, timber production must retain a "buffer" alongside any stream. This is called a streamside management zone. The addition of roads will bring some visitors to this area. The timber harvest and regeneration will have a minimal effect on the three indicator species, since sustainable management will ensure regeneration of the forest. It will cost money to build and maintain the roads and for management, but the harvested trees can be sold to generate revenue.
Trails	
Graded trails allow different types of visitors to enjoy a forest area, including walkers, cyclists, families with strollers, and wheelchair users. Trails should not be built near a cultural site.	Trails will bring more visitors, but they will also disturb the wildlife, particularly the owls and wood salamanders. It costs money to build and maintain trails, and trees will need to be cut to make room for the trails. But you may sell the cut trees and charge an entrance fee to visitors.
Campground	
A campground allows visitors to enjoy a forest area overnight or over the weekend. It typically has campsites, picnic tables, fire pits, parking spaces, and bathrooms. A campground also needs to have a road winding through it. Campgrounds should not be built near a cultural site.	A campground will bring more visitors, but it will cause all three indicator species—owls, wood rats, and salamanders—to disappear from the area. Trees will need to be removed to build the road and campsites. It costs money to build and maintain the campground. But you may sell the cut trees and charge a camping fee.

NAME _____ DATE_____

Forest Use	Effects
Hunting and Foraging	
Some forest areas are managed to encourage game animals (deer, turkey, and quail) for hunters and edible items (medicinal plants, mushrooms, and berries) for foragers.	Hunting and foraging will bring some visitors, but with regulations to keep game populations constant, there should be no effect on the three indicator species—owls, wood rats, and salamanders. It will cost money to manage the area. But you may charge visitors a license fee.
Reservoir	
To supply water to the nearby community, a forest stream can be dammed to form a freshwater reservoir. A reservoir will bring visitors for canoeing, kayaking and other nonmotorized boating. Trees will need to be removed to create the reservoir.	The reservoir will cause all three indicator species—owls, wood rats, and salamanders—to disappear from the flooded area. It will cost money to build the dam and to manage the reservoir. But the cut trees can be sold, and you may charge visitors a recreation fee.
Cultural Sanctuary	
The purpose of a cultural sanctuary is to honor the people who lived there before and to respect the history, culture, and beliefs of Indigenous people today. A cultural sanctuary has no roads, graded trails, or campsites.	A cultural sanctuary will not change the number of visitors, trees, or amount of wildlife. It will cost money to monitor the area.

CAREER CORNER

I LOVE MY GREEN JOB!

FORESTERS manage forests for public and private use. They may develop short- and long-term plans for the forest. Their plans may include planting, growing, and monitoring trees for healthy growth, and making sure forest practices are sustainable and meet environmental regulations.

NAME _____ DATE _____

- This map shows 400-Acre Wood, including the stream and cultural site.

- Each small square represents 1 acre and is 209 feet per side.

- The diagonal distance across one square measures 294 feet.

LEGEND

 Stream

 Cultural site

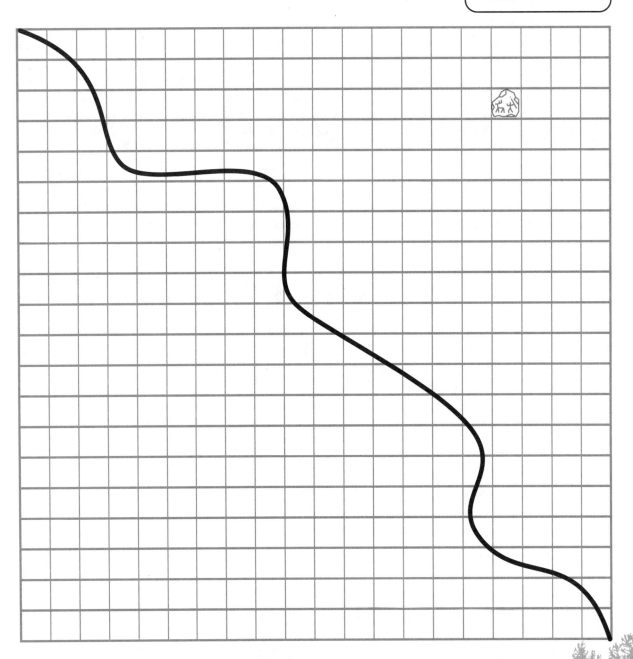

 I LOVE MY GREEN JOB!

CAREER CORNER

GEOGRAPHIC INFORMATION SYSTEMS (GIS) SPECIALISTS work with computers to create graphic images and maps that show different kinds of data. Maps of forest areas may depict land use or tree cover, and help inform decision-makers about the forest.

What's the Score?

NAME _____ DATE _____

FOREST USE

Identify how many acres you will devote to each forest use. The total must equal 400 acres.

	FOREST USE							
	Wildlife	Timber	Trails	Campground	Hunting/ Foraging	Reservoir	Cultural Sanctuary	TOTAL
Area (acres)								**400** Acres

ENVIRONMENTAL FACTORS

Step 1: Wildlife Conservation

Determine how your plan will affect the wildlife management indicator species. Put the number of planned acres for each forest use in all the blank boxes below for that use (a black space means that the species won't live in an area with that use). Multiply the total acres per species by the number of animals per acre. (For owls and wood rats, round down to the nearest whole animal.) Compare the new population totals with the original population of 8 owls, 400 wood rats, and 10,000 salamanders.

	FOREST USE							TOTALS		
	Wildlife	Timber Production	Trails	Camp-ground	Hunting/ Foraging	Reservoir	Cultural Sanctuary	Total Acres Per Species	Animals Per Acre	New Population
Owls			■	■					.20	
Wood Rats				■		■			1.0	
Salaman-ders			■	■		■			25	

NAME _____ DATE _____

Step 2: Number of Trees

Trees will need to be removed in order to build any trails, roads, or campground, or to harvest timber. Put the number of planned acres for each forest use in the blank boxes below for that use. Multiply the total acres for each use by the number of trees removed per acre. Add up the total trees removed. Initially, 400-Acre Wood contains 37,000 trees. Calculate how many trees will remain with your plan.

| | FOREST USE | | | | | | | TOTAL | |
	Wildlife	Timber	Trails	Campground	Hunting/ Foraging	Reservoir	Cultural Sanctuary	Trees Removed	Trees Remaining
Area (acres)									
Trees Removed per Acre	0	40	10	20	10	150	0		
Total Trees Removed									
Total Trees Remaining Per Plan									

Step 3: Stream Protection

To protect the stream, any timber activities in your plan must include a "buffer" along the stream. Check that your plan does not have any timber squares touching the stream.

SOCIAL FACTORS

Step 4: Number of Visitors

Calculate the number of visitors your plan will attract to the forest each year. Multiply the number of acres for each forest use by the numbers below. Then, add the totals.

| | FOREST USE | | | | | | | TOTAL |
	Wildlife	Timber	Trails	Campground	Hunting/ Foraging	Reservoir	Cultural Sanctuary	
Area (acres)								
Visitors per Acre per Year	5	5	25	50	2	60	0	
Visitors per Plan per Year								

What's the Score? (cont.)

NAME _____   DATE _____

Step 5: Cultural Site Protection

Calculate how well your plan safeguards the cultural site. For each forest use in your plan, measure on your map the shortest distance (in feet) to the cultural site, and place that distance in the table below. Assign 1 point for each 500 feet in distance to the site (rounded to the nearest whole number). Wildlife and Cultural Sanctuary are worth 10 points each, as they do not affect the site. The final score is the lowest of the points that is not 0.

	FOREST USE							SCORE
	Wildlife	Timber	Trails	Campground	Hunting/ Foraging	Reservoir	Cultural Sanctuary	
Area (acres)								
Distance (in feet)								
Points	10						10	

ECONOMIC FACTORS

Step 6: Construction Costs and Revenue

Calculate the net cost of developing the site for your plan. To determine the construction cost, multiply the number of acres for each forest use by the dollar amounts below, and then add the numbers to find the total. To calculate the revenue, multiply the number of trees removed for each forest use (from Step 2 above) by $50 per tree, and then add the numbers to find the total. Subtract the total revenue from the total construction cost to determine the net cost. (If the number is positive, it is a cost; if it is negative, it is a revenue.)

		FOREST USE							TOTALS
		Wildlife	Timber	Trails	Camp-ground	Hunting/ Foraging	Reservoir	Cultural Sanctuary	
	Area (acres)								
COSTS	Construction Cost per Acre		$2,025	$1,200	$6,000	$2,025	$16,200		
COSTS	Total Construction Cost								
REVENUE	Revenue: Sale of Trees ($50 per Tree)								
NET COST	Net Cost (Total Construction Cost Minus Income)								

PROJECT LEARNING TREE K–8 ACTIVITY GUIDE © SUSTAINABLE FORESTRY INITIATIVE

NAME_____ DATE_____

Step 7: Annual Costs and Revenue

Calculate the annual management costs for your plan. Multiply the management costs per acre by the number of acres for each forest use, and then add the numbers. To determine the income from fees, multiply the fees per visitor by the number of visitors for your plan (from Step 4), and then add the numbers. Subtract the Total Revenues from the Total Management Costs to determine the annual cost or revenue. (If the number is positive, it is a cost; if it is negative, it is a revenue.)

		FOREST USE							TOTALS
		Wildlife	Timber	Trails	Camp-ground	Hunting/ Foraging	Reservoir	Cultural Sanctuary	
	Area (acres)								
COSTS	Management Costs per Acre	$4	$40	$20	$100	$8	$20	$4	
	Total Management Costs								
REVENUE	Revenues: Fees per Visitor	$1	$2	$2	$8	$6	$6	$0	
	Total Revenues								
NET COST	Net Cost or Revenue (Total Management Costs minus Total Revenue)								

CAREER CORNER

__NATURAL RESOURCE ECONOMISTS__ are concerned about the sustainable use of energy, food, forests, and other natural resources. They may work to find the most efficient and least expensive ways to manage forests and to supply or manufacture forest products.

Every living thing has a habitat—a place that meets its needs. Human beings' habitat is the community in which they live. Students plan and, if possible, carry out a service-learning project that focuses on making positive environmental changes in their community.

IMPROVE YOUR PLACE

SUBJECTS
Science, English Language Arts, Social Studies

PLT CONCEPTS
5.8, 5.10

STEM SKILLS
Collaboration, Communication, Problem Solving

DIFFERENTIATED INSTRUCTION
Cooperative Learning, Multiple Solution Pathways, Nonlinguistic Representation, Personal Connections

MATERIALS
Chart paper, rulers, drawing pencils or markers, sticky notes or index cards. Optional: Camera.

TIME CONSIDERATIONS
Preparation: Varies, depending on project.

Activity: Varies, depending on project.

OBJECTIVES
Students will

• Identify ways they can improve their local area.

• Create and carry out a plan to improve the area.

BACKGROUND

Close your eyes and picture a familiar place such as your home, your neighborhood, or anywhere in your community. Think of this place as your habitat. It is important to you because it's where you live and where your needs are met.

Use this activity to encourage students to develop and implement a project to improve their habitat. Simple projects might include planting flowers, grass, shrubs, or trees; painting benches; finding ways to reduce or eliminate litter; or designing a mural for a wall in a public park. Students might also coordinate with a local park or forest to help remove invasive plants, enhance wildlife habitat, pick up trash, or complete another project. A more elaborate project might be designing an environmental study area.

Students can plan their project to coincide with Earth Day (April 22) or Arbor Day (date varies by state, so contact your state forester or visit arborday.org).

GETTING READY

• Before tackling a project, consider the scope of the project and your limitations. Your group can simply survey the project area and make recommendations for improvement to the appropriate authorities. Or you can seek funding from the PTA, school board, garden club, or other organization to carry out the project.

• Make copies of the Project Action Plan student page.

• Get approval from appropriate individuals for the project. Arrange for students to present their plan to the individual or group charged with making decisions about the project area.

• For more information about planning and implementing a service-learning or environmental action project, see PLT's *GreenSchools Investigations* available at plt.org/greenschools.

DOING THE ACTIVITY

1. **PERSONAL CONNECTIONS** Ask students to list as many adjectives as possible that describe your site, school grounds, or other project area. Which adjectives describe physical characteristics? Which describe the feelings the area evokes? Is there anything about the project area that students wish was different?

2. Take your students outside to investigate the area. They should look for things they like about it, as well as any possible problems (such as excess litter, lack of trees and plants, soil erosion, or broken play equipment or benches).

3. As they investigate the area, have students sketch a simple map of it. Students might also take pictures of what they observe.

4. If possible, have students interview or poll people who use the area to get other opinions on how the area could be improved.

5. **NONLINGUISTIC REPRESENTATIONS** After the initial survey is complete, help students create a single, large map of the site as it currently exists. You may need to make a large grid on which to lay out the map. Use simple symbols such as circles for trees, squares or triangles for play equipment, and so on.

6. Have the group create an affinity map of the issues they identified by writing one issue per sticky note or index card, placing them where all can see, and clustering similar issues into categories.

7. **MULTIPLE SOLUTION PATHWAYS** Form student teams to brainstorm ideas for addressing each category of issues from the affinity map. Teams should discuss possible solutions to the issues in their category and agree on one solution to present to the group. After the presentations, invite the group to vote for the idea or ideas they would like to try.

8. Help students determine whether they need approval for their project from the PTA, school board, or another decision-making body. If they do, have students present or submit their project plan to decision makers. You might also look to your community for other supportive parents, individuals, and organizations who can help.

9. **COOPERATIVE LEARNING** Give student teams copies of the Project Action Plan student page and have them select which pieces of the action plan they will prepare. Give them time to draft their parts of the plan, using a word processing or presentation app.

10. When students have finished a draft of their plan, they should evaluate it using the following questions:

    - Is there enough evidence to warrant doing this project?

    - What alternative actions could we take?

    - Is the proposed action the best one? Why?

    - What are the ecological, social, and economic consequences of this project?

- Are there legal consequences to consider? If so, what are they? (If any parents are lawyers, students might ask them for their input.)

- Do we have the skills, time, and materials needed for the project? If not, who can help?

- What outcomes will we use to determine success?

Using this evaluation, students can adjust their plan. They should be prepared to answer questions like these when they propose their plan to the decision-making individual or group.

11 Have students present their final version of the plan to the decision-making individual or group, and to ask for approval of the plan.

12 If the plan is approved, help students carry out the project.

VARIATION: GRADES 3–5

1 Read aloud a true story about a child or group of children who worked to improve their community's environment. (Check with your librarian or see plt.org/myk8guide for ideas.) Ask students for their reactions to the story and thoughts about doing a similar project.

2 Take students on a walk around your site or neighborhood. Have them record on a T-chart some pluses (things they like) and minuses (things they wish were different) about the surrounding area.

3 Invite students to examine their list and brainstorm things they could do as individuals or as a group to improve the site or neighborhood.

4 Help students carry out one or more of their ideas.

ACADEMIC STANDARDS

SCIENCE

Practices

- Constructing explanations and designing solutions
- Obtaining, evaluating, and communicating information

Concepts

- Human impacts on Earth systems
- Cause and effect

ENGLISH LANGUAGE ARTS

Practices

- Writing: production and distribution of writing
- Speaking and listening: presentation of knowledge and ideas

SOCIAL STUDIES

Practices

- Developing questions and planning inquiries
- Communicating conclusions and taking informed action

Concepts

- Civics: participation and deliberation
- Geography: geographic representations

ASSESSMENT

Ask students to

- Present their plan and ask the decision-making individual or group to provide feedback on the thoroughness and clarity of the plan and presentation.
- After completing their project, (1) evaluate the effectiveness of the project, based on the criteria they identified in the plan; (2) describe intended and unintended consequences of the project; and (3) reflect on ways the project could be more effective by providing either next steps or tips for others trying to do a similar project.

ENRICHMENT

- Invite students to draw or map their dream scenario for the project area, assuming money or other potential roadblocks are not factors. Pairs or individuals can design their "ideal sites" and present them to the group.
- Have students contact their state or local forestry office for information on site improvement projects using trees and shrubs.

Project Action Plan

NAME _____ DATE_____

Project Location: _____

Project Goal: _____

BACKGROUND INFORMATION

1. What is the area identified for the project?

2. Who uses it?

3. What need will this project address?

THE PROBLEM

1. What site investigations and opinion surveys have you done for the area?

2. What problem did you identify from this information?

3. Where is the problem located?

RECOMMENDATIONS

1. What actions could be taken to solve the problem?

2. Which action do you recommend and why?

3. What are possible future projects?

NAME _____ DATE _____

PROJECT DETAILS

1. Who will be involved?

2. How much will it cost?

3. Who will do the work?

4. How will the project benefit the community?

MAPS

1. What does the project area look like now?

2. How would it look after the project is complete?

EXPECTED RESULTS

1. What results do you hope to achieve?

2. How will you know whether the project was successful?

CAREER CORNER

PROJECT MANAGERS work with team members to successfully complete projects. They determine a project's scale, plan its budget and schedule, manage communications, and carry out other tasks needed to deliver results.

Throughout history, people have intentionally and unintentionally moved plant and animal species to new environments. Some of these species have proved beneficial, but others invade natural habitats, causing environmental and sometimes economic harm. Students research invasive species to determine how these species got to their new locations and what characteristics make their control so challenging.

INVASIVE SPECIES

SUBJECTS
Science, English Language Arts, Social Studies

PLT CONCEPTS
1.1, 1.6, 2.8

STEM SKILLS
Communication, Creativity, Problem Solving, Technology Use

DIFFERENTIATED INSTRUCTION
Multiple Solution Pathways, Nonlinguistic Representations, Student Voice

MATERIALS
Map of the world, access to the internet.

TIME CONSIDERATIONS
Preparation: 20 minutes

Activity: One 50-minute period, and time for research and making student presentations

OBJECTIVES

Students will

- Learn what invasive species are and why they sometimes cause problems.
- Research and create a presentation on an invasive species in their local area.
- Identify actions to help prevent the spread of invasive species.

BACKGROUND

A **native species** is a plant or animal that occurs naturally in a certain area. Native species co-evolved with neighboring species to maximize the resources available to them, ultimately attaining balance with other species in the ecosystem. Species with the capacity to spread aggressively are typically kept in check through predation, competition, or disease.

Non-native species (also known as exotic species or alien species) have been introduced or moved by human activities to an area where they do not naturally occur. A non-native species is not necessarily harmful, and in fact, some non-native species are beneficial (such as apple trees, which originated in Central Asia but now grow across North America). However, when a non-native species overruns or outcompetes native species in natural communities or ecosystems, it is called an **invasive species**. Many such species can ultimately cause ecological or economic problems.

In their new locations, non-native species tend to become invasive when they do not have the natural controls that limit their population in their native range. If they also have a high rate of reproduction and can tolerate a range of conditions, they have the potential to take over in these new areas. (See the box *Common Characteristics for Invasive Species* on the next page.)

Invasive species are a problem worldwide, as they may degrade and alter habitats, crowd out native species, choke waterways, alternative fisheries, prevent forests from regenerating, and compete with agricultural crops. Once established, invasive species can be very difficult to remove. Controlling invasives is very time-consuming and expensive.

Invasive species are not a new phenomenon, but **globalization** has increased worldwide travel and shipment of goods, increasing the number of new invasions. In the United States alone, scientists estimate about 6,500 invasive species have established themselves. These species include plants, mammals, birds, amphibians, reptiles, fish, arthropods, and mollusks. Some have caused major environmental damage and economic losses—totaling about $120 billion per year—in agriculture, forestry, and other segments of the economy.

There are many pathways by which invasive species end up in a new location, far from their native range. In some cases, people intentionally introduce them to the new area, not realizing the untold damage they could cause. For example, people purposely brought nutria and purple loosestrife to the United States (see the Space Invaders student page). In other cases, the introduction of invasive species is unintentional. People unknowingly transport species on barges, boats and trailers, animals, vehicles, commercial goods, packing materials, produce, footwear, or clothing.

Many aquatic invasive species are transported to new regions in the ballast water of ships. Ballast water is taken into partially empty cargo ships to provide stability during ocean crossings and then is pumped out when the ships pick up their loads somewhere else. Some ships transport millions of gallons of water, laden with organisms, to other locales. Species such as zebra mussels and spiny water fleas were unintentionally introduced this way, then spread throughout interior waterways via recreational boats and other means. Some species may also find their way past natural barriers like mountain ranges or vast prairie regions as human activities alter environments, creating habitable corridors for invasive species to cross. For example, garlic mustard is an invasive weed that has spread aggressively along road corridors.

The best way to manage invasive species is to prevent their spread. See the box *How to Prevent Invasive Species* on the facing page for suggested actions that individuals can take to prevent invasive species.

COMMON CHARACTERISTICS OF INVASIVE SPECIES

These factors or characteristics make a species more likely to be invasive:

- New location has climate and environmental conditions similar to native habitat, allowing non-natives to establish.
  Example: Nutria thrive in marsh conditions in the United States that are like those in South America.

- Species has few natural controls such as predators, disease, or insects.
  Example: In North America, feral swine have no natural predators.

- Species produces lots of offspring, seeds, or eggs.
  Example: One zebra mussel can release up to one million eggs per year.

- Species tolerates a wide range of conditions.
  Example: The European starling can live in a variety of habitats, from woodlands to open fields to cities.

Climate change may have numerous potential effects on species invasions. For example, extreme weather events like hurricanes may transport non-native species a long way, and warming climates may push non-native species into new environments like high altitudes or Arctic regions.

HOW TO PREVENT INVASIVE SPECIES

You can help stop the introduction and spread of harmful invaders in your community.

GARDENING

- Avoid growing plants that are known to be invasive. If you don't know it, don't grow it!
- Be cautious when buying plants from nurseries or seeds from other regions of the country.
- Avoid using seed mixtures, especially ones labeled "wildflowers."
- Landscape using plants that are native to your area.
- Never dispose of unwanted plants or garden clippings in a nearby park, local body of water, or natural area.

BOATING AND FISHING

- Never transport water, animals, or plants from one body of water to another.
- Do not release live fish, including bait, into a new body of water.
- Remove all aquatic plants and animals from hulls, propellers, intakes, trailers, and gear before leaving a launch area.
- Wash all fishing tackle, downriggers, and lines to prevent spreading small, larval forms of aquatic invaders.

PETS

- Don't buy any non-native pets that are known to be invasive.
- Don't release any pets or aquarium fish into a local area or natural body of water.
- Purchase locally grown or certified weed-free hay for horses.

TRAVELING

- Never carry fruit, seeds, live plants, soil, or animals into or out of the country.
- Within the country, don't transport items such as hay, wood, soil, sod, or gravel from region to region.
- Wash your boots and tires to remove soil and weed seeds before you hike in a new area.
- Abide by local and international quarantines to prevent the spread of serious pests, weeds, and diseases.

TAKE ACTION!

- Tell others about the harm that invasives cause.
- If local nurseries sell invasive plants or seeds, or if pet stores sell potentially invasive pets, let them know your concerns.
- Volunteer to help remove invasive plants from your local park or nature reserve.
- Learn to recognize common invaders and keep an eye out for signs of new ones. Check trees, gardens, vacant lots, roadsides, yards, agricultural areas, wetlands, ponds, and lakes.
- If you think you've found a new infestation, contact your county agricultural agent or state Department of Natural Resources. Early detection is crucial to stopping an invasive from becoming permanently established!

Source: Adapted from U.S. Fish and Wildlife Service. "Invasive Species: What You Can Do." https://www.fws.gov/invasives/what-you-can-do.html

GETTING READY

- Make copies of the Space Invaders and Comparing Invasive Species student pages. Cut out each species on the Space Invaders student page or provide students with an electronic version.

DOING THE ACTIVITY

1 Begin the activity by asking students what the word "invasive" means. Ask them whether they have heard the term "invasive species," what they think this term might mean, and why invasive species might be a problem.

2 Divide students into teams and give each team two or more different species from the Space Invaders student page. Have students read about their species and complete the Comparing Invasive Species student page.

3 **NONLINGUISTIC REPRESENTATIONS** Ask teams to discuss the following questions. You might have them create a concept map or other graphic organizer to support the discussion.

- What do these species have in common? How do they differ?
- What are typical characteristics of invasive species?
- How do invasive species spread?

4 **MULTIPLE SOLUTION PATHWAYS** Explain to students that they will research an invasive species (different from the ones on the cards) that is a problem in your area. After learning about this species, they will create a presentation to inform friends, family, neighbors, or the city council about the invasive species, its effects on the environment, and how to prevent its spread. Presentations may be in the form of a video, slideshow, poster, skit, or other form of their choosing. Their presentations should include:

- Where the species originated.
- How and why it got to your area.
- The characteristics that help it thrive.
- The problems it creates.
- What people can do to get rid of it or prevent it from spreading.

Students can begin by searching for "invasive species [name of state or city]" on the internet. They might also check the websites of local or state parks, the state natural resources agency, or the agriculture department for problem species in your state or region. Visit plt.org/myk8guide for more resources.

5 **STUDENT VOICE** Give students time to research and create their presentations, and then share them with the group and the community.

TAKE IT OUTSIDE

Arrange for students to participate in an invasive species control project in your community. This may involve removing invasive plants or planting native species in parks or nature areas. Contact your local parks or natural resources department to find out about volunteer opportunities for your group.

ACADEMIC STANDARDS

SCIENCE

Practices
- Obtaining, evaluating, and communicating information

Concepts
- Ecosystem dynamics, functioning, and resilience
- Human impacts on Earth systems
- Cause and effect

ENGLISH LANGUAGE ARTS

Practices
- Reading informational text: integration of knowledge and ideas
- Writing: production and distribution of writing

SOCIAL STUDIES

Practices
- Evaluating sources and using evidence
- Communicating conclusions and taking informed action

Concepts
- Geography: human–environment interactions
- History: change, continuity, and context

ASSESSMENT

Ask students to

- Present their research on an invasive species. Assess students on the following: How well they understand the concept of invasive species? How well did they communicate why invasive species are a problem? Did they offer solutions for preventing further spread of invasive species? How creative were they in getting across their message?

- Write about an invasive species found in your state and what people can do to help increase awareness about it.

ENRICHMENT

- Have students work in small teams to design and create their own invasive species board game. The purpose of the game is to educate players about the biology, impact on ecosystems and biodiversity, control or prevention, and identification of invasive species. The new game can be created from students' imagination or it can be modeled after a popular board game. Students should write the rules and instructions for the game and test their game to determine if it works as intended.

- Invasive species are a problem worldwide, not just in the United States. Have students research species that originated in the United States but are considered invasive in other countries. For example, the American slipper limpet was brought unintentionally to Europe in 1870 with shipments of oysters and is now found all along the Atlantic coast from the Mediterranean to Norway. Students could create a world map showing where each species originated and where it is found now. Ask them to compare the environments of the original locations with those of the current distributions.

- Once invasive species get a foothold in a new environment, they often reproduce at a geometric rate. Present the following math problem as an example of how a species population can grow so quickly (students may want to use a spreadsheet program to calculate their answer): An invasive weed species produces enough seeds to start 10 new seedlings each year. Each of the new seedlings can start producing seeds after a year. How many plants will be there be in five years? (Answer 111,111 plants!)

STUDENT PAGE

Space Invaders

An invasive species is an organism that is not native to an area and that has the potential to spread at an unhealthy rate. Invasives often take over, making it difficult for native species to thrive, and sometimes causing environmental or economic damage. Here are some invasive species found in the United States that are particularly harmful.

✂ -

FERAL SWINE

These wild pigs are descendants of domesticated pigs that either escaped or were released into the wild. They are sometimes called wild boars, wild hogs, and piney woods rooters. Although they look similar to domestic pigs, they are generally thinner with coarse bristly hair and longer tusks.

These animals arrived in North America in the 1500s, when colonists brought them from Europe for food. But since the 1980s, their populations have nearly tripled and they are now found in at least 35 states. They are also quickly spreading across Canada. In North America, they have relatively few natural predators—except humans—to keep their numbers in check.

They use their snouts to dig or root in the soil for food, pulling up wild plants and destroying crops. They eat just about anything and actively hunt and eat small mammals, reptiles, amphibians, and insects. Their rooting, trampling, and feeding can do extensive damage to natural ecosystems. In the United States, feral swine cause millions of dollars in crop damage every year. They also carry diseases that threaten humans, pets, and safe meat production.

✂ -

KUDZU (KUUD-ZOO)

This plant is nicknamed the "vine that ate the South." It is native to Asia and was brought to the United States from Japan in 1876 for the Centennial Exposition in Philadelphia. Gardeners were attracted to the kudzu's large leaves and sweet-smelling blossoms. In the southern United States, it became a popular plant for shading porches. Today, it covers extensive areas in 23 states and the District of Columbia, particularly in Georgia, Alabama, and Mississippi.

This climbing vine can grow up to a foot a day and reach 100 feet long. A single root crown may produce as many as 30 vines, which become hairy and woody and expand in all directions. It can also thrive in drought conditions and poor soil.

Kudzu can kill native trees and other plants by completely covering them, smothering them with its leaves and blocking out light for photosynthesis. The weight of its vines can break or uproot trees, bring down power lines, and damage buildings. Because it is difficult to get rid of it once it takes hold, a kudzu infestation can make land unusable for growing trees or crops.

✂ -

ZEBRA MUSSELS

These invertebrates first came to North America in the 1980s as stowaways in cargo ships from western Asia. If a large ship is only partially loaded, people pump water into it to stabilize it for long ocean voyages. This ballast water is then pumped out at the destination. Scientists believe this is how zebra mussels first came to North America.

Zebra mussels begin their lives as tiny larvae carried by water currents. As they mature, they attach themselves to hard substances like rocks, other mussels, boat hulls, and even the interiors of pipes. They are a major problem for power plants and public water systems because they grow in thick masses. In Lake Erie, 700,000 mussels per square yard have been found in some utility water pipes.

One adult zebra mussel may release up to a million eggs each year! Adults can also reattach themselves if they break off and can survive out of water for days. Zebra mussels can move to new locations as larvae and attach to boats, anchors, or ropes when they are adults. Mussels feed by filtering water and removing plankton (tiny plants and animals) from it. The problem is that they can filter out all the plankton from a lake or stream, leaving nothing for native animals to eat.

PURPLE LOOSESTRIFE

This is a lovely plant—or so it first seems. It has a tall stalk of pinkish-purple flowers that bloom in the late summer. But ever since it was brought to North America in the early 1800s as an ornamental garden plant, this plant has earned the nicknames of beautiful killer, marsh monster, and purple plague.

Soon after coming to the United States, purple loosestrife started spreading into natural areas. By 1830, it could be found all along the New England coast. The construction of the Erie Canal and other canals in the 1880s allowed it to spread farther inland. Today it is found in wetlands throughout all the lower 48 states except Florida. In some areas, it grows so densely that scientists have counted up to 20,000 seedlings in one square meter.

In Europe, where it is a native plant, purple loosestrife is not invasive because a variety of insects feed on it and keep it in check. None of these insects occur naturally in North America. This, and the fact that a single plant grows very quickly and can produce more than 2.5 million seeds annually, has allowed purple loosestrife to spread uncontrollably.

When purple loosestrife invades a wetland area, it crowds out native plants, reduces the food and cover available to wildlife, and chokes waterways.

- ✂ -

NUTRIA (NEW-TREE-UH)

These water-loving animals from South America have big front teeth and dense, warm fur, like their cousin the beaver. People brought nutria to the United States in the 1930s to raise them for their fur. But nutria fur never became popular, so some people released their nutria into the wild. They are now found in 22 states.

Nutria are herbivores with very large appetites. They eat about one-fourth of their body weight every day. While they will eat any almost any plant, their favorite food is the roots of marsh plants. They dig under the plants and turn them over to eat the root mat, often killing the plants. Nutria breed year-round and reproduce very quickly. An adult female can have two or three litters a year, with up to 11 young per litter.

As there are few predators to keep them in check, nutria have destroyed thousands of acres of marsh plants in the United States. This harms nesting water birds and songbirds, as well as fish and crabs, that depend on the marsh to live.

- ✂ -

HEMLOCK WOOLLY ADELGID (UH-DEL-JID)

This tiny, sucking insect has killed many hemlock trees in the eastern United States. (Hemlocks are tall trees with evergreen needles.) It feeds on the sap at the base of the hemlock needles, causing them to fall off. Without needles, the tree starves to death, usually within a few years of the first attack.

The hemlock woolly adelgid was accidentally brought from Japan to the western United States in 1924 through wood shipments. Western hemlocks are naturally able to resist the insect. But when the adelgid traveled to the eastern United States in the 1950s, it became clear that eastern hemlocks could not resist it.

The adelgid now threatens entire hemlock forests in the eastern United States. As the trees die, the plants and animals that depend on the forest may also die. Because eastern hemlock trees are an important in forests along streams in the Appalachians, their loss can lead to drier soils and higher stream temperatures in that environment.

Hemlock woolly adelgids are spread by wind or carried by birds, mammals, and humans. They reproduce rapidly; one individual can produce up to 90,000 new adelgids in a year.

TAMARISK

These trees guzzle up tons of water in the dry southwestern United States. Tamarisk roots grow deep into the desert earth, sucking springs dry. And as its nickname— salt cedar—suggests, tamarisk oozes salt from its leaves, making the soil around it unsuitable for native plants.

Western settlers in the 1800s brought this Eurasian tree to the region as a source of wood and shade. It has now spread all over the Southwest.

Tamarisk thrives because it has no natural predators or known diseases. It is also very quick to multiply. Each plant produces up to a half million seeds, and some varieties can grow as much as 10 feet in height each year. When tamarisk replaces native plant species, the numbers of birds, small mammals, and other animals in the area may decrease.

EUROPEAN STARLINGS

Starlings came to the United States in 1890 when a man named Eugene Schieffelin released 40 pairs of them in New York's Central Park. He said he wanted to bring all the birds mentioned by William Shakespeare to America.

By 1930, European starlings had spread all the way to the western states. Two hundred million starlings are now found over most of North America, Mexico, and parts of the Caribbean.

Starlings are intelligent and interesting birds, but they are bad news for native birds such as woodpeckers, bluebirds, and swallows. Starlings compete with these birds for nest cavities in trees, often destroying eggs and young birds in the process. Also, because they form large wintering flocks, they are considered pests by people.

GYPSY MOTHS

These moths have lived in Europe and Asia for thousands of years. They were first brought to the United States in 1869 by a scientist who wanted to try using them to produce silk. By accident, several of the caterpillars blew off the windowsill of his home in Massachusetts and escaped.

Twenty years later, there was a gypsy moth outbreak in the surrounding areas. Today, the gypsy moth is one of the most damaging forest pests in the northeastern United States. The caterpillars emerge from their eggs beginning in early spring. They are not fussy eaters. While they prefer oak, maple, and elm tree leaves, they will feed on approximately 500 different plants. When food is scarce, the caterpillars will eat almost any vegetation. They destroy the leaves of millions of acres of trees each year.

Gypsy moths are spread in two different ways. Newly hatched caterpillars spin short lengths of silken thread, which allow them to be carried by the wind. More often, they spread when people move their outdoor belongings— like cars, RVs, firewood, or lawn furniture—to new places, not knowing that they harbor gypsy moth eggs.

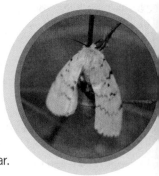

I LOVE MY GREEN JOB!

CAREER CORNER

ENVIRONMENTAL EDUCATORS lead school and community groups in learning activities that focus on trees and forest ecosystems. They may conduct field trips where learners can experience nature firsthand.

NAME _____ DATE _____

Species	Where is its native region? Where is it found now?	How did it get to the new location?	What characteristics help it thrive?	What problems does it cause?	What can people do?

CAREER CORNER

I LOVE MY GREEN JOB!

__FOREST ECOLOGISTS__ study the relationships between living and nonliving components of forest environments and the effects of humans on forests. They work outdoors, spending a lot of time in the field.

Students model processes that can lead to species becoming rare or endangered. Then, they become advocates for rare or at-risk species of plants or animals and create "public relations campaigns" on behalf of these species.

LIFE ON THE EDGE

SUBJECTS
Science, English Language Arts, Social Studies

PLT CONCEPTS
2.8, 5.1, 5.2, 5.10

STEM SKILLS
Collaboration, Creativity, Problem Solving, Technology Use

DIFFERENTIATED INSTRUCTION
Cooperative Learning, Higher-order Thinking, Nonlinguistic Representations

MATERIALS
Part A: Mats or carpet squares

TIME CONSIDERATIONS
Preparation:
Part A: 30 minutes
Part B: Time to gather species list and materials

Activity:
Part A: 50-minute period
Part B: Two to three 50-minute periods, plus time to conduct research

OBJECTIVES

Students will

- Identify the habitat components that organisms need to survive.
- Research a rare, threatened, or endangered species and give a persuasive media presentation on safeguarding that organism.

BACKGROUND

The fossil record indicates that the number and type of species on Earth have changed continuously throughout time. There have been several periods of mass extinction in the Earth's history. During these events, many species were not able to adapt to large-scale changes, such as climate change.

Since life on Earth first began, species extinction has been nearly as common as species origination. Although we know that change is normal, scientists are observing large numbers of organisms facing extinction at a faster rate than is healthy for Earth's ecosystems. Human activities that change the environment are putting these species at risk.

Under the Endangered Species Act (ESA) in the United States, plant and animal species may be listed as either **endangered species** or **threatened species**. "Endangered" means a species is in danger of extinction throughout all or a significant portion of its range. "Threatened" means a species is likely to become endangered within the foreseeable future. "Rare" and "at-risk" are not legal terms under the ESA, but generally refer to animals and plants that are in decline and that may be in danger of extinction.

While habitat loss can happen naturally due to earthquakes, floods, tornadoes, wildfire, volcanoes, changes in climate, and other processes, a significant cause of habitat loss is human activity. Conversion of natural areas to agriculture, deforestation, urban and suburban development, dam building, and more can destroy, degrade, or fragment habitats. In addition to causing direct habitat loss, some human activities may threaten the health of habitats. Examples include burning fossil fuels that contribute to climate change, introducing invasive species that can outcompete the native species, or carelessly sparking a wildfire.

A lot of attention is focused on rare or at-risk animals, but we should not overlook rare or at-risk plants. Plants form the basis of ecosystems, and people directly depend on plants for food, clothing, building materials, medicine, and much more.

PROJECT LEARNING TREE
An initiative of SFI

Most of the world's plant species have not yet been identified, let alone studied to determine their usefulness to humans or their unique role in natural systems.

The welfare of one species of plant or animal is likely to have a direct effect on other species, as well as on the functioning of the entire ecosystem. Scientists are working to determine the habitat requirements of various species, how we can restore habitats that have been lost or seriously diminished, and how we can balance human needs with the needs of other life forms on the planet.

Many times, removing the problem that threatens a rare species will allow it to recover on its own. But sometimes ensuring the survival of a rare species requires more extensive human intervention. These efforts may take the form of habitat protection in parks, preserves, and managed areas; habitat restoration; and zoos and botanical gardens that breed animals and plants, thereby preserving genetic diversity.

GETTING READY

PART A:

- Prepare 4–10 large mats or carpet squares, depending on your group and the size of the mats. Label them to present different types of natural habitat, such as forest, field, pond, ocean, and so on. You may choose to have two or three mats representing each habitat.

PART B:

- Obtain a list of locally rare, threatened, and endangered plant and animal species in your region from your state natural resource agencies, the U.S. Fish and Wildlife Service, the U.S. Department of Agriculture, NatureServe, or your state Natural Heritage data center. Outside the United States, contact the comparable agencies in your country.

- Arrange for students to have internet access. You might also ask your local librarian to set aside books on rare, threatened, and endangered species.

- Make copies of the Life on the Edge Research Questions student page or share it electronically.

PART A: HABITAT SCRAMBLE

1 What happens to wildlife when their habitat is altered, either naturally or by humans? Invite students to model the process to find out. Place the mats on the ground. Have each student choose one of the habitats and assume the identity of an animal (bird, fish, mammal, etc.) that lives there. They should stand with at least one foot on the appropriate mat. (More than one animal can occupy a habitat mat.)

2 When everyone is in place, tell a brief story describing the loss or alteration of a particular habitat (for example, a wetland is drained to build a housing development, or an invasive species is accidentally introduced and outcompetes the native species). After the story, pull away the mat representing that habitat. The animals that were standing there must scramble to find a new habitat that is suitable and stand with one foot on it. If they cannot adapt to another habitat, they do not survive and must stand to the side for the duration of the model.

3  **NONLINGUISTIC REPRESENTATIONS** Continue telling stories of habitat change and removing habitat mats after each one. As habitats disappear, students must scramble to find another suitable habitat mat to stand on or they die. Crowding, tension, and aggressive behavior will result, mimicking what often occurs in nature. End the model when most animals have lost their habitat.

4 Afterward, discuss the principles that the model demonstrated. Point out how learning about species needs and habitats when planning for development or land-use change is important for wildlife and people. Also point out that many plants and animals can adapt to minor changes in their habitat or can be accommodated by careful management.

PART B: SPECIES SPECIFICATION

1 Discuss with students the definitions of rare, threatened, and endangered species that are provided on the student page. Give students a short list of rare, threatened, or endangered species in your state (or have students develop a list from internet resources).

2 **COOPERATIVE LEARNING** Ask student teams to select a species from the list to research. Instruct them to gather as much information as they can from the internet and other resources, and to put together a profile for that species. (See plt.org/myk8guide for links to good starting places.) As students investigate, they should consider the questions on the student page.

TAKE IT OUTSIDE

Conduct the modeling activity in an open space outdoors. Afterward, invite students to look around their immediate surroundings for clues to how animals or plants get the food, water, and space they need to survive. For example, they might find chewed leaves (food), a stream (water), or a bird nest in a tree (space). Challenge them to find as many clues as they can to represent each requirement.

3  **HIGHER-ORDER THINKING** Challenge student teams to take the role of an advocate for the species they selected. They should imagine that they work for a public relations or advertising firm that has been hired to communicate to the public that the species is rare, threatened, or, endangered and to share what actions people are taking or could take to help it. Teams should create campaign materials that may include social media messages, websites, TV commercials, posters, or other materials. The information they present should come from their research.

4 Have teams present their campaign materials to the rest of the group.

VARIATION: GRADES 3–5

1 Ask students what they think happens to animal species when there isn't enough food, water, or space to go around. To find out, invite students to pick an animal species to portray in the following model.

2 **NONLINGUISTIC REPRESENTATIONS** Give each student a mat or sheet of paper to represent their habitat and spread the students out about 4 feet (1.2 m) apart. Randomly scatter on the floor three colors of poker chips, math cubes, or squares of construction paper to represent food, space, and water. (There should be about two of each color per person in the group.) Explain that each "animal" will try to gather as many of the chips as they can while always keeping at least one foot on their habitat.

3 Give a signal to start. Have the "animals" reach with their arms to gather requirements for 10 seconds and then record how many squares of each color they gathered. Explain that if animals don't have any of a particular requirement, they "die."

4 Try several more rounds. For each round, gather and redistribute the requirements, and have students record their results. Here are suggestions for additional rounds:

- Have students stand in groups of two or three per habitat (representing crowding or reduced habitat).
- Have only half the group participate (with the same number of chips).
- Use fewer water chips (representing drought or water contamination).
- Use fewer space chips (signifying a smaller habitat caused by humans or non-native species).
- Use fewer food chips (illustrating decreased availability of food due to disease, natural disaster, or climate change).

5 Invite students to compare the different rounds. Ask them to share what the model tells them about species that don't have enough food, water or space. Introduce the terms rare, threatened, and endangered species, as appropriate for the group.

ACADEMIC STANDARDS

SCIENCE

Practices
- Developing and using models
- Obtaining, evaluating, and communicating information

Concepts
- Human impacts on Earth systems
- Cause and effect

ENGLISH LANGUAGE ARTS

Practices
- Reading informational text: integration of knowledge and ideas
- Writing: production and distribution of writing

SOCIAL STUDIES

Practices
- Evaluating sources and using evidence
- Communicating conclusions and taking informed action

Concepts
- Geography: human–environment interactions
- History: change, continuity, and context

ASSESSMENT

Ask students to

- Write a paragraph describing what they learned about endangered species from conducting the model in Part A.

- Explain what they learned when they developed their presentations for Part B. You may use the following criteria to assess their presentations: Do students give a complete description of the organism, including where it lives, its range and distribution, other organisms that depend on it, and its population status? Do they give possible reasons the organism is listed as endangered or threatened? Do they describe actions that people are taking to protect the organism? Do they offer possible solutions to the threats the organism is facing and discuss trade-offs involved in providing for the organism's needs? Are their arguments convincing?

ENRICHMENT

- Hold a rare species "bee" (like a spelling bee) to see who can identify the most species. Have students create clue cards about the species they researched. They should write five descriptive statements about the species, listed in order from general to specific, on one side of the card (see Example Clue Card). Then they should write the name of the species on the back of the card. The students should line up in order and you should move down the line as you read them clues. For each species, read one clue to a student and allow them one guess. If they're correct, they win the point; if they are not correct, read the next clue to the next student. Students may only guess when it is their turn.

  Example Clue Card
  - » I live in open areas, with steep rocky slopes.
  - » My fur is brown, with a white patch near my tail.
  - » I eat grasses, shrubs, twigs, and shoots.
  - » I am very sure-footed—or you might say, "sure-hooved."
  - » Males of my kind have large, curling horns.

  [Answer: Bighorn sheep]

- Invite students to develop a game related to rare species. They might create a web quest about their specific animal or plant species, looking on the internet for examples. Or they might use presentation software to develop a Jeopardy-type game focusing on endangered species in your region. See plt.org/myk8guide for an example.

- Learn about rare species success stories: species that have recovered from the threat of extinction thanks to habitat protection and other conservation efforts. Encourage students to identify the most effective strategies and incorporate those strategies into the public relations materials they developed.

NAME _____ DATE _____

DEFINITIONS

Endangered Species: a native species or subspecies that is in serious danger of becoming extinct throughout all, or a significant portion, of its range as a result of one or more causes, including loss of habitat, overexploitation, competition, or disease. Endangered species are defined by the U.S. Fish and Wildlife Service based on factors listed in the Endangered Species Act.

Threatened Species: a native species that is not presently threatened with extinction but is likely to become endangered in the foreseeable future if not given special protection and management efforts. Threatened species are defined by the U.S. Fish and Wildlife Service based on factors listed in the Endangered Species Act.

Rare Species: a native species that is not presently threatened with extinction but exists in such small numbers throughout its range that it may become threatened if its present environmental conditions worsen. A species may be identified as rare based on scientific data, but the term is not defined legally.

SPECIES NAME: _____

1. What is the status of this species? (See definitions above.) _____

2. Where does it live? _____

    _____

3. What does it look like? _____

    _____

    _____

4. What is its habitat? _____

    _____

    _____

5. What is the current range of its population? _____

    _____

6. Why is it rare, threatened, or endangered? _____

    _____

    _____

    _____

NAME _____ DATE _____

7. What current actions are people taking to improve its chances of survival? _____

_____

_____

_____

_____

8. What are some ways in which individuals or groups can help this species? _____

_____

_____

_____

9. What other species depend on it? _____

_____

_____

_____

10. Why is it important that this species survive? (Give several reasons.) _____

_____

_____

_____

_____

_____

_____

_____

I LOVE MY GREEN JOB!

CAREER CORNER

ENDANGERED SPECIES BIOLOGISTS conduct research to determine whether species are rare or should be listed as threatened or endangered. They work to answer questions like: Why is this species rare or at risk? What are the causes of threats to this species? What can we do to remedy the problem?

Students learn about the three elements a fire needs to burn and find out how this "fire triangle" can be used to prevent and manage wildland fires, particularly in the wildland–urban interface.

LIVING WITH FIRE

SUBJECTS
Science, Social Studies

PLT CONCEPTS
4.8, 5.3

STEM SKILLS
Investigation, Leadership, Problem Solving

DIFFERENTIATED INSTRUCTION
Hands-on Learning, Multiple Solution Pathways

MATERIALS
Part A: Birthday candles, modeling clay, glass jars with lids, matches, safety goggles.

Part B: Five metal containers or pans, different-sized fuels (see Getting Ready), fire extinguisher, buckets or other containers filled with water, safety goggles, art materials.

TIME CONSIDERATIONS
Preparation: 50 minutes

Activity: One to two 50-minute periods

OBJECTIVES

Students will

- Describe the three elements of the fire triangle and explain how eliminating one (or more) can help prevent or control a fire.
- Describe ways to reduce the fire risk to homes in the wildland–urban interface.

BACKGROUND

From an ecological standpoint, fire is neither "good" nor "bad." Fire occurs naturally through lightning strikes in the presence of dry fuel. Fires also occur when humans start them, intentionally or accidentally.

Fire is a natural event in many forest ecosystems and can help to recycle nutrients back into the soil or help some plants regenerate. Fire is also an important component in the life cycle of several tree species: they need intense heat to open their cones and release seeds, and they thrive after a fire opens the forest canopy and allows more light to reach the ground.

Fires need heat, fuel, and oxygen to burn; these three elements are known as the "fire triangle." Initially, the heat is provided by an ignition source such as lightning, matches, or sparks. Fuels include dry trees, dead trees and limbs, leaf litter, and dry grass. Oxygen is available in the air. If you remove any of the elements of the fire triangle, the fire will not burn.

THE FIRE TRIANGLE

FOREST FACT

Closely spaced small trees and branches in the understory can act as ladders that allow fire to spread more easily into the upper canopy. The resulting "crown" fire can become extreme in certain forest types and weather conditions.

did you know?

Wildland fires are also influenced by the "fire behavior triangle," which includes other factors, particularly weather, fuel composition, and topography.

- Weather conditions have a great influence on when fires occur and how they spread. Sustained high temperatures and low humidity dry out forest debris, making the landscape more susceptible to fire. The stronger the winds, the more quickly moisture evaporates from the vegetation, and the faster fire can spread.

- Fuel composition, including moisture level, chemical makeup, and density, determines the degree of flammability.

- Topography, which describes an area's slope and steepness and whether it has canyons, valleys, or rivers, determines how hot and dry an area is and how quickly a fire can spread.

THE FIRE BEHAVIOR TRIANGLE

Historically, different regions of North America had distinct "fire seasons" when wildland fires were more likely to occur. Conditions such as earlier winter snow melt, drought, and tree mortality from insect infestation have extended the traditional fire season in many areas. Wildfires now sometimes occur year-round, forcing some forest managers to consider the "fire year" when making fire management decisions.

Fire has been an important tool in Indigenous cultures in North America and in other cultures around the world. Fire has traditionally been used to attract game animals by stimulating new growth, reducing populations of unwanted animals, fertilizing the soil to enhance crop growth, and clearing areas of forests. It has also been used as a management tool to bring back endangered species such as the Kirtland's warbler and the Karner blue butterfly.

PROJECT LEARNING TREE
An initiative of SFI

Over the years, fire management techniques have shifted to an active management strategy. A **prescribed burn** (one that is lighted by trained fire personnel when prescribed fuel and weather conditions are right) can prepare a harvested area for reforestation, enhance wildlife habitat and berry production, protect native species, manage invasive species, or reduce future fire hazard by reducing burnable fuels. Prescribed burns can also be used to prevent the spread of wildfires and protect communities.

In the United States, the human population continues to grow from urban areas into outlying rural and wildland areas. This demographic change is increasing the extent of the wildland–urban interface, the area where human-built structures and development meet or intermingle with undeveloped wildlands.

As more homes and other buildings are constructed near forests and other wildland areas, there is an increased likelihood that wildfires will threaten both structures and people. Because fires can readily move between buildings and vegetative fuels, it is becoming more difficult to manage fires in the wildland–urban interface. Homes, property, and lives within the wildland–urban interface are increasingly threatened by wildfire, and preventing, controlling, and suppressing it remains a challenge.

Ultimately, healthy forests are resilient forests. In fire-adapted ecosystems, a healthy forest has openly spaced trees and underbrush, a mosaic of different size and aged patches of forests, and the regular presence of fire. By promoting healthy forests, forest managers help to reduce the risk of wildland fire and also prevent unwanted effects of fire.

BURNABILITY

Different types of fuels burn differently, depending on their unique characteristics.

- Dead pine needles and other dead fuels ignite quickly and burn easily.

- Green or live fuels contain lots of moisture, preventing the fuel from getting hot enough to ignite. If they are really wet, water also keeps oxygen from reaching the fuel.

- Green pine needles are hard to ignite, but once they start burning, they are consumed quickly due to the oils and other volatile compounds they contain.

- Small pieces of fuel (like twigs) are much easier to ignite than large pieces (like a log) because they have more surface area exposed to oxygen and to the ignition source.

- Charred wood is hard to ignite because carbon (the fuel) is burned off from the surface, leaving unburnable minerals such as silicon.

GETTING READY

PART A:

Gather materials for the investigation. Invite a local firefighter or forest fire management professional to visit your group.

PART B:

Set up five metal containers and fill each one halfway with the following fuels:

1. Different-sized live branches, leaves, and needles (all green).

2. Different-sized dead and dry branches, leaves, and needles.

3. Different-sized dead and damp branches, leaves, and needles (or a dry assortment that has been sprayed lightly with water).

4. Large-diameter fuels, such as branches or whole pieces of wood (not kindling).

5. Partially burned pieces, such as from a fireplace or campfire (used but not completely consumed).

> ⚠️ **SAFETY CHECK!** Place metal containers outside on a fire-resistant surface (concrete, asphalt, or bare earth) away from cars, buildings, and dry vegetation. Be sure to have water and a fire extinguisher readily available. Ask another adult to assist with the demonstration, and wear safety goggles.

DOING THE ACTIVITY

PART A: FIRE TRIANGLE

1 Ask students, "What things do you think a fire needs to burn? What do you think happens if one of these things is missing?"

2 **HANDS-ON LEARNING** Divide the group into teams of 3–4 students. Provide each team with a birthday candle, modeling clay, a jar, a lid, and a set of matches.

3 Pass out copies of the Fire Triangle Investigation student page. Invite teams to conduct the investigation described and answer the questions.

4 When everyone is finished, ask the group what three things are needed for fire to burn. Draw a picture of the fire triangle where everyone can see it.

5 Have a local firefighter or forester talk with your group about the equipment and techniques used to put out fires, relating each technique to the fire triangle. Have them also discuss ways to prevent fires. Alternatively, share a video about techniques people use to fight wildland fires (see plt.org/myk8guide for suggestions).

PART B: THE WILDLAND-URBAN INTERFACE

1 As city populations expand, the urban boundary expands into wildland areas. This means that more and more people are building homes in woodland and grassland areas. Ask:

- What might be the risks in living next to or within wildland areas?

- How might people reduce the risk of fire in these wildland–urban interfaces?

- How might the type of fuel around the homes affect the fire risk?

2 Take students outside and show them the five different containers you have prepared, describing the contents of each. Tell them that you will try to start a fire in each container. Have students predict which fire will be easiest to start, and which will be most difficult.

3 Use matches to try to light a fire in each container, one at a time. Follow the safety guidelines listed in Getting Ready. Lead a discussion about the results and the implication for wildland fires:

- Which fuel burned the most readily?

- Which fuel was most difficult to burn?

- What types of plant materials would be best to have around residences in wildland–urban interfaces?

- How do prescribed burns help to reduce the risk of wildfires?

- How do healthy forests depend on wildland fires? How do they help to prevent high-intensity wildland fires that are particularly damaging in wildland–urban interfaces?

4 Challenge students to research ways to make homes in your community safer from wildfires or provide them with copies of the Wildfire Safety Checklist student page.

5  **MULTIPLE SOLUTION PATHWAYS** Have students work either individually or in teams to design a home that is safer from wildfire. They can use art materials to draw a picture or make a model. Ask them to share their designs with the rest of the group, pointing out the safety features.

TAKE IT OUTSIDE

Introduce the concept of the wildfire behavior triangle (see Background), discussing how an area's slope and fuel density can affect fire conditions. Take students on a walk through your site or nearby natural area to identify elements of the wildfire behavior triangle.

ACADEMIC STANDARDS

SCIENCE

Practices
- Analyzing and interpreting data

Concepts
- Natural hazards
- Cause and effect

SOCIAL STUDIES

Practices
- Communicating conclusions and taking informed action

Concepts
- Geography: human–environment interactions
- Geography: spatial patterns and movement of human populations

ASSESSMENT

Ask students to

- Create a picture board story—like a comic book without dialogue—of a wildland fire. Picture boards should have at least 10 frames showing how the area looked before the fire, what fuel was present, how the fire was ignited (natural or human causes), whether any structures in the area followed fire-safe guidelines, and which part(s) of the fire triangle was removed to stop the fire.

- Draw and label the fire triangle and detail two ways in which it relates to the fire behavior triangle.

- Identify steps people can take to reduce wildfire risk in the wildland–urban interface.

ENRICHMENT

- Research your state's primary causes of wildfires. Consult the state forestry agency (usually found within the state department of natural resources or department of agriculture) or the state office of the USDA Forest Service. Students can use this information to create tables, graphs, or other visual representations showing numbers and percentages of fires from different causes.

- Have students compare the number, sizes, and costs of prescribed fires and wildland fires in the United States over the past several years. These statistics are available from the National Interagency Fire Center (nifc.gov). Students may graph data to support their analysis.

- Changes in climate—such as higher temperatures, drier conditions, and more frequent and intense storms—can increase the risk and extent of wildfires. Lead a discussion about what communities might do to prepare for the possibility of greater fire risk.

- Invite students to research fire-adapted plant species to learn how they are adapted to wildfires. Possibilities include ponderosa pine, shortleaf pine, lodgepole pine, Ceanothus species (California lilac), and coffeeberry. Challenge them to design a new species that is adapted to fire and to describe its characteristics that enable it to thrive in a fire-prone ecosystem.

PROJECT LEARNING TREE
An initiative of SFI

Fire Triangle Investigation

NAME ____ DATE ______________

Fires need three things to burn: heat, fuel, and oxygen. This is known as the "fire triangle."

1. Draw a triangle here. You will add to this picture as you conduct your investigation.

2. Attach a birthday candle to the inside of the jar lid with modeling clay. Place the lid and candle on a tabletop and use a match to light the candle. What element of the fire triangle does the match demonstrate?

   ____

   Label one side of your triangle above with the word and draw a picture that shows this element.

NAME _____ DATE_____

3. Screw the jar onto the lid to cover the lit candle (so the jar is upside down). What happened?

_____

What element of the fire triangle does this demonstrate?

_____

Label another side of your triangle above with the word and draw a picture that shows this element.

4. Open the jar, relight the candle, and put the jar back onto the lid. When the flame starts to go out, reopen the jar. What happened?

_____

What does this show?

_____

5. Take the jar completely off the lid and allow the candle to burn until the flame goes out by itself. What happened?

_____

_____

How long did it take?

_____

What element of the fire triangle does this demonstrate?

_____

Label the last side of your triangle above with the word and draw a picture that shows this element.

6. Fire needs heat to burn. Initially, the heat is provided by a spark or flame, which can be produced by natural causes or generated by humans. Name two natural and two human-caused sources of heat that could start a fire.

Natural

• _____

• _____

Human-caused

• _____

• _____

NAME _____ DATE _____

7. Fires need fuel to burn. Name three possible fuels you might find in a forest.

_____

_____

_____

8. Fires need oxygen, which is available in the air. Hot temperatures and dry winds can create severe fire conditions. How might dry winds increase the chance of wildfires?

_____

_____

_____

9. If you cut off any one of the three elements—heat, fuel, and oxygen—a fire will not burn. What is one way that fire-fighters might cut off each of the three elements of the fire triangle?

Heat: _____

Fuel: _____

Oxygen: _____

CAREER CORNER

I LOVE MY GREEN JOB!

WILDLAND FIREFIGHTERS protect and maintain the health of the forest by preventing, controlling, and putting out forest fires, and lighting and managing prescribed burns. They may also talk to the public about ways they can help prevent fires.

Wildfire Safety Checklist

NAME_____ DATE_____

Wildland fire is an element of nature, just like weather, soils, minerals, plants, animals, and water. In fact, some landscapes depend on periodic fire to maintain a healthy ecosystem. As with other natural elements, fire is unpredictable and cannot always be controlled. Householders in fire-prone areas must make their homes "defensible" against wildfire.

Use this checklist to assess wildfire safety in three zones around your home. (Note: Check with your local fire safety agency for requirements in your area, which may be different.)

Immediate Zone (within 5 feet)

❏ Nothing flammable within 5 feet of any structure

❏ No plants, mulch, woodpiles, furniture, or stored or decorative items within 5 feet of structure

Intermediate Zone (5–30 feet)

❏ Area is "lean, clean, and green"

❏ All dead plants, grass, and weeds are removed

❏ Tree branches are trimmed so that they are a minimum of 10 feet from other trees

❏ Plants are watered regularly

❏ No woodpiles (move them to Zone 2)

❏ Trees and shrubs are separated from items that could catch fire, such as patio furniture or swing sets

Extended Zone (31–100 feet)

❏ Annual grass is cut or mown to a maximum height of 4 inches

❏ Trees branches are removed if less than 6 feet from the ground

❏ Shrubs and trees are planted in "islands" with space around them

❏ Shrubs and trees are pruned to eliminate fire ladders (places where fire could climb from the ground to the plant's crown)

❏ Fallen leaves, needles, twigs, bark, cones, and small branches are removed (but may be permitted to accumulate on the ground to a depth of 3 inches)

I LOVE MY GREEN JOB!

CAREER CORNER

FIRE PREVENTION SPECIALISTS work to reduce the risk and extent of forest fires. They may inspect outdoor public and residential areas for fire hazards, enforce fire regulations, and recommend fire prevention measures.

Trees come in many shapes and sizes. Students become familiar with tree structure and scale by using different methods to measure them and by making comparisons. They learn the importance of standardized measurements and proper measuring techniques.

NATURE'S SKYSCRAPERS

SUBJECTS
Science, Math

PLT CONCEPTS
3.2, 4.1

STEM SKILLS
Data Analysis, Investigation, Technology Use

DIFFERENTIATED INSTRUCTION
Hands-on Learning, Personal Connections

MATERIALS
Scrap paper; metric ruler (or yardstick) and large ball of string or measuring tape; large sheets of paper and marking pens, or other way to record group measurements; ruler for each pair of students.

TIME CONSIDERATIONS
Preparation: 20 minutes

Activity: One to two 50-minute periods

OBJECTIVES

Students will

- Explain how and why people use standard units of measure.

- Develop an understanding of measurement and tree scale.

- Measure trees in a systematic, consistent way.

BACKGROUND

Have you ever looked closely at neighborhood trees? You might notice that they have an assortment of sizes, shapes, colors, and textures. Some tree species, such as firs, tend to be tall and straight, with relatively short branches. Other species, such as dogwoods, tend to be shorter with long, broad branches.

An experienced forester or arborist may be able to judge the age of a tree simply by looking at its diameter and location. The growth rate of trees depends on the species and on local environmental conditions. The world's most massive tree species is the giant sequoia (*Sequoiadendron giganteum*), which grows in scattered groves in central California. This species can grow more than 250 feet (76 m) tall and more than 20 feet (6 m) in diameter. It is also among the world's longest lived trees: some sequoias are more than 3,000 years old!

FOREST FACT

did you know

Forest inventories play a key role in sustainable forest management, as they provide information for site management, forest thinning, timber harvests, and site quality assessment.

Foresters measure trees as part of a forest inventory to help them make forest management decisions. To determine the approximate timber yield of a tree stand, foresters perform a "timber cruise" in which they calculate the volume of timber in a given area, examine the health of the forest, and survey the species found there. This information helps them make forest management decisions and calculate the economic value of timber and other natural resources.

The volume of wood in a tree can be measured in board feet (a piece of lumber 12 inches square and 1 inch thick, or 0.002 cubic meters), cords (a stack of logs 4 ft x 4 ft x 8 ft, or 1.2 m x 1.2 m x 2.4 m), cubic feet, or cubic meters. One giant sequoia could yield more than 500,000 board feet (1,190 cubic meters)—enough to make 33 houses!

FULL CORD OF WOOD = 128 cubic feet (3.62 m³) and weighs up to 5,000 lbs

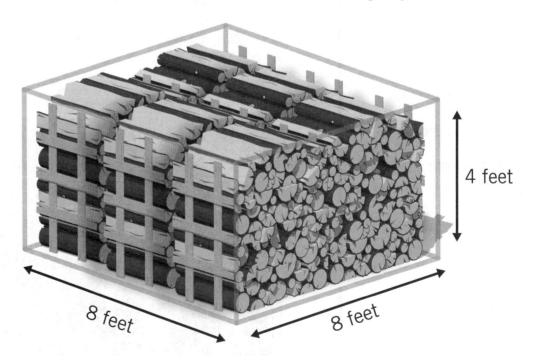

4 feet

8 feet

8 feet

PROJECT LEARNING TREE
An initiative of SFI

GETTING READY

- Preselect tree(s) for students to measure. The tree ideally should be in an open area so that students can measure its shadow.
- Make copies of the How Big Is That Tree? and Giant Comparisons student pages.

FOREST GIANTS

Giant sequoias (*Sequoiadendron giganteum*) are the most massive tree species on Earth. They are one of three species of closely related trees commonly known as redwoods because of their red bark and heartwood. While giant sequoias aren't quite as lofty as coast redwoods (Sequoia sempervirens), they still get mighty tall.

- The tallest known giant sequoia is 316 feet (96 m) tall, or about as high as a 31-story building. Giant sequoia trunks can grow up to 31 feet (9 m) wide at the base, or wider than a three-car garage!

- Giant sequoias grow so large because they live a very long time and grow relatively quickly. They can live more than 3,000 years.

- The high tannin content of their wood makes giant sequoias remarkably resistant to fungal disease and insect infestation. Their thick bark insulates them from fires and harsh weather.

- The only place giant sequoias grow naturally is on the western slopes of the Sierra Nevada mountains of California. Giant sequoias require lots of water, which is supplied by the Sierra snowpack that accumulates during the winter and soaks into the ground when it melts.

- Giant sequoias are conifers, meaning that their seeds grow in cones. Each 2- to 3½-inch-long (6- to 9-cm-long) cone contains about 200 seeds.

- Giant sequoias have evergreen leaves that look like small overlapping scales.

1 Take students to their adopted tree or other tree you have chosen. Ask students why a person might want to measure a tree like this. (One reason may be to determine how much wood or other natural resources it contains.)

2 ⬅ **PERSONAL CONNECTIONS** Invite them to think about how they would measure tree height, trunk circumference, and crown spread. Have students share their ideas with a partner. As a group, come up with a list of possible tree measurement methods.

3 ⬅ **HANDS-ON LEARNING** Ask students to estimate the circumference of the tree's trunk in inches or centimeters. Then have them measure the circumference using a piece of string and a metric ruler or yardstick, or a tape measure. Have students record their findings and compare their actual measurement with their estimate.

4 Explain that when foresters inventory forest areas, they always measure the width of a tree's trunk at a distance 4.5 feet (1.4 m) above the ground. To see why this is an important measurement standard, have students measure the circumference of the tree at 1 foot (.3 m), 2 feet (.6 m), and 4.5 feet (1.4 m) above the ground to see how their measurements differ (trees usually get wider toward the base). Ask students what would happen if everyone measured the circumference of a tree at a different height (everyone would get different results). Explain that foresters use a measurement called diameter at breast height (DBH) as their standard when they want to compare tree width. (For more information, see *Measuring DBH* box.)

CROWN SPREAD

To find the tree's average crown spread, measure the width of the crown at two different places (A-B and C-D). Add these two numbers together and divide by two for the average crown spread.

5 Show students what is meant by **crown spread** (the distance a tree's branches spread away from its trunk). Ask: Why would the measurement of a tree's crown be important? (The bigger the crown, the more leaves it has, the more food it can make, and the bigger it can grow.)

6 Ask students to estimate the tree's crown spread in feet or meters. Help students measure and calculate the average crown spread using the How Big Is That Tree? student page. Record their findings.

7 Have students determine the height of a tree using their ideas or one of the two methods shown on the How Big Is That Tree? student page.

- On a sunny day, students measure their own height and then immediately measure the length of their shadow. Show students how to use a ratio comparison to determine tree height. Ask students to compare their calculations: What might explain any differences?

- If it is not possible to measure shadows, try using proportions to estimate height (as shown on the How Big Is That Tree? student page). Ask students to compare their calculations. What might explain any differences?

8 Ask students whether they think a tree's leaves (or needles) are all the same size. Divide students into pairs, asking each to measure the length and width of a leaf (or needle) using a ruler. Record their findings.

MEASURING DBH

Foresters use a measurement called **diameter at breast height (DBH)** as the standard way to measure the width of a tree's trunk. Because tree trunks are often wider at their base, foresters always measure the width at a standard distance of 4.5 feet (1.4 m) above the ground, or roughly the height of a person's chest from the ground ("breast height").

Foresters typically use one of three instruments to accurately measure the diameter at this height: (1) a special measuring tape, called a diameter tape or d-tape, which shows the diameter of the tree when it is wrapped around the trunk's circumference (the distance around the trunk); (2) a Biltmore stick, which is a specially designed ruler; or (3) calipers, placed with arms on either side of the trunk, that indicate the trunk diameter. Without these instruments, it is easiest to measure the circumference, as in the activity.

9 Back inside, review the group's findings. Ask students how they think their tree would compare with the largest known tree on Earth. Use the Giant Comparisons student page to introduce them to the giant sequoia. Challenge them to do the calculations to compare their tree with the General Sherman Tree. Point out that though it is not the tallest, widest, or oldest tree on Earth, the General Sherman Tree is the largest known single-stem tree by volume.

10 ➡ **PERSONAL CONNECTIONS** To help students visualize the General Sherman Tree's size, invite them to stretch out their arms to create a circle 79 feet (24.1 m) in circumference to model its width, and to pace out 275 feet (83.8 m) to model its height.

VARIATION: GRADES 3–5

1 ➡ **HANDS-ON LEARNING** Challenge students to find the tree with the largest trunk at your site or a local park. Have students measure trees by joining arms around a large tree or using hand spans around a small one.

2 For each tree, help students measure the trunk by wrapping string around it and cutting the string to fit each tree's circumference. Staple or tape the strings to a wall. Help students to compare the strings and measure them using a ruler or different body parts: foot, hand span, arm span, length of finger, or paces.

3 Challenge students to find a very small tree (alternatively, bring in a potted tree). If the tree is small enough for students to reach the top, ask whether they think the tree's height is greater than or less than its crown spread. Have the students measure the height of the tree in hand spans and using standard units of measurement. Record findings and ask the students to compare the measurements with their estimate.

ACADEMIC STANDARDS

SCIENCE

Practices
- Using mathematics and computational thinking

Concepts
- Scale, proportion, and quantity
- Natural resources

MATH

Practices
- Reason abstractly and quantitatively
- Use appropriate tools strategically

Concepts
- Ratios and proportional relationships
- Expressions and equations

ASSESSMENT

Ask students to

- Write a paragraph or draw a diagram describing, step by step, how to measure a tree. Describe how this information might be used.

- Explain why, when teams measured tree height, they got slightly different results for the same tree.

- Complete the Giant Comparisons student page and explain the thought processes behind the problems presented (answers provided).

ENRICHMENT

- Help students make a life-sized drawing of a giant sequoia tree on the parking lot or other surface using tape, string, or chalk for the outline.

- "Champion Trees" are the largest known trees of their species. They are recorded online in the National Register of Big Trees at americanforests.org. Each state also has a record of its state champions. Find local champions to compare with the national or state champions. Champions are determined by using a tree's dimensions to calculate a total number of points. Calculate points for a tree of your choice by adding:

tree circumference at 4.5 feet (1.4 m) off the ground (in inches) **tree height (in feet)** **one-fourth of the average crown spread (in feet)**

- Invite a local forester to talk with your group about why they measure trees. You can find foresters working at the federal government, state agencies, companies that make paper products, universities, etc.

- Use i-Tree, a suite of free online tools used by urban foresters in the field (available at itreetools.org) to assess the benefits of trees. See PLT's *Teaching with i-Tree* at plt.org/i-tree for three hands-on activities using i-Tree that you can do using the measurements your students collected.

ANSWERS TO GIANT COMPARISONS STUDENT PAGE

Answers will vary depending on the data collected. Here's how the problems should be set up:

1. $$\frac{\text{height of General Sherman Tree}}{\text{height of your tree}} = \frac{\text{275 feet (or 83.8 m)}}{\text{height of your tree}} = \text{answer}$$

2. 1,250 feet* (or 381 m) — 279 feet (or 83.8 m) = 971 feet (or 297.2 m)

   (height of Empire State Building)   (height of General Sherman Tree)

   * The height here is the building height, not including the antenna.

3. **The answer will depend on the specific building used for comparison.**

4. $$\frac{\text{length of longer leaf}}{\text{length of shorter leaf}} = \text{answer}$$

5. $$\frac{\text{circumference of General Sherman Tree}}{\text{length of armspan}} = \frac{\text{79 feet (or 24.1 m)}}{\text{length of armspan}} = \text{answer}$$

6. bigger crown spread — smaller crown spread = answer

NAME _____ DATE _____

ESTIMATING TREE HEIGHT

METHOD 1

1. Have a friend stand at the tree's base.

2. Hold a ruler at arm's length and walk backward, keeping your arm stiff, until the top and bottom of the ruler line up with the top and bottom of the tree.

3. Note where the top of your friend's head appears on the ruler (for example, at 2 in or 5 cm). _____

4. Divide the length of the ruler by this number.

   _____ ÷ _____ = _____

5. Multiply your friend's actual height by your answer to number 4:

   _____ (friend's height) x _____ (answer to number 4) = _____ (tree height)

METHOD 2

1. Measure the length of the tree's shadow and measure the length of your shadow, both in inches (cms).

2. Calculate the height of the tree using this formula:

   $$\text{height of tree} = \frac{\text{length of tree's shadow} \times \text{your height}}{\text{length of your shadow}}$$

ESTIMATING CROWN SPREAD

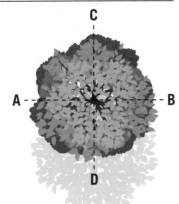

To find the tree's average crown spread, measure the width of the crown at two different places (A-B and C-D). Add these two numbers together and divide by two for the average crown spread.

CAREER CORNER

FOREST TECHNICIANS help to maintain forestland. They may conduct a forest survey—or "cruise"—to estimate the size, quality, and species of trees and timber in an area.

Giant Comparisons

STUDENT PAGE

NAME _____ DATE_____

Record each of the estimates and measurements for your tree below. Compare your tree with the biggest tree in the world, the General Sherman Tree. It's the largest giant sequoia—and the largest known living plant—on Earth!

	Your Tree		General Sherman
	Estimate	Measurement	
Circumference (at breast height)			79 feet (24.1 m)
Height			275 feet (83.8 m)
Average crown spread			106.5 feet (32.5 m)
Leaf or needle length (from base of stem to tip)			.25 inches (6 mm)

GENERAL SHERMAN

1. How many of your trees would you have to stack on top of one another to equal the height of the General Sherman Tree?

   _____

2. Which is taller: The General Sherman Tree or the Empire State Building? How much taller?

   _____

3. Which is taller: The General Sherman Tree or the tallest tree in your community? How much taller?

   _____

4. Which is longer: Your tree's leaf or the leaf (needle) of the giant sequoia? How many times longer is it?

   _____

5. How many of you would it take to wrap your arms around the General Sherman Tree? (You'll need to measure the distance of your outstretched arms from fingertip to fingertip.) How about your tree?

   _____

6. Which is bigger, the average crown spread of your tree or that of the General Sherman Tree? How much bigger is it?

   _____

CAREER CORNER

I LOVE MY GREEN JOB!

FORESTRY ENGINEERS design and supervise the building of roads, trails, bridges, and other construction projects in managed forests. They must understand forest ecosystems and the impacts of projects on forest resources.

PROJECT LEARNING TREE K-8 ACTIVITY GUIDE © SUSTAINABLE FORESTRY INITIATIVE

Succession is a natural pattern of change that takes place over time in a forest or other ecosystem. Students read a story about succession and investigate the connections among plants, animals, and successional stages in a local ecosystem.

NOTHING SUCCEEDS LIKE SUCCESSION

SUBJECTS
Science, English Language Arts, Math, Social Studies, Visual Arts

PLT CONCEPTS
5.1, 5.3

STEM SKILLS
Collaboration, Investigation, Nature-based Design

DIFFERENTIATED INSTRUCTION
Cooperative Learning, Hands-on Learning, Nonlinguistic Representations, Student Voice

MATERIALS
Part A: Journals. Optional: Presentation app, wax paper or transparency film sheets, permanent or wet-erase markers.
Part B: Journals, colored pens or pencils.
Part C: Materials for roping off study area (such as rope or string, scissors, stakes, hammer), journals, camera.

TIME CONSIDERATIONS
Preparation: 30 minutes

Activity:
Part A: 50-minute period
Part B: One 50-minute period
Activity, Part C: An hour once a month

OBJECTIVES

Students will

- Explore basic relationships between species diversity and ecosystem changes.

- Identify successional stages in ecosystems based on the plant and animal species that are present.

- Draw conclusions about the process of succession based on study test plots that are in different stages of succession.

BACKGROUND

Like all ecosystems, forests are in a constant state of change. Disturbances—such as fires, pest infestations, and changes in climate—can alter the structural development and composition of a forest. Even without such a disturbance, the composition of the forest will gradually change as the forest community matures. The scientific word for change over time in plant communities is **ecological succession**.

Ecologists distinguish between **primary succession** and **secondary succession**. Primary succession occurs in areas where there is little or no soil, such as after a lava flow, severe landslide, or retreating glacier. These areas gradually begin to populate with living organisms, starting with **pioneer species** that are able to survive without soil and in very harsh conditions. Secondary succession occurs in areas after less-severe disturbances, such as a fire or flood, where some life forms and nutrients survive the disturbance.

Primary and secondary succession both create a continually changing mix of species within communities. The progression of species is not random, however: at every stage, certain species are adapted to the environmental conditions of that stage, and there is a somewhat predictable sequence of changes in the community's composition.

When a disturbance occurs in a forest, such as wildfire, it may clear space and bring in sunlight. The first plants to move into the open space are often fast-growing, sun-loving annuals. Over time, these plants grow dense and start to shade the forest floor, enabling the vegetation to gradually shift to more and more woody **shrubs** and

PROJECT LEARNING TREE
An initiative of SFI

FOREST FACT

Foresters use various techniques to minimize weather-related damage to their forests. For example, they may clear dead trees and debris to help reduce the spread of wildfire, or plant "wind-firm" (deep-rooting) species in windy areas so they won't topple.

trees. Eventually, as the community matures, different sizes and ages of trees may form a layered canopy, with a ground layer of shrubs and **herbs** underneath.

Succession doesn't end with a mature plant community. Rather, the ecosystem continues to change. Minor disturbances, such as a tree dying and creating a gap in the forest canopy, can affect the growing conditions in small areas, while major disturbances, such as wildfire or hurricanes, can affect hundreds of forest acres.

Like other successional disturbances, **climate change** can be viewed as a disturbance that affects the composition of forest communities. A shifting climate can bring changes in temperature, precipitation, storms, fires, and other factors, making it difficult for some species to survive in a given location. Either the range or geographical area where those species live could shift, or the species could begin to die out. For species or forest communities that are already at the edge of their range, the effect of a changing climate may be particularly severe.

GETTING READY

PART A:

- Make copies of the student pages, The Story of Mount St. Helens and Pictures of Succession, or plan to share them electronically.

PART B:

- Identify a study site that exhibits several stages of succession (such as a grassy area, an area with shrubs, and an area with trees), or plan a field trip to a natural area. If a walk or a field trip is not possible, use the pictures of various stages of succession provided on the Pictures of Succession student page or find pictures on the internet.

PART C:

- Get permission to set aside three 10.75-sq ft (1 sq m) study areas on or near your site. The first should be a bare, unpaved area. The second should be a patch of lawn that is regularly mowed and watered. The third should be a lawn or grassy area that you rope off and leave untouched (no mowing, watering, or fertilizing).

- Coordinate with maintenance staff to leave the third study area undisturbed.

PART A: THE STORY OF SUCCESSION

1 Ask students to name ways that a forest might change over time.

2 **NONLINGUISTIC REPRESENTATIONS** Have students read The Story of Mount St. Helens student page aloud as a group. Ask them to stop after each part of the story and record descriptive words about this stage in a journal. After you have read the story, discuss the changes that the story described.

3 Hand out copies of the Pictures of Succession student page to let students see how succession typically proceeds in a forested area. Point out how each successional stage has its characteristic plants and animals. Emphasize that even if a forest appears to reach an "endpoint," small- or large-scale disturbances can still occur, creating a variety of plant communities and habitat types within different forest stands.

4 **COOPERATIVE LEARNING** Divide your group into teams. Using a presentation app, or wax paper or transparency film sheets and colored markers, each team will create a sequence of pictures to show succession.

- The base drawing on a presentation slide or piece of 8.5" x 11" (21.6 cm x 28 cm) white paper should show a disturbed area (such as a site burned by fire or harvested by people).

- Overlay drawings on successive slides or 8" x 11" (20.3 cm x 28 cm) pieces of wax paper or transparency film sheets should show successive phases of growth. Have teams tape or staple their overlays to the base picture. For example:

  » The base picture could show blackened ground with stumps of trees (perhaps with an animal passing through).

  » Overlay 1 could display grass, flowers (seeds borne by wind or animals), and small animals returning.

  » Overlay 2 could add small bushes, shrubs, and more animals.

  » Overlay 3 could add young, small trees with characteristic animals.

  » Overlay 4 could add full-grown, mature trees with characteristic animals.

- When the teams are finished, they can share their work with the group and describe what is happening in each successive scene.

PART B: IN THE FIELD

1 **HANDS-ON LEARNING** Take your students on a field trip through an area that has several types of vegetative communities (for example, an urban park with wooded areas). Have them try to find areas where plant communities appear to be changing in composition. Tell them not to worry about plant or tree names, only types (such as grasses, herbs, shrubs, or trees). Have them look for animals and signs or sounds of animals. They should also look for evidence of disturbance (such as erosion, tire tracks, fire, or construction) that might have altered the

PROJECT LEARNING TREE
An initiative of SFI

natural succession. They can try to find the following compositions (note that not all of them may be present or in discrete locations):

- Grasses and herbs only

- Grasses, herbs, and shrubs

- Grasses and shrubs, with young tree saplings (stem < .5" [1.3 cm])

- Ground vegetation and young trees (stem .5" to 2" [1.3 cm to 5 cm])

- Mature trees (stem > 2" [5 cm], can still be under canopy)

2 Call the group together and define the stages of succession evident at your site. Discuss disturbances that could change the vegetation you see at the site, including disease, insects, fire, wind, lightning, pollution, and drought.

3 **COOPERATIVE LEARNING** Divide the groups into teams of three students. Have students draw a general map of the study area, including major landmarks (such as major trees, trail junctions, parking lots, benches, creeks, etc.), and then identify and draw areas on the map that fall into the different categories of succession identified in Step 1.

PART C: AT YOUR SITE

1 Ask students what changes they might see over time if they were to make careful observations of the site's lawn area. Discuss whether any changes would occur if the lawn continued to be mowed, as well as if the mowing stopped. Ask for their ideas on how they might investigate the changes.

2 Suggest that one way to observe changes would be to compare three different areas: one that has no lawn, one with lawn that is regularly mowed and watered, and one with lawn that is no longer mowed or watered. Show the group the three study areas you have designated (see Getting Ready), and have students describe the similarities and differences between the areas and how they might continue to change over time.

3 **NONLINGUISTIC REPRESENTATIONS** Over the next several months, encourage students to make weekly observations of the three sites, recording their observations in journal writings, drawings, and photographs. When they take photos, they should mark the camera position on the ground or take the picture from a particular location, so they can use the same position each time. Students can use a presentation app to create a slideshow of the photos, or print them and make a wall display. Photos can show the following:

- Types of plants (record changes)

- Plant growth rate (measure in centimeters and graph each week)

- Changes in plant density (count the number of stems per square meter)

- Changes in species composition (note whether some plants gradually become more abundant and others less abundant)

- New plant species (record the types)

- Evidence of animal or human life at the site

4 ◑ **STUDENT VOICE** After each observation period, ask the students to make a general statement about the changes or apparent succession they observe, and to describe similarities and differences in species at the three sites.

VARIATION: GRADES 3–5

1 Read aloud a fictional story told from the perspective of siblings who observe forest changes over several decades. (Find the Tree Tops Valley student page at plt.org/myk8guide.) Stop after each part of the story and have students draw a picture of the stage in their journals. After reading, discuss the changes described in the story and shown in their drawings.

2 Share copies of the Pictures of Succession student page to show students how succession typically proceeds in a forested area.

3 Have students recreate the story of succession using a felt board, in which the bottom third is brown (for soil) and the top two-thirds are blue (for sky). Assign teams for each of the successional stages described in the story. Allow teams to use different colors of felt to cut out the shapes of plants, animals, and other elements (such as fire) to depict that stage.

4 Invite teams to come up and place their felt pieces in appropriate places on the felt board to describe their stage.

5 Discuss the idea that major and minor disturbances affect each stage and help to shift the ecosystem to another stage.

ACADEMIC STANDARDS

SCIENCE

Practices
- Obtaining, evaluating, and communicating information
- Planning and carrying out investigations

Concepts
- Ecosystem dynamics, functioning, and resilience
- Patterns
- Stability and change

ENGLISH LANGUAGE ARTS

Practices
- Reading informational text: integration of knowledge and ideas
- Speaking and listening: presentation of knowledge and ideas

MATH

Practices
- Reason abstractly and quantitatively

Concepts
- Statistics and probability

SOCIAL STUDIES

Practices
- Applying disciplinary concepts

Concepts
- Geography: human–environment interactions
- History: change, continuity, and context

ASSESSMENT

Ask students to

- Take notes and create a map by looking for accurate and detailed descriptions (both written and visual) of topography, nonliving things, plants, and animals at a site. To assess their understanding of the concepts, look for accurate placement of identified features and successional stages on the map.

- Write a summary report of what happened at all three sites and what stages of succession they observed. They should describe the life cycles and stages of plant growth, disturbance factors, and evidence of animal life.

ENRICHMENT

- Suggest that students write a short story or interactive play to tell the history of the forest through its succession.

- Have students create a succession flipbook that illustrates change over time in an environment.

- Challenge students to find locations in their community that have experienced different stages of succession. For example, what existed on the school's land 20, 50, or 100 years ago?

- Research the plant and animal species involved in the Mount St. Helens story to learn about the adaptations that may have helped them survive.

NAME _____ DATE _____

On May 18, 1980, the Mount St. Helens volcano in Washington State erupted violently, causing the top to blow off the mountain. A 300-mile-an-hour (480 kilometers per hour) blast of hot air, rocks, and debris flattened the surrounding forest, and a cloud of ash climbed to 80,000 feet (24,300 meters) in the air.

When the blast was over, more than 230 square miles (596 square kilometers) of forests, lakes, meadows, and streams were covered in gray ash and volcanic debris. In many places, the once-lush forest looked like a lifeless moonscape.

But, surprisingly, some smaller plants and animals survived the blast. Protected by snow, ice, or moist soil, they lived through the intense heat and wind. Within days and weeks, these animals scurried out of hiding, and the plants began to grow again.

Before long, winds blew in seeds and insects, bringing more life to the blast zone. Over time, the plants and insects attracted birds, deer, and elk from nearby areas, carrying seeds "hitchhiking" on their feathers or fur.

Today, many areas around Mount St. Helens still have a moon-like appearance, but most of the plant and animal species that were there before the eruption have returned. The landscape is gradually becoming a forest again.

Tiny red alder tree seedlings that were living under the snow at the time of the blast are now over 40 feet tall. These fast-growing deciduous trees create shade for other trees to grow. With time, evergreen trees that prefer shady areas—like Douglas-firs and hemlocks—will return.

Scientists predict it will take several hundred years for the blast area to look like it did before the eruption. Imagine all the plants and animals that will live in the forest then.

Mount St. Helens, 1981
One year after eruption

Mount St. Helens, 2010
30 years after eruption

Source: Adapted from Mount St. Helens–A Story of Succession in PLT's Secondary Environmental Education Module *Exploring Environmental Issues: Focus on Forests.*

I LOVE MY GREEN JOB

CAREER CORNER

VOLCANOLOGISTS (vole-can-AWL-uh-jists) have an exhilarating job! These scientists study the formation of volcanoes and investigate past and current volcano eruptions.

NAME_____ DATE_____

As the diagram below shows, plant communities change over time in a process called succession. It's important to remember that succession is ongoing and cyclical in nature. Changes will still occur after the community reaches the mature stage shown in the drawings. Both major disturbances (such as hurricanes, wildfires, or prescribed fires) and minor disturbances (such as several trees dying due to disease or being thinned by a **forester**) will bring different results to the landscape.

STAGES OF FOREST SUCCESSION

| PIONEER SPECIES | GRASSES & HERBS | SHRUBS | YOUNG FOREST | MATURE FOREST |

CAREER CORNER

I LOVE MY GREEN JOB!

FOREST BIOTECHNOLOGISTS use science and genetic engineering to test new ways to develop wood products and to make forests more sustainable. They must be creative and innovative, as well as detail oriented.

Our nation's forests are managed to support multiple outcomes. Students learn how forests can be managed to meet a variety of human and environmental needs and examine national parks or forests to identify challenges that forest managers face meeting different needs.

OUR FEDERAL FORESTS

SUBJECTS
Science, English Language Arts, Math, Social Studies

PLT CONCEPTS
2.7, 4.5, 5.3, 5.9

STEM SKILLS
Communication, Data Analysis, Problem Solving

DIFFERENTIATED INSTRUCTION
Cooperative Learning, Multiple Solution Pathways, Personal Connections

MATERIALS
Internet access.

TIME CONSIDERATIONS
Preparation: 15 minutes

Activity: One to two 50-minute periods

OBJECTIVES

Students will

- Identify ways that people use forest resources.

- Explore how forests are managed to satisfy a variety of human and environmental needs.

- Offer possible solutions to problems facing federal forestland.

BACKGROUND

Both in the United States and across the globe, about one-third of the total land base is covered in forest. To be classified as forestland, the area must be at least one acre (0.4 ha) and contain about 10% tree cover. About two-thirds of U.S. forestlands are also classified as commercial timberland (forests capable of growing trees for commercial purposes). Almost 60% of U.S. forests are privately owned, mostly by families and corporations. The remaining 40% of forests are owned by the federal government and by state and county governments. See the *Forestland in the United States* graphic on page 341 for a breakdown of forest ownership and management in the United States.

Federal public lands are held in trust for all Americans. They are intended to be managed for both the long-term health of the land and the long-term benefit of citizens. Much of the federal forestland belongs to national forests, national wildlife refuges, and national parks. These lands have different mandates and are managed by different federal departments.

NATIONAL FORESTS

National forests are managed by the U.S. Forest Service, under the U.S. Department of Agriculture. There are more than 150 national forests in 43 states and Puerto Rico. National forests include approximately 190 million acres (77 million ha) of forestland, of which about two-thirds is classified as commercial timberland.

The U.S. Forest Service is required by law to manage its forests for multiple uses, such as generating wood products, protecting watersheds, conserving soil and wildlife habitat, and providing public recreation and **ecosystem services**. See the *Multiple Use Management* box for more details.

NATIONAL WILDLIFE REFUGES

The National Wildlife Refuge System is managed by the U.S. Fish and Wildlife Service for the conservation and management of fish, wildlife, and plant resources and the habitats on which they depend. It includes more than 560 wildlife refuges covering over 145 million acres (59 million ha) of land. These refuges include a range of ecosystems, from hardwood forests in the Southeast to prairies in the Heartland and deserts in the Southwest.

NATIONAL PARKS

National parks are managed by the U.S. National Park Service, under the U.S. Department of the Interior. More than 400 areas covering over 85 million acres (34 million ha) of land are part of the national park system. These areas include monuments, battlefields, military parks, historical parks, historic sites, lakeshores, natural areas, seashores, recreation areas, and scenic rivers and trails.

National parks emphasize strict preservation of natural areas, with a focus on protecting natural and historic resources "unimpaired for the enjoyment of future generations." Activities that are conducted in national forests, such as mining, oil and gas drilling, livestock grazing, hunting, and other activities, are limited in national parks.

FORESTLAND IN THE UNITED STATES

57% PRIVATE
- 36% Individuals & Families
- 19% Private Corporations
- 2% Other

43% PUBLIC
- 32% Federal Government
- 11% State/Local Government

MULTIPLE USE MANAGEMENT

Managed forests typically are managed to provide several resources at the same time, such as timber, wildlife habitat, recreational areas, and environmental benefits (like shade, watershed protection, and carbon storage). They are managed to protect all these resources through **multiple use management**. Both public and private forests may be managed for multiple use. For example, forests owned by a forest product company may be used for hiking, fishing, and camping, at the same time that they are managed for timber production and ecosystem protection.

Multiple use management involves making choices about the types of activities that can take place in designated areas. Some forest ecosystems cannot support certain activities, and some activities should not be allowed to occur in the same area at the same time. For example, hiking or camping near an active forest management area could pose safety risks. Also, activities such as roadbuilding or mining could affect watershed resources.

Some forest owners or managers have their forests certified to demonstrate that they are responsibly managed. For more information, check out the What's in a Label? activity.

GETTING READY

For Part B, make copies of the Shaping Solutions student page. Choose national parks, national wildlife refuges, or national forests for students to research or plan to have them choose. To find U.S. federal forestlands in your state or region, check the following websites:

- Find a Park, U.S. National Park Service: nps.gov/findapark
- Refuge Locator, U.S. Fish and Wildlife Service: fws.gov/refuges/refugelocator.html
- Find a Forest, U.S. Forest Service: discovertheforest.org

DOING THE ACTIVITY

PART A: FOREST OF MANY USES

1 **PERSONAL CONNECTIONS** Divide students into teams of four and challenge teams to list different ways that people and wildlife use or benefit from forests. Help to expand their lists by asking:

- What kinds of recreational activities have you or your family done in forests?
- What kinds of products do people get from forests?
- What animals live in forests (including less obvious ones like fish, insects, worms, and microorganisms)?
- How do forests affect water and air?

2 Display the words "Wildlife," "Recreation," and "Products" where all can see, and have teams share ideas from their lists that fit under each category. For example, they may put food or water under "wildlife," camping and fishing under "recreation," and wood or hydroelectricity from a dam under "Products."

3 Explain that people manage forests with an emphasis on different needs. For example, some forests may be managed to meet the needs of wildlife, others to meet recreational needs, and still others to meet the need for forest products. Some forests may be managed to meet all these needs.

4 Assign each team one of the three categories to explore in depth. Team members should imagine they are forest managers and need to manage a forest for that category. What strategies could they use to promote it? What requirements would they need to address? How might they manage for that category while also addressing the other two categories?

5 Have each team brainstorm ideas and then share with the group. Record ideas in the corresponding location from Step 2.

6 Explain that, in many cases, forests today are managed for more than one use at a time. Point out that by law, U.S. national forests must be managed for multiple uses. Have your students look at the lists they created and consider:

- What adjustments might be necessary to meet all these uses in a single forest area?

- Which activities on the list might conflict with one another if someone tried to manage both at the same time?

- Would those activities always conflict, or would they conflict only at certain times and under certain conditions?

- What could people do to ensure both the long-term health of the forest and long-term use for people?

PART B: SHAPING SOLUTIONS

1 PERSONAL CONNECTIONS Begin by asking students whether they have ever visited a national park, national wildlife refuge, or national forest in the United States or another country. Where did they go? What did they see? Were there many people there? If none of the students has been to such a place, have them research options to take a virtual field trip.

2 Refer to the list of forest benefits from Part A, Step 2, and ask students which uses would be allowed on federal forestlands. Then explain that although some public lands such as national forests are managed for multiple uses (wildlife, recreation, timber), national parks in the United States are more restricted. For example, timber harvesting, mining, oil and gas drilling, and livestock grazing are typically limited in national parks.

3 COOPERATIVE LEARNING Divide your group into teams of two to four students. Assign or have teams choose a national park, national wildlife refuge, or national forest. Challenge teams to find that area's most pressing challenges in providing multiple uses, and to propose solutions to at least one challenge. Suggest that they do an internet search using terms such as "[name of national forestland] challenges" or "[name of national forestland] issues and concerns."

4 MULTIPLE SOLUTION PATHWAYS Have students work in teams to complete the student page, discussing their findings and recommendations. What solutions do they recommend? How do other students feel about those recommendations? What are the pros and cons of each recommendation?

5 Encourage students to back up their recommendations with existing data about their area. For example, they might research visitor trends, public approval ratings, amenities offered, or overnight stays and show how their recommended solution would affect specific datapoints. Challenge them to display this information visually, using graphs, tables, illustrations, and more.

TAKE IT OUTSIDE

Pocket parks are small outdoor spaces where a few people can gather, relax, and enjoy a bit of nature. They may include a bench, some trees, or a small community garden. In urban settings, they are often located between commercial buildings or private homes or on part of a vacant lot. If there's a pocket park on or near your site, take students to it and have them identify its features and the qualities that make it inviting. If there isn't one nearby, invite students to map the outdoor area at your site, suggest possible locations for a pocket park, and draw a schematic showing what the park could look like.

VARIATION: GRADES 3–5

1 🔄 **COOPERATIVE LEARNING** Invite students working in pairs or small teams to identify different ways that people use forests, as in Step 1 of the activity. Create a group list of their ideas. If you notice that particular areas are missing from the list (such as products or recreation), ask questions to elicit further additions to the list.

2 Challenge students to create silent charades that show different uses of a forest area. Have pairs or teams choose two or more ideas from the list to act out as a group. Give teams a few minutes to plan and practice their charades, which must involve everyone in the team.

3 After a team has presented, invite other teams to guess what forest use was being portrayed.

PROJECT LEARNING TREE
An initiative of SFI

ACADEMIC STANDARDS

SCIENCE

Practices
- Constructing explanations and designing solutions
- Obtaining, evaluating, and communicating information

Concepts
- Natural resources
- Cause and effect

ENGLISH LANGUAGE ARTS

Practices
- Writing: research to build and present knowledge

Concepts
- Speaking and listening: comprehension and collaboration

MATH

Practices
- Reason abstractly and quantitatively

Concepts
- Statistics and probability

SOCIAL STUDIES

Practices
- Evaluating sources and using evidence
- Communicating conclusions and taking informed action

Concepts
- Civics: civic and political institutions
- History: change, continuity, and context

ASSESSMENT

Ask students to

- Create a visual presentation showing strategies that promote one of the categories of forest uses: products, recreation, or wildlife.

- Use a claim, evidence, and reasoning to share their recommendation for the forestland explored in Part B. Challenge them prepare a written claim that states their recommendation, and then describe supporting evidence and reasoning to support the claim. See Appendix K: Making a Scientific Argument for a sample student page to use.

ENRICHMENT

- Invite a forest manager or private forest owner in your area to talk to your class about how local forests are managed for multiple uses.

- Invite a state forest or state park employee (e.g., manager, forester, naturalist, ranger, police officer) to visit your group and address forest management goals, guidelines, and enforcement. To find state parks in your area, see stateparks.org. Have students discuss their ideas for solving forest management issues with your guest.

- Explore potential careers involved in managing forestlands or national parks. See PLT's *Green Jobs in Green Spaces: Exploring Forest Careers* at plt.org/greenjobs for a set of activities to guide their exploration.

Shaping Solutions

NAME ______________________________ DATE ______________

Name of national park, national wildlife refuge, or national forest:

____

1. What are the most pressing challenges facing this area?

____

____

____

____

2. What are possible solutions to address one of those problems? Identify at least three.

- ______________________________
- ______________________________
- ______________________________

3. How would each of your proposed solutions solve the problem?

- ______________________________
- ______________________________
- ______________________________

4. What problems might each solution create?

- ______________________________
- ______________________________
- ______________________________

5. Would your solutions also work for other forest areas, or just this one?

____

____

NAME _____ DATE _____

6. What other information would you like to know before making a recommendation?

_____

_____

_____

7. What would you recommend for this area?

_____

_____

_____

8. Use the space below to create a visual display that supports your recommendation, such as a map of the area or graph of land use.

CAREER CORNER

I LOVE MY GREEN JOB!

PUBLIC RELATIONS ASSOCIATES work to provide news and information about forests through blogs, press releases, or media coverage. They may develop advertising and speak at public events about the benefits of forests.

Never underestimate the power of a tree! In addition to giving us an amazing array of paper and wood products, trees provide a host of other benefits—from shading our backyards to reducing air pollution to helping stabilize the global climate. Students can express their appreciation of trees by planning and carrying out their own tree-planting project.

PLANT A TREE

SUBJECTS
Science, English Language Arts, Social Studies

PLT CONCEPTS
1.10, 2.1, 2.2

STEM SKILLS
Collaboration, Leadership, Technology Use

DIFFERENTIATED INSTRUCTION
Cooperative Learning, Hands-on Learning, Higher-order Thinking, Student Voice

MATERIALS
Paper and pencils, native sapling or seedling, shovel, mulch, watering hose or watering can

TIME CONSIDERATIONS
Preparation: 60 minutes

Activity: Two to five 50-minute periods

OBJECTIVES

Students will

- Identify ways that urban trees enrich our lives.

- Determine how people care for urban trees.

- Identify areas in their local community that would benefit from having more trees.

- Organize and execute a project to plant a tree.

BACKGROUND

Trees are invaluable assets to our communities. They shade and cool our streets and buildings and protect homes from cold winds. They give us flowers, fall colors, and lovely scents. They provide homes for animals. Their branches create beautiful shapes that soften the urban landscape and even hold tree houses. They contribute to a community's sense of place.

Here are some of the most important things that trees do, particularly those planted in urban or residential areas:

- Store carbon, helping to reduce atmospheric carbon dioxide and fight climate change

- Help settle out, trap, and hold small particles (dust, ash, smoke) that can damage lungs

- Absorb sulfur dioxide and other pollutants

- Hold soil with their roots, preventing erosion

- Provide homes and food for birds, squirrels, insects, and other animals

- Serve as a windbreak, keeping buildings warmer

- Provide shade, keeping buildings cooler

- Muffle traffic noise

- Provide beauty and enjoyment and improve our overall health

Planting a tree is a long-term investment that can repay the community again and again for the duration of the tree's life. But it's important to put thought into planting a tree. In order for the tree to grow well and have a long life, it should be a suitable tree species for the region and should be placed in a suitable planting

FOREST FACT

The "Right Tree Right Place" (RTRP) concept was developed by Dr. Richard Harris in 1982 to ensure the appropriate selection and planting of trees.

location. The tree must be cared for not only during the planting event, but also for several years after. With a healthy start and proper ongoing care, a tree may live decades or even hundreds of years.

For specific information about planting trees, see the Tree Planting Checklist student page and remember to check for online resources and local resources in your community (see Getting Ready). There are lots of great videos online about planting trees!

GETTING READY

- Make copies of the Tree Planting Checklist student page or have it available electronically.

- Find out which agencies or organizations are responsible for planting and maintaining trees in your community or in your schoolyard. They might include your municipality's parks department, the city's urban forestry department, nonprofit organizations, or independent garden or community clubs. Within your school, it may be the maintenance department. Students can check the websites of those agencies or organizations for tree-planting information specific to your area.

DOING THE ACTIVITY

1 **COOPERATIVE LEARNING** Ask students to name some areas in the community (such as along city streets and in other public areas, including the school grounds) where trees have been planted. Then have them work in teams to list the benefits that trees provide to people and wildlife in those areas.

2 Use the teams' lists to develop a group list, adding any other benefits you can think of (see Background). Have everyone make a copy of the list.

3 **STUDENT VOICE** Suggest that planting trees is a great way to do something good for the community—and for the planet. Have students work in teams to identify areas in the community or on your site that would be improved by the presence of one or more trees. Remind students to refer to their lists of tree benefits as they consider different planting sites. If you're working with younger students, take them on a walk around the school to locate areas that could be improved by adding a tree.

4 After the students have identified possible sites, have a group discussion about the feasibility of each site. Have students decide which site or sites should be the focus for their tree-planting campaign. With proper supervision, teams can work on multiple sites. Consider the pros and cons of selecting a site on school grounds or city property.

5 ➤ **HIGHER-ORDER THINKING** If you're working with older students, talk to them about contacting the appropriate officials to get permission to plant in the areas they've chosen. Help them learn about tree planting in your community so you can answer these questions together:

- How much money is spent annually on tree care in the community or within the school? How many trees are planted, and where?

- Which species are most often chosen for planting?

- Do any criteria exist for selecting the species that will be planted? If so, what are they? Whether or not such criteria exist, suggest that students consider many factors before deciding on which trees to plant. For example, depending on where they'll be planting, they may want to consider species that are resistant to shade, air pollution, drought, and so forth. It is also important to discuss **invasive species** and why it is important to only plant native, non-invasive species.

- What are some hardships that urban trees face? What is the average lifespan of a city tree?

- How can citizens become involved in planting and maintaining trees on public property? Help students use this information to compose a letter to the appropriate officials requesting permission to plant.

- Who takes care of the trees once they are planted, and how do they care for them?

6 Discuss the importance of a tree maintenance plan. The plan should include a watering schedule, mulching, pruning, damage assessment, and overall care of the tree. It is important to consider who will tend the tree in the summer, when schools are generally not in session and trees experience excessive growth. Work with students to develop a maintenance plan that leverages community resources, including volunteers from the community.

7 After the students have received permission to plant, help students develop the plans for their tree-planting project. For instance, they may decide to raise money to buy trees from a local nursery, or they might ask people to donate trees. You may contact local foresters or nurseries to get help with planning and carrying out the planting. Students can do internet research to find out what kind of tree to plant and the specific requirements for that tree.

8 ➤ **HANDS-ON LEARNING** Have students plant trees and care for them. Start with the planting recommendations on the student page, but also get directions on how to plant and care for the chosen tree species from a nursery. Have students can take digital pictures before and after planting the tree. Keep a scrapbook (digital or print) of the tree over time.

VARIATION: GRADES 3–5

1 Lead a discussion about trees, asking students questions such as: What do you like about trees? How do trees help us? What is your favorite tree? How does planting trees help the world?

2 Choose a location and a tree sapling to plant (see Background and Getting Ready) and involve students in planting the tree. Invite students to write a wish for the tree on butterflies made from recycled paper that they tie to the tree.

3 Have students record data on the tree's height, width, number of branches, and other observations. Collect weekly or monthly data on the tree to track its growth over time.

4 Make a plan for regularly watering the tree until its roots are established and tending the tree into the future.

ACADEMIC STANDARDS

SCIENCE

Practices
- Constructing explanations and designing solutions
- Obtaining, evaluating, and communicating information

Concepts
- Natural resources
- Developing possible solutions
- Cause and effect

ENGLISH LANGUAGE ARTS

Practices
- Speaking and listening: presentation of knowledge and ideas

SOCIAL STUDIES

Practices
- Developing questions and planning inquiries
- Communicating conclusions and taking informed action

Concepts
- Geography: human–environment interactions

ASSESSMENT

Ask students to

- Create a care plan for the newly planted tree in words or pictures. Plans should meet both short- and long-term requirements for trees to live healthy lives.

- Assemble information booklets that other groups could use to plan, execute, and publicize a community tree-planting project. Teams can work on different sections of the booklet that cover, for example, the benefits of tree planting, how to select a site, whom to contact for permission, how to organize volunteer help, securing funding, determining what species to plant, and planting and caring for the trees. Students can include photos, diagrams, drawings, and videos.

ENRICHMENT

- Arrange for a tree-planting ceremony, possibly in conjunction with a special occasion such as Earth Day or Arbor Day. Students should plan the event and contact local media to ask them to cover it.

- Have students make a map of the planting site using graph paper. The map should show the site as it is now and the area the tree canopy will cover when the tree reaches maturity. In order to ensure adequate space for the tree, students should determine its size at maturity and compare the current canopy with what it will be when the tree is mature.

- Have students educate the rest of the school (or community) about the importance of the new tree, including how to take care of it. This would be a great time to discuss and discourage common activities that cause tree damage, including bark stripping, root trampling, and branch breaking.

- Use i-Tree, a suite of free online tools developed by the U.S. Forest Service and other partners (available at itreetools.org), to calculate the dollar value and ecosystem services of trees planted. See PLT's *Teaching with i-Tree* at plt.org/i-tree for this and other activities to use with i-Tree.

- After a tree is planted, the most important aspect of care is to ensure it receives plenty of water. Challenge students to design a catchment system or suitable irrigation system to ensure that their tree receives the water it needs.

NAME _____ DATE _____

Choose Your Site Wisely

The tree you plant today could eventually reach 40–100 feet (12–30 meters) in height, depending on its species.

❏ When choosing a site, look up, around, and down to make sure there will be room for your tree. Plant the tree where its roots will not grow into sewers and pipelines, or under driveways and sidewalks.

❏ Plant your tree well away from buildings and power lines, so that it won't do any damage or need pruning later in its life.

Planting Your Tree

As you prepare the site for planting, keep the tree cool and shaded. Try not to handle the exposed roots during planting, and keep them moist.

If you're planting a sapling (1–4 inches in diameter):

❏ Dig a hole twice as wide and as deep as the root ball.

❏ Build a mound of soil and place the sapling on top of the mound so that it is 2 inches (5 cm) above the hole's bottom.

❏ If the roots are wrapped, remove the burlap.

❏ Fill the hole with soil, tamping it down with your foot and wetting it with water.

❏ Soak the soil around the tree with water to encourage deep rooting.

If you're planting a seedling (less than 1 inch in diameter):

❏ Dig a hole a little deeper than the roots are long.

❏ Fill the hole around the seedling with dirt.

❏ Gently pull the trunk of the seedling up slightly to straighten the roots. Tamp the soil firmly, but not too tightly, or the roots won't be able to collect appropriate amounts of water and nutrients.

❏ Soak the soil around the tree with water to encourage deep rooting.

Giving TLC

A tree is most vulnerable during the first years of its life, and during this time it requires TLC (tender loving care) from friends and stewards.

❏ Protect your tree from pests and animals. You could put a plastic or mesh tree guard around it to keep animals from chewing the bark.

❏ Water it as appropriate for the tree type.

❏ Add a 3- to 4-inch (8 to 10 cm) layer of mulch around the base of the tree to help keep the soil moist and improve soil aeration (mulch should not touch trunk).

Then sit back and enjoy! If it is cared for properly, each tree you plant will flourish, providing you—and all of us—with benefits and beauty for many years.

CAREER CORNER

I LOVE MY GREEN JOB!

TREE NURSERY TECHNICIANS are plant experts who grow and care for trees, either for sale or for planting on public lands. They may water, prune, and weed young trees and maintain a database to track the trees.

By examining trash, students can learn a lot about how and why they throw things away. Students find ways to reduce their community's waste production and improve its management through participation in a service-learning project.

REDUCE, REUSE, RECYCLE

SUBJECTS
Science, Math, Social Studies

PLT CONCEPTS
2.5, 2.7, 5.10

STEM SKILLS
Collaboration, Data Analysis, Problem Solving

DIFFERENTIATED INSTRUCTION
Hands-on Learning, Multiple Solution Pathways, Personal Connections

MATERIALS
Part A: Boxes, pails, or other containers for sorted waste; rubber gloves; scale; labeled recycling bins.

Part B: As needed for chosen project.

TIME CONSIDERATIONS
Preparation: 15 minutes

Activity: Several periods over 1–2 weeks

OBJECTIVES

Students will

- Analyze the solid waste that they generate over a period of time.

- Describe what happens to various types of waste when it's discarded.

- Develop and implement a plan for reducing the amount of solid waste in their community.

BACKGROUND

What is trash? Trash—also called solid waste, rubbish, refuse, and garbage—is the solid materials that we no longer want or need. The EPA estimates the United States produces nearly 270 million tons of trash from homes, businesses, and schools each year (2017 data). On average, each person in the United States generates 4.5 pounds (2 kg) of trash a day. Half of that trash can be recovered from the waste stream and reused, as it is composed of paper (which can be recycled), food waste, and yard trimmings (both of which can be composted).

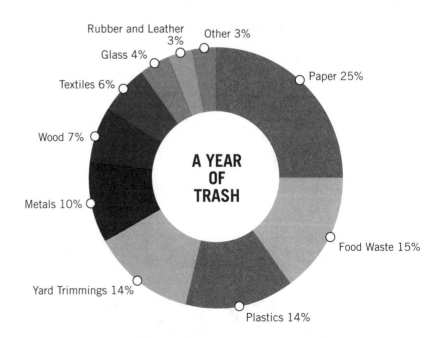

In 2017, Americans generated 270 million tons of trash (before recycling). Paper accounted for 25% (by weight) of the solid waste generated, followed by food waste, plastics, and yard trimmings.

There are several ways to eliminate trash, and some ways are better for the environment than others. You can think of the options as a hierarchy, in which the most environmentally benign approach is used first (see the *Waste Management Hierarchy* reverse pyramid).

SOURCE REDUCTION

The best way to "manage" trash is to not generate it in the first place. Source reduction or waste prevention means decreasing the amount of waste that is produced. People can prevent the creation of trash by buying the right amount of food (not so much that it spoils before they can eat it) or using reusable containers and products instead of accepting disposable ones.

REUSE

Reusing items in a similar or new application instead of tossing them in the trash saves natural resources and cuts down on the amount of waste. Repairing a broken device, reusing a lunch bag, or donating "hand-me-down" clothes to a friend or a thrift store instead of throwing them away are some ways to reuse.

RECYCLING

Recycling means recovering materials like paper and glass for remanufacture into new products or containers. In the United States, 30% of all solid waste and nearly 70% of all paper is recycled, which helps to reduce municipal solid waste, saving both energy and money. However, recycling by itself does not reduce how much waste people generate. Recycling still requires energy and other natural resources. It also requires an end market for the collected materials and reprocessed products. If there is no market for the recycled goods, recycling can't happen.

COMPOSTING

A good method for recycling organic materials like food scraps and yard trimmings is composting. When organic trash is composted, microscopic organisms decompose the material to produce a rich soil that is good for plants and gardens. Many communities have compost programs for yard and kitchen waste to help reduce solid waste.

WASTE MANAGEMENT HIERARCHY

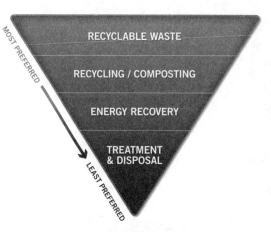

This hierarchy ranks waste management strategies from most to least environmentally preferred.

Source: Sustainable Materials Management, U.S. Environmental Protection Agency, epa.gov

TREATMENT AND DISPOSAL

When trash is not reduced, reused, recycled, or composted, then the final option is disposal. This can occur in several ways:

- **Landfill.** Most of the solid waste in the United States ends up in a landfill, a site where trash is dumped. Once the site has been filled up and the trash is allowed to settle, it is possible to grade a landfill, cover it with sod, and use it as a park, golf course, or wildlife area. Methane gas, a product of the decomposition of trash, is sometimes collected from the landfill and burned to generate electricity. Landfills take up a lot of space, and it is difficult to find sites for them because nobody wants to live near one. Even though they have a special liner to prevent leaking, landfills also can leach hazardous materials (like motor oil and pesticides) into the ground and contaminate the groundwater.

- **Incineration.** Incinerators burn waste and can turn huge piles of garbage into much smaller piles of ash, which must then be disposed. Some incinerators also produce electricity. However, incinerators put greenhouse gases into the atmosphere and can also emit harmful materials.

- **Hazardous Waste.** Household hazardous waste, which consists of cleaning products, oils, paints, electronic devices, batteries, etc., requires special disposal because it is harmful to humans and the environment. Many communities have collection programs for disposing of this waste in the safest manner.

THE WASTE STREAM

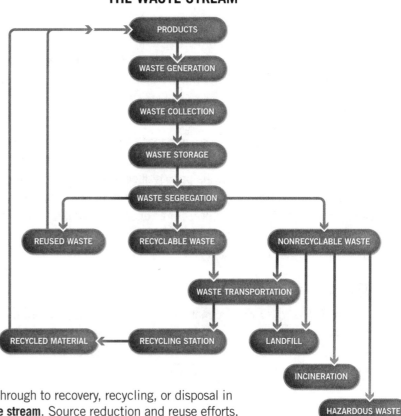

Waste flows from its source through to recovery, recycling, or disposal in a process known as the **waste stream**. Source reduction and reuse efforts, as well as composting, reduce the quantity of waste in the stream. Recycling reduces the quantity that goes to landfills or incineration.

GETTING READY

PART A:

- Procure a large container (or several containers) to hold a week's worth of the group's trash. A large cardboard box, large trash barrel, or several plastic trash bags all work well.

- Be sure to prearrange that the group's collected trash is not removed by maintenance, janitorial services, etc.

- Optional: If you are using the Talking Trash: The Hype on Type student page, make copies or have it available electronically.

PART B:

- See the activity Improve Your Place for more information on planning and carrying out a service-learning project.

DOING THE ACTIVITY

PART A: TAKING OUT THE TRASH

1 Discuss whether it is truly possible to throw something away. Where is "away?" Do these things truly disappear? Can trash continue to affect us even after we've thrown it away? Ask students to guess how much and what kinds of trash they produce. Invite them to propose ways to find out.

2 **PERSONAL CONNECTIONS** Suggest that one way for students to understand how much trash they produce is for them to inspect the amount they generate in a week. Explain that for the next week, everything they want to throw away will be saved for inventory. Use large containers, like the one you've prepared (see Getting Ready), to organize the trash collection. Have students make trash predictions, guessing how much (in pounds or kilograms) they will generate, what categories (paper, food, plastic, etc.) the trash will compose, what category will be the largest, etc. Provide copies of the student page for recording data, if desired.

> ⚠️ **SAFETY CHECK!** Students should wear rubber gloves when sorting trash. Food waste can be collected in a separate container, weighed, recorded, and then eliminated each day to add to the weekly total. Otherwise, they are likely to grow mold by the week's end.

3 **HANDS-ON LEARNING** At the end of a week (or at the end of each day), have students look at their trash. How did the results compare to their predictions? You can sort through the trash and hold up items for examination or have student teams sort the trash to identify and quantify each category. Record results where everyone can see.

4 Challenge students to create graphs or other representations of their data. They can calculate percentages of specific items or categories (such as paper or plastic) and graph them. They may also graph the number of pieces in each category over time.

5 A **waste stream** describes the entire life cycle of garbage produced. Discuss:

- What are the components of the waste stream? (Share a supporting diagram, such as *A Year of Trash* in the Background.)

- What usually happens to trash at the end of each day? (Someone collects it and takes it to a dumpster. You might want to take students to see the dumpster on site).

- Where does the trash end up? (In most cases, someone collects it from the dumpster and takes it to a local landfill, where it is buried, or to a combustor, where it is burned. Recyclable materials that are separated are often taken to a recycling facility.)

- What are the pros and cons of landfills? (Landfills provide easy disposal for large amounts of waste in a relatively sanitary fashion. However, the existing landfills are filling up and it is difficult to find new landfill sites. Landfills can also contaminate the soil and water around them.)

- What are the pros and cons of burning trash? (Burning greatly decreasing the volume of waste, but it emits carbon dioxide and harmful pollutants into the air.)

- What raw materials make up the items in the trash? (Paper comes from trees, metal cans from minerals in the earth, plastics from fossil fuels, fruit from trees and other plants.) How could they be better used or reused?

- What are the effects of single-use items on our supply of natural resources? (Using items only once and then disposing of them means that we must use more nonrenewable raw materials and fossil fuels for energy to create new products.)

6 Have the students look at the trash categories and think of ways to keep some items out of the waste stream. Ask students to suggest how they could reduce, reuse, or recycle specific items they found (for example, only use one paper towel when they are drying their hands; store lunch items in reusable containers; compost food waste; or recycle paper, glass bottles, and aluminum).

TAKE IT OUTSIDE

Lead students on an excursion to pick up litter nearby. Bring along plastic bags for collecting trash (with a separate bag for recyclables), as well as gloves and a pick-up stick, if you have one. Afterward, invite students to reflect on where litter comes from, what kind of litter they saw the most, what can be done to reduce litter, and how it felt to clean up the area.

SAFETY CHECK! Be sure to point out safety precautions. Students should wear gloves when picking up trash and only adults should handle dangerous items.

PROJECT LEARNING TREE
An initiative of SFI

PART B: MAKING A DIFFERENCE

1 ➡️ **MULTIPLE SOLUTION PATHWAYS** Have students develop and carry out a service-learning project to reduce the amount of trash they generate or persuade others to do so. Some suggestions include:

- Set up a "recycling center" for your group. Before beginning a collection, select an appropriate material (aluminum, glass, plastics, and/ or paper) and determine what you will do with it after collection. Find out what your local school, community, or city is already doing, and locate local recycling centers online. Create a pamphlet or poster showing how to set up a group recycling program.

- Set up a swap table. If students have useful items they no longer want, such as old books, toys, games, or clothes, they can bring in items to put on the swap table for others to take.

- Encourage students to create a video, web page, or other product that teaches others why and how to reduce the trash they generate.

- Create a compost pile at your site for grass clippings and other yard debris. Contact your local or state environmental agency for composting regulations.

- Set up a worm box to compost food waste. All you need is a sturdy, ventilated box; some soil and shredded newspaper for "bedding" material; and some worms. Soon you'll have rich compost that's great for gardens and indoor plants. (For more information about setting up a worm box, see the activity Soil Builders [in Grades K–2].)

- Determine whether any disposable or nonrecyclable products used at your site (or at home) could be replaced with reusable products. Have students analyze the costs and benefits of each option (including, for example, the cost of hot water and labor to wash reusable utensils). In some situations, they may find that it is more economical and environmentally sound to use disposable products.

2 After completing the project, help students evaluate and share their results with other students or members of the community.

VARIATION: GRADES 3–5

Challenge students to come up with new inventions or alternate uses for broken items, such as turning a broken aquarium into a planter. Have students bring an item from home that is broken and that they were planning to put in the trash. Put all the items on a table and have students select something they would like to try to fix or find an alternate use for. Your group could have a "trashion" show in which students exhibit the new creations they have made from trash.

ACADEMIC STANDARDS

SCIENCE

Practices
- Analyzing and interpreting data

Concepts
- Human impacts on Earth systems
- Patterns
- Cause and effect

MATH

Practices
- Reason abstractly and quantitatively
- Attend to precision

Concepts
- Ratios and proportional relationships
- Statistics and probability

SOCIAL STUDIES

Practices
- Developing questions and planning inquiries
- Communicating conclusions and taking informed action

Concepts
- Economics: economic decision-making
- Geography: human–environment interactions

ASSESSMENT

Ask students to

- Write about or create a visual display detailing what steps or individual actions they will take to reduce, reuse, or recycle waste.

- Create a waste stream diagram showing what happens to waste that is not reused or recycled, inserting possible pathways to offer diversion, reuse, and recycling.

ENRICHMENT

- Organize a field trip to a landfill, incinerator, or recycling center. Or invite a guest speaker (such as a professional from a solid waste management company) to visit and speak with students.

- Provide each student with three large sturdy paper bags. Label the bags "glass," "aluminum," and "paper." Direct students to take the bags home and set up a home recycling station. Have students keep track of how many days it takes to fill their bags and report back to the group. The information can be recorded on a group chart and used to make graphs, calculate averages, and estimate recycled material.

- Divide the group into teams and have them challenge each other to see which can reduce the most waste from their group average at the beginning.

- PLT's *GreenSchools Investigations* provides a blueprint to create more green and healthy learning environments. Visit plt.org/greenschools to access five investigations for greening your environment: energy, environmental quality, the school site, waste and recycling, and water. Students can conduct a waste and recycling audit to monitor the waste at home, school, or other site, and design and carry out a collaborative plan to reduce the total amount of waste.

PROJECT LEARNING TREE
An initiative of SFI

NAME _____ DATE_____

Collect your daily trash and sort it into different categories. Weigh and count the pieces in each category.

Date	Category	Weight	Number of Pieces

SUM IT UP

At the end of the investigation, total the weight and number of pieces in each category. Calculate the percentage of the total for each category and create a graph comparing them.

Category	Total Weight	Total Pieces	Percent of Total Weight	Percent of Total Pieces
TOTALS				

CAREER CORNER

I LOVE MY GREEN JOB!

RECYCLING MANAGERS oversee and promote recycling programs for communities or businesses. They may also investigate new opportunities for materials to be collected and recycled.

Students model what happens to renewable and nonrenewable resources over time and discover why sustainable use of natural resources is so important.

RENEWABLE OR NOT?

SUBJECTS
Science, English Language Arts, Math, Social Studies

PLT CONCEPTS
1.9, 2.7, 3.7

STEM SKILLS
Collaboration, Communication, Problem Solving

DIFFERENTIATED INSTRUCTION
Cooperative Learning, Higher-order Thinking, Literacy Skills, Multiple Solution Pathways, Nonlinguistic Representations, Student Voice

MATERIALS
Part B: Model 1—popcorn, marbles, math cubes, pennies, or other small tokens in a large jar, 14 paper bags; Model 2—plates, napkins, popcorn; Model 3—signs for world regions, 86 small tokens. Optional: 125 feet (38 m) of rope; Model 4—materials for student-designed models.

TIME CONSIDERATIONS
Preparation: 60 minutes

Activity: One to two 50-minute periods (depending on number of models)

OBJECTIVES

Students will

- Identify and define renewable and nonrenewable resources, explaining the key differences between them.
- Model societal resource use to explore factors that make renewable resources sustainable.

BACKGROUND

Natural resources are the raw materials we use for housing, clothing, transporting, heating, cooking, and more. They include the air we breathe, the water we drink, the land we farm, and the space we use for living and recreation. In short, they are all the things we use in our physical environment to meet our needs and wants. We can put resources into two categories: nonrenewable and renewable.

Nonrenewable resources exist in finite or limited amounts. For example, **fossil fuels** like oil and gas are formed through natural processes that take millions of years. If we use all the available fossil fuels, no additional amounts of them will ever be available to us—at least not for millions of years. Other nonrenewable resources such as copper and other metals were created billions of years ago during the explosions of giant stars. These nonrenewable resources are not created through Earth's natural processes. The only way we could get more of them is to mine other planets.

Renewable resources can be replenished through natural or human processes. For example, even though trees die naturally or are harvested, new trees are naturally reseeded or can be replanted by humans. And even though people consume livestock, new animals are constantly being born. Solar energy and wind energy are renewable resources that are constantly, perpetually restored.

Renewable resources must be managed in **sustainable** ways. This means not using them so fast or in a way that they cannot recover. For example, in the early 1900s, passenger pigeons were hunted so heavily and irresponsibly that the species became extinct. **Grasslands** can become overgrazed to the point that the soil loses its ability to support plant life and the area becomes barren. **Groundwater** supplies may be pumped out of the ground faster than **precipitation** can trickle down to replenish them. Forests may be cut down and converted to housing developments, after which forest will never grow on that land again.

The maximum rate at which people can use a renewable resource without reducing the ability of the resource to renew itself is called the **sustainable yield**. A sustainable yield of timber means harvesting only the volume of trees that the forest can grow during that same time period. This term also applies to water and wildlife. The sustainable yield of any resource varies from region to region, and it can be altered through management.

When people reduce or reuse natural resources, they decrease demand, save energy, and reduce pollution. For example, using a reusable water bottle instead of single-use plastic bottles reduces the need for oil to produce the bottles, releases less carbon dioxide into the atmosphere, and reduces the amount of waste going to landfills.

Another way to reduce the use of natural resources is through **recycling**, which involves treating or processing waste to make it reusable. Recycling requires energy to both collect and process the materials. It also depends on a reliable end market for the collected materials and reprocessed products. While recycling helps sustain natural resources, it is less effective than reducing their use in the first place.

To support using renewable resources sustainably, the United Nations created 17 Sustainable Development Goals. One of the goals is "Life on Land," which protects, restores, and promotes the sustainable use of terrestrial ecosystems, managing forests sustainably, combating desertification, reversing land degradation, and halting biodiversity loss. For more information about wise use of resources, see the activity Reduce, Reuse, Recycle.

GETTING READY

- Make copies of the Clues and Cues student page.

- Decide which models to conduct and prepare accordingly:

MODEL 1—POPCORN GENERATION
- » Fill a large jar or other container with popcorn or other small tokens. Mark 14 slips of paper as follows: two "1st Generation," four "2nd Generation," and eight "3rd Generation." Put the slips into a paper bag or other container.

MODEL 2—GREED VS. NEED

» Gather materials: plates, napkins, and popcorn.

 SAFETY CHECK! If you are using popcorn or other food items, be aware of any allergies among your students. If students will be eating the popcorn, have them wash their hands before doing the modeling exercise.

MODEL 3—GLOBAL MARKETPLACE

» Make signs to post in different parts of the room: Africa, Asia, Europe, Oceania/Australia, North America, and South America.

» Prepare slips of paper, one per student, labeled with a region, according to the *Global Market Allocations* chart. Numbers are provided for a group of 20. For groups of different sizes, adjust these numbers, keeping similar ratios.

» Post (or project) a world map.

» Optional: In lieu of posting signs, have students create their own world map from pre-cut pieces of rope. You will need 15' x 25' of open space. The Global Market Allocations chart offers suitable rope lengths, proportional to actual region size.

GLOBAL MARKET ALLOCATIONS

Region	Students (group of 20)	Resources (or tokens)	Rope length
Africa	4	2	27 ft (8.2 m)
Asia	12	32	40 ft (12.2 m)
Europe	2	22	9 ft (2.7 m)
Oceania/Australia	0	2	7 ft (2.1 m)
North America	1	24	23 ft (7.0 m)
South America	1	4	16 ft (4.9 m)
Totals	**20**	**86**	**122 ft (37.1 m)**

PROJECT LEARNING TREE
An initiative of SFI

DOING THE ACTIVITY

PART A: SORTING WHAT'S WHAT

1  **LITERACY SKILLS** Divide the group into teams of four to examine component parts of the terms "renewable" and "nonrenewable" (without telling them the terms). Assign each team one of the following word parts to define or to provide examples in context: -able, -new, re-, non-

2 Call on teams to report, starting with "-able" and building the two terms in reverse, one part at a time. Record relevant ideas from the group where everyone can see. Once the two terms are revealed (renewable and nonrenewable), ask if anyone has heard these terms before and, if so, in what context. If they don't mention it, point out that these terms are often used to describe different kinds of natural resources.

3 **COOPERATIVE LEARNING** Give each team a copy of the student page. Direct teams to take turns reading the clues aloud to their team. Then, challenge each team to use their clues to synthesize a one-or two-sentence definition for "renewable resources" and "nonrenewable resources." Everyone on the team should understand each of the clues and agree with their team's definitions.

4 Teams should then discuss the questions on the student page, with one member designated to record their responses and one designated to report them.

5 Review the questions with the entire group, asking each team to report. Have students compare their earlier responses with the group's definitions.

PART B: RESOURCE MODELING

Apply these simulations to explore sustainable use and offer students a context for renewable and nonrenewable resources. Use a spreadsheet program to have students record and analyze data from the modeling demonstrations.

MODEL 1—POPCORN GENERATION

1 Have 14 students each draw a slip of paper from the bag. They should not tell anyone what the paper says. Give each of these students a paper bag and explain that they will be part of a modeling exercise.

2 Ask the two 1st Generation students to come up to the big jar of popcorn. Explain that the food in the jar represents the world's supply of a nonrenewable resource. Tell them they can take as much of it as they want. Let them fill their bags while the rest of the group watches.

3 When the 1st Generation students are finished, invite the four 2nd Generation students to go up and take as much of the remaining popcorn as they want. After they've finished, have the 3rd Generation students come up and take what they want.

TAKE IT OUTSIDE

Take students outdoors to look for objects made from renewable and nonrenewable natural resources. For example, a wood fence or bench is made from a renewable resource (trees), while asphalt or blacktop is made from a nonrenewable resource (petroleum). Use a T-chart to record observations.

RENEWABLE	NONRENEWABLE
trees	petroleum

4 Discuss what is happening to the world's popcorn supply:

- What happened to the total amount of the resource?

- How much was left for each successive generation?

- Was anything left for a 4th generation?

- Did any of the students who were part of the demonstration think about those who might be eating after them, or were they only trying to get as much popcorn as they could?

- What parallels do the students see between what happened in the demonstration and what happens in the real world?

- Why does the 1st Generation have only two students, while the 2nd has four and the 3rd have eight? In real life, what happens to the world's population with each successive generation? What does that mean for the use and availability of resources?

5 **STUDENT VOICE** You may choose to have students repeat the demonstration and try different variations. For example, vary the number of students in each generation while the distribution of resources remains the same. Or, students can come up with their own variations to try. Students should realize that as new generations come along, there will be less and less of the resource available to them, and eventually there will be nothing.

MODEL 2—GREED VS. NEED

1 Divide the group into teams of four. Give each team 16 pieces of popcorn on a plate and each student a napkin.

2 **NONLINGUISTIC REPRESENTATIONS** Explain that students will conduct a model in which the popcorn represents the team's supply of a renewable resource that is replenished after each round of play. Each student can take freely from the team's plate supply for their personal napkin supply, minding the following rules:

- At the end of each round, students can eat all the popcorn in their personal supply.

- Each team member needs to take at least one piece per round from the team supply to survive.

3 Round One: Allow students on each team to take freely from their team's popcorn supply. Ask students to record the results.

4 Ask each team how many pieces it has in its team pile and give the team half that number of new pieces. Some teams may run out of resources right away. If so, invite them to observe other teams where all members have survived.

5 Play three or four more rounds, stopping after each to find out if anyone didn't survive. Then provide each team with the prescribed amount of new popcorn.

6 After four or five rounds, have the students share what happened in their teams. In which teams did all the students survive? Which students had the most popcorn in their personal supplies? Which team had the most popcorn in its collective supply? Which teams think they would be able to keep a resource forever as long as the resource kept renewing itself? On these teams, how many pieces were these students taking each round?

7 **HIGHER-ORDER THINKING**
Discuss as a group:

- What are the advantages and disadvantages of using a resource in a sustainable way?

- What advantages and disadvantages are there to using a resource in a nonsustainable way?

- Sustainable yield is the maximum rate that people can use a renewable resource without reducing the ability of the resource to renew itself. What was the sustainable yield in our model? What happened if people used more than the sustainable yield?

- In the model, the popcorn was resupplied each round. What does this represent in real life?

- In this model, the population of each team stayed the same. However, the human population is increasing rapidly. What would have happened if one or two or three more people were added to your team each round?

- How would a natural disaster affect the quantity and quality of resources? How would it affect education systems? Disease? Advanced technology systems?

MODEL 3—GLOBAL MARKETPLACE

1 Optional: Have students create a world map from pre-cut pieces of rope. Split students into six equal teams and give each a piece of rope to outline the general shape of their region. Have them use a world map for reference. They may need some help positioning the regions relative to each other.

2 Have each student pick one of the slips you've prepared (see Getting Ready) and go to the section of the room or the world map for that region. Tell them that they represent the relative population of the regions. Each team should appoint an "ambassador" to represent their region. Display a large world map for reference.

3 Tell the regions that they will receive a certain number of tokens, which represent their Gross Domestic Product (GDP), the total value of goods and services that their region produces in a year). Distribute the tokens according to the Global Market Allocations chart (see Getting Ready).

4 Explain that each person must have at least one token to survive. Students can exchange tokens freely between regions but only the appointed ambassador can leave the team's designated area.

5 ⬅ **MULTIPLE SOLUTION PATHWAYS** Allow the modeling activity to go on for 15 minutes. Let the students work out the token ("resource") inequalities any way they like. Take notes on what you hear and see happening.

6 Announce the end of the model. Discuss the group's experience:

- What was your initial reaction to the distribution of resources? How did you feel when you saw who had what?

- Did you think you would survive? Were you more concerned for others or yourself?

- How did you ask for help? How did it make you feel?

- What did you do with your team's resources? How did the group react?

- What choices are available to nations that do not have enough money to buy resources from other countries?

- What are some important ideas involved in this model?

- What is missing from the model that would make it more realistic?

- What was your overall experience?

MODEL 4—MAKE YOUR OWN

1 After experiencing at least one of the given Models in Part B, challenge student teams to design their own model that examines the sustainability of renewable and nonrenewable resources. Their model can be a physical simulation— like the ones presented here—or it can be a diagram, 3D constructed item, mathematical representation, analogy, or computer simulation.

2 Invite students to begin by formulating a question about renewable and nonrenewable resources. Next, brainstorm possible ways to answer that question using a model. Finally, choose one idea to develop further.

3 Support teams in creating a plan for their model that includes the materials needed and details how the model will be used to answer the question.

4 Optional: Provide materials for them to construct their model, as appropriate.

5 Invite teams to present their models or plans to the group.

ACADEMIC STANDARDS

SCIENCE

Practices
- Developing and using models
- Obtaining, evaluating, and communicating information

Concepts
- Natural resources
- Systems and system models
- Stability and change

ENGLISH LANGUAGE ARTS

Practices
- Language: vocabulary acquisition and use

MATH

Practices
- Model with mathematics

Concepts
- Statistics and probability

SOCIAL STUDIES

Practices
- Applying disciplinary concepts

Concepts
- Economics: economic decision-making
- Economics: exchange and markets

ASSESSMENT

Ask students to

- Write definitions for renewable and nonrenewable resources.

- Use scientific argumentation to explain:

  » If a resource is renewable, does that mean it will always exist?

  » What two factors are most important in determining how fast natural resources are used?

  See Appendix K: Making a Scientific Argument for an example student page using claim, evidence, and reasoning.

- Draw a Venn diagram showing the similarities and differences between renewable and nonrenewable resources, including advantages and disadvantages of each.

- Identify one change that would make a model in Part B more realistic and explain why.

ENRICHMENT

- Choose a familiar or commonly used product, and research what renewable and nonrenewable resources are used to make it. Suggest alternative materials, processes, or products that would be more sustainable. For example, some products, like disposable food containers, are increasingly being made from wood fiber and other renewable sources.

- Research and draw a global map (or regional map) showing where the greatest amounts of resources, such as oil, water, coal, and timber are located. Consider dividing the group into teams and having each research and draw a map for a specific region. Students can then compare their maps with other maps detailing GNP, consumption, or energy use. What conclusions can be drawn? What effects does resource location have on global issues?

ANSWERS TO CLUES AND CUES STUDENT PAGE

1. **Renewable:** corn, geothermal energy (hot springs), sunlight, tides, trees, wind, water. (Although these resources are considered renewable, some can be regionally depleted by nonsustainable management practices.)

   Nonrenewable: coal, gold, natural gas, petroleum (oil), sand.

2. **Answers will vary depending on students' location.** For example, students may suggest using wood as a substitute for plastic or metal in chairs and other equipment.

3. **Answers will vary.** For the list of pros, students may suggest that the materials to make products from renewable resources can always be available, or that making these products creates less pollution. For the list of cons, they may suggest that some materials from nonrenewable resources are superior because they're lighter, stronger, or have other properties, or that using nonrenewable resources is more convenient.

4. **If the students don't come up with answers to this question, don't worry. But, don't give them an answer!** The modeling in Part B should provide students with ideas about conditions under which this could occur.

NAME _____ DATE_____

Have each person in your team read one of the following clues aloud. Then, working as a team, use the clues to write definitions for the terms **renewable resource** and **nonrenewable resource**.

CLUE 1: On Earth, there are limited amounts of fossil fuels such as oil, coal, and natural gas. There are also limited amounts of minerals such as iron, copper, and phosphates. These resources either cannot be replaced by natural processes or require millions of years.

CLUE 2: Some nonrenewable and renewable natural resources can be reused or recycled, to reduce the total amount of new material used. Using a reusable water bottle instead of single-use plastic bottles is an example of reuse. Recycling involves processing waste to make it reusable. For example, the motor oil from a car can be reprocessed into fuels or refined again into lubricating oils.

CLUE 3: Renewable natural resources include plants, animals, and water, when they are properly cared for. Minerals and fossil fuels, such as coal and oil, are examples of nonrenewable natural resources.

CLUE 4: Trees, wildlife, water, and many other natural resources may be restocked by natural processes or by people. Water is continuously cycled and reused. Sunlight, wind, geothermal heat, tides, and flowing water are resources that are constantly renewed or restored.

Renewable resource:

_____
_____
_____
_____

Nonrenewable resource:

_____
_____
_____
_____

CAREER CORNER

I LOVE MY GREEN JOB!

NATURAL RESOURCE ECONOMISTS study the economic effects of decisions about natural resource use. They may analyze the costs and benefits of different options or use sophisticated computer programs to model various scenarios.

STUDENT PAGE

Clues and Cues (cont.)

NAME _____ DATE_____

Work as a team to respond to the following prompts.

1. Categorize the following as renewable or nonrenewable resources and place them in the chart.

    - Coal
    - Corn
    - Geothermal energy (hot springs)
    - Gold
    - Natural gas
    - Petroleum (oil)
    - Sand
    - Sunlight
    - Tides
    - Trees
    - Water
    - Wind

Renewable Resources	Nonrenewable Resources

2. In the chart below, list items you can see around you that are made from renewable and nonrenewable resources. In the third column, list renewable natural resources that could be used instead of the nonrenewable ones.

Items Made from Renewable Resources	Items Made from Nonrenewable Resources	Renewable Resources that Could Be Used Instead

3. What are pros and cons for using renewable natural resources in place of nonrenewable ones?

    Pros: _____

    _____

    Cons: _____

    _____

4. When might a renewable natural resource not be renewable?

    _____

    _____

Using data collected from Mauna Loa, students graph changes in atmospheric levels of carbon dioxide (CO_2) over the course of several decades and identify possible reasons for those changes. They will also explore the relationship among CO_2, the Earth's climate, and local ecosystems and suggest ways to reduce the effects of increased CO_2 levels in the atmosphere.

THE GLOBAL CLIMATE

SUBJECTS
Science, English Language Arts, Math, Social Studies

PLT CONCEPTS
2.8, 4.3, 5.10

STEM SKILLS
Collaboration, Data Analysis, Problem Solving

DIFFERENTIATED INSTRUCTION
Cooperative Learning, Higher-order Thinking, Literacy Skills

MATERIALS
Graph paper, colored pencils, materials for making exhibits.

TIME CONSIDERATIONS
Two to three 50-minute periods

OBJECTIVES

Students will

- Examine and analyze trends in CO_2 levels.
- Learn how an increase in temperature can affect ecosystems.
- Suggest ways to reduce the effects of elevated CO_2 in the atmosphere.

BACKGROUND

The Earth's climate system is complex. **Climate** is the long-term average weather condition in a particular location or region at a particular time of the year. It is affected by what happens not only in the atmosphere, but also in the oceans, the cryosphere (glaciers and ice caps), the geosphere (land areas), and the biosphere (living things).

Earth's atmosphere is a critical component of climate and is vital for life on Earth. This thin blanket of gases and dust includes gases—known as **greenhouse gases**—that allow infrared radiation from the sun to penetrate and also trap heat radiating from the Earth's surface, similar to how a greenhouse traps heat. Earth's greenhouse gases include carbon dioxide (CO_2), nitrous oxide, methane, and water vapor, and occur naturally in the atmosphere. In fact, without this natural process—called the **greenhouse effect**—the planet would be too cold for life.

GREENHOUSE EFFECT

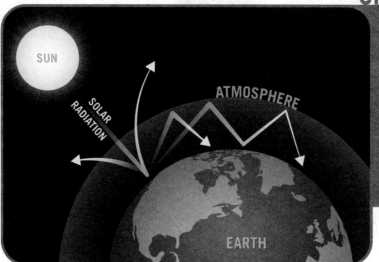

1. The sun's energy warms the Earth's surface.

2. Some of the sun's energy is radiated from the Earth's surface, through the atmosphere, and back into space.

3. When greenhouse gases and water vapor accumulate in the atmosphere, they absorb heat radiated from the Earth's surface and direct it back toward the Earth. As a result, the temperature at the earth's surface may increase.

The concentrations of many greenhouse gases have fluctuated over Earth's history. For several thousand years, however, CO_2 levels were stable at about 280 parts per million (ppm). By looking at air in ice core samples, scientists can see that those levels started to rise at the start of the Industrial Revolution around 1860. By 1958, they were up to 315 ppm and, in 2013, they topped 400 ppm for the first time.

Many natural processes affect CO_2 levels in the atmosphere. Carbon dioxide levels go through an annual cycle: as plants start growing aggressively in the spring, they take up CO_2 and reduce the level in the atmosphere, while in the fall they die back and the levels of CO_2 rise again. Other natural fluctuations that influence CO_2 levels include oceans and soil taking up and releasing CO_2, volcanic eruptions, and weather patterns like El Niño.

The recent increases in CO_2 levels are beyond what are considered normal. They are leading to changes in the Earth's climate that are referred to as **global climate change** or **global warming**. Increased levels of this greenhouse gas trap more heat in the atmosphere, causing a rise in average global temperature.

Most increases in atmospheric CO_2 come from burning fossil fuels to run cars, trucks, airplanes, power plants, and industries. Today, approximately 80% of carbon dioxide emissions are attributed to fossil fuel combustion. The second largest CO_2 source is land-use change, mainly clearing forests for agriculture or development.

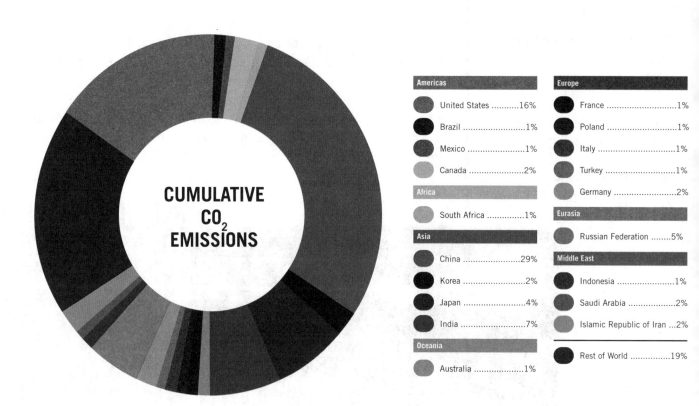

CUMULATIVE CO₂ EMISSIONS

Americas
- United States 16%
- Brazil 1%
- Mexico 1%
- Canada 2%

Africa
- South Africa 1%

Asia
- China 29%
- Korea 2%
- Japan 4%
- India 7%

Oceania
- Australia 1%

Europe
- France 1%
- Poland 1%
- Italy 1%
- Turkey 1%
- Germany 2%

Eurasia
- Russian Federation 5%

Middle East
- Indonesia 1%
- Saudi Arabia 2%
- Islamic Republic of Iran ...2%

- Rest of World 19%

The world's countries emit vastly different amounts of CO_2 into the atmosphere.
Source: "Each Country's Share of CO_2 Emissions." Union of Concerned Scientists, 2020.

FOREST FACT

U.S. and Canadian forests capture more carbon than they release. In one year, for example, carbon storage in U.S. forests can offset approximately 9% of the nation's greenhouse gas emissions.

did you know?

Some effects of global climate change are already evident, including more extreme storm and weather patterns, coastal flooding, and increased wildfires. Understanding the changes in the Earth's climate is one of the biggest questions facing scientists today, particularly in terms of the effects of those changes.

Forests play an important role in atmospheric CO_2. Trees take up CO_2 and release oxygen (O_2) through photosynthesis, transferring the carbon to their trunks, limbs, and roots as they grow. Through this process, forests can store considerable carbon and their growth provides an essential **carbon sink**.

Approximately 2.86 billion tons of CO_2, one-third of the CO_2 released from burning fossil fuels, are absorbed by forests every year. Trees store the carbon, and release helpful oxygen back into the atmosphere. However, scientists predict that the impacts of climate change, including insect outbreaks, fire, drought, and storms, could reduce forests' ability to absorb CO_2. Thus, **sustainable forest management**, which helps ensure the vigor and adaptability of forests, is a critical component of addressing climate change. For more on sustainable forest management, see the activities If You Were the Boss, Every Tree for Itself (in Grades 3–5), and Trees in Trouble (in Grades 3–5).

GETTING READY

- Make copies of the Mauna Loa Atmospheric CO_2 Concentrations student page.

- For Part B, find a podcast, video, or journal article describing a scientific study on the effects of climate change on forests or other ecosystems. If possible, find one specific to your location or region. Make sure that the level is appropriate for your students and identify any vocabulary terms you may need to introduce. Depending on your group, you might have students search for the study. See plt.org/myk8guide for suggestions.

- Note: Be sure to use sources that are reputable. Credible sources will list the author and date of the material and cite their sources.

PART A: CO$_2$ PAST, PRESENT, FUTURE

1 Ask students what carbon dioxide is and where it can be found. Point out that air is about 78% nitrogen, 20% oxygen, 0.9% argon, and 0.04% carbon dioxide. (Rare gases, including helium, krypton, neon, xenon, and radon together make up 0.06%.) Explain that students will be examining the concentration of CO$_2$ in the atmosphere over time.

2 Have students read the Mauna Loa Atmospheric CO$_2$ Concentrations student page. Help students understand that 400 parts per million (ppm) is equal to 0.04% of the total atmosphere.

3 ➡ **COOPERATIVE LEARNING** Divide the group into teams and, depending on the number of teams, assign each team a 5- to 10-year period to graph. Give each team a sheet of graph paper or provide access to graphic software and direct the teams to create the x-axis and y-axis so that the graphs will be uniform in scale. The x-axis should show the years the teams will graph, and the y-axis should show values of CO$_2$ ranging from 300 to 425 ppm.

4 Have the teams graph the data for May and October in one color, connecting the dots, and then graph the annual average in a different color. Ask students to share with the whole group their observations about their graphs.

5 ➡ **HIGHER-ORDER THINKING** Post the graphs in chronological order, linking them along the x-axis to make one large graph. Discuss:

- What pattern do you notice in the graph over 10 years? What pattern do you notice within each year? What could potentially cause this pattern?

- How do the last five years of data compare with the first five years?

- The level of CO$_2$ in the year 1750 was approximately 280 ppm. How does the rise from 1750 to 1958 compare with the rise from 1958 to now?

- What factors might contribute to these patterns?

- Do you think the increase in CO$_2$ was caused by human activities or a different source? Explain.

- How might the change in CO$_2$ affect global society?

- What global societal changes may impact the amount of CO$_2$ in the atmosphere?

- What do you predict the CO$_2$ concentration will be in the year 2050? What assumptions did you make to arrive at this prediction? What impact might this concentration have on climatic conditions?

TAKE IT OUTSIDE

Many people find that getting outside can be an antidote to climate anxiety (feelings of fear or distress about the possibility of environmental change). Invite students to do something physical outside or in nature, such as going for a walk, planting a garden bed, or clearing weeds from a park or nature area. Encourage them to notice how they feel before and after doing the activity.

PART B: ECOSYSTEM EFFECTS

1 Ask your students what they think the term "global climate change" (or "global warming") means. What is the connection between CO_2 levels in the atmosphere and global climate change?

2 Using information from the Background, help students understand the relationship between the levels of CO_2 and air temperature. Ask students: What effect do you think increasing the air temperature by a few degrees (2 degrees Celsius = 3.7 degrees Fahrenheit) will have in our region over time? List their responses where all can see.

3 **LITERACY SKILLS** Share the podcast, video, or journal article describing a scientific study on the effects of climate change on forests or other ecosystems. Introduce any key vocabulary terms. As they listen, watch, or read, direct students to identify what the study tells about the effects of climate change.

4 **HIGHER-ORDER THINKING**
Discuss:

- What were the results of the study?

- Is there anything about the results that surprised you?

- What conclusions might we draw from the study?

- What weaknesses can you identify in the study?

- What might be the impacts of the study?

- Looking at the list of effects we started (in Step 2), what might we add?

5 Challenge student teams to create a physical or virtual exhibit describing what they learned from the study and suggesting something people could do to reduce the effects. Explain that teams will display their exhibits for others to see.

6 **COOPERATIVE LEARNING** Have teams work together to develop a plan for their exhibit, making sure that all team members contribute to the product and are familiar with the content. Encourage students to be creative in presenting the information, including visuals and even sound as appropriate.

7 Allow at least one to two class periods for students to create their exhibits and to share them with the group.

ACADEMIC STANDARDS

SCIENCE

Practices
- Analyzing and interpreting data
- Obtaining, evaluating, and communicating information

Concepts
- Global climate change
- Patterns
- Stability and change

ENGLISH LANGUAGE ARTS

Practices
- Reading informational text: integration of knowledge and ideas
- Speaking and listening: presentation of knowledge and ideas

MATH

Practices
- Model with mathematics

Concepts
- Statistics and probability

SOCIAL STUDIES

Practices
- Evaluating sources and using evidence
- Communicating conclusions and taking informed action

Concepts
- Geography: human–environment interactions

ASSESSMENT

Ask students to

- Extend their graph from Part A to show their prediction for CO_2 levels in 20 years if present trends continue.

- Present their exhibit from Part B and explain its key points.

- Construct an argument related to atmospheric CO_2 levels or the effects of climate change on forests or other ecosystems, using data from the activity to support it. See Appendix K: Making a Scientific Argument for a sample student page for organizing a claim, evidence, and reasoning.

ENRICHMENT

- Conduct an energy audit of your school to look for ways to save energy and reduce CO_2 emissions using PLT's *Energy Investigation*, available at plt.org/greenschools. This is one of five *GreenSchools Investigations*, which provide a blueprint for students to assess energy, environmental quality, waste and recycling, and water at their school site.

- Have students investigate the carbon cycle and make a diagram of the different components of the cycle. See PLT's Carbon & Climate E-Unit (plt.org/eunits) for ideas on how to introduce the carbon cycle to students.

- Encourage students to use internet resources to research the ice core data from the Law Dome and Vostok, Antarctica. These data provide information on CO_2 levels going back about 400,000 years. Students can compare these findings with the levels being measured today.

- Investigate ambient CO_2 levels in your region and at your site. Many public health offices have CO_2 monitoring devices that they can loan to educators. You can also purchase CO_2 monitoring devices from science supply vendors.

- Participate in Budburst, a community science program that collects data about the effects of climate change by looking for and report the timing of different plants' first leaf, first flower, and first fruit each year.

- Invite students to conduct a survey of the trees on or near your site to find out how much carbon they store. Using i-Tree, a suite of free online tools developed by the U.S. Forest Service (available at itreetools.org), students can identify and measure trees and calculate the ecosystem services they provide, including carbon storage. For more information, see PLT's *Teaching with i-Tree* at plt.org/i-tree.

- Plant a tree at your site and have students determine how much carbon the tree could store store (sequester) over its lifetime. See *Teaching with i-Tree* (above) and the activity Plant a Tree for more information.

PROJECT LEARNING TREE
An initiative of SFI

Mauna Loa Atmospheric CO₂ Concentrations

STUDENT PAGE

NAME _____ DATE _____

Since 1958, scientists have measured the amount of CO_2 in the Earth's atmosphere from a site on the Mauna Loa volcano in Hawaii. This site is one of the best locations in the world for measuring CO_2 because there are no plants or human activities nearby to influence the measurements. Any volcanic venting of gas may be excluded from the record. The Mauna Loa data are a precise record of the concentration of atmospheric CO_2 in the region.

Using the data in the table, graph the concentrations of CO_2 for May and October from 1958 to 2020. Using a different color, graph the annual average for each year.

	May	Oct	Annual Average		May	Oct	Annual Average
1958	317.50	312.44	--	1990	357.16	351.18	354.19
1959	318.29	313.26	315.98	1991	359.33	352.21	355.59
1960	320.03	313.84	316.91	1992	359.66	353.31	356.37
1961	320.58	315.38	317.64	1993	360.28	353.99	357.04
1962	321.01	315.42	318.45	1994	361.68	355.99	358.89
1963	322.24	315.99	318.99	1995	363.79	357.76	360.88
1964	322.24	316.79	--	1996	365.41	359.60	362.64
1965	322.16	317.30	320.04	1997	366.79	360.77	363.76
1966	324.01	318.10	321.38	1998	369.30	364.23	366.63
1967	325.00	319.31	322.16	1999	371.00	365.13	368.31
1968	325.57	320.25	323.05	2000	371.82	366.73	369.48
1969	327.34	321.78	324.63	2001	374.02	368.09	371.02
1970	328.07	323.16	325.68	2002	375.55	370.25	373.10
1971	328.92	323.57	326.32	2003	378.35	373.01	375.64
1972	330.07	325.06	327.45	2004	380.63	374.24	377.38
1973	332.48	327.18	329.68	2005	382.28	376.88	379.67
1974	333.09	327.37	330.25	2006	384.95	379.06	381.84
1975	333.96	328.34	331.15	2007	386.39	380.81	383.55
1976	334.87	328.94	332.15	2008	388.45	382.73	385.34
1977	336.74	331.16	333.90	2009	390.18	384.38	384.35
1978	338.01	332.55	335.51	2010	392.94	387.18	389.78
1979	339.47	333.86	336.85	2011	394.16	389.00	390.45
1980	341.46	336.02	338.69	2012	396.74	391.05	392.46
1981	342.91	336.86	339.93	2013	399.78	393.70	395.19
1982	344.13	337.86	341.13	2014	401.78	396.03	397.12
1983	345.75	339.99	342.78	2015	403.96	398.29	399.41
1984	347.43	341.35	344.42	2016	407.72	401.59	402.85
1985	348.93	342.80	345.90	2017	409.69	403.63	405.00
1986	350.21	344.17	347.15	2018	411.24	406.00	407.38
1987	351.84	346.36	348.93	2019	414.66	408.52	411.43
1988	354.22	348.88	351.48	2020	417.31	411.51	414.24
1989	355.67	349.99	352.91				

Mauna Loa Observatory, NOAA Global Monitoring Division.

Source: National Oceanic and Atmospheric Administration. https://www.esrl.noaa.gov/gmd/ccgg/trends/data.html.

CAREER CORNER

I LOVE MY GREEN JOB!

CARBON MODELERS work with forest owners to quantify the carbon being stored or sequestered in their forest. Using this information, owners sell "carbon credits" to companies that emit carbon dioxide (and are required to offset their emissions by buying credits) as a way to reduce overall carbon emissions.

Students explore the environmental, social, and economic criteria of forest certification and consider possible benefits and limitations of certification for both forests and people. They then examine the steps involved in making a certified forest product and the importance of certifying each step of the process.

WHAT'S IN A LABEL?

SUBJECTS
Science, English Language Arts, Math, Social Studies

PLT CONCEPTS
1.9, 2.6, 2.9, 5.5

STEM SKILLS
Collaboration, Creativity, Organization

DIFFERENTIATED INSTRUCTION
Multiple Solution Pathways, Personal Connections

MATERIALS
Part A: Two identical spiral-bound notebooks, sticky notes or other labels.

Part B: Scissors, tape or glue, large pieces of drawing paper.

TIME CONSIDERATIONS
Preparation:
Part A: 20 minutes
Part B: 20 minutes

Activity:

Part A: Doing the Activity: One 50-minute class period
Part B: Doing the Activity: One 50-minute class period

OBJECTIVES

Students will

- Describe and define forest product certification.

- Articulate ways that certification benefits the environment, the people who rely on forests, and the end consumer.

- Identify how chain of custody substantiates the certification process.

BACKGROUND

Healthy forests are a critical part of the web of life. Forests provide a range of **ecosystem services**: they support biodiversity, purify water, release oxygen through leaves, filter air pollutants, and absorb carbon dioxide, which helps to stabilize the global climate. They also provide us with valuable resources like wood, food, and medicines.

Forest certification is one approach to ensure that a forest is managed in a sustainable way. Sustainable forestry may be defined as forest management that meets the needs of the present without compromising the ability of future generations to meet their own needs. (Source: Sustainable Forestry Initiative Standards Rules and Regulations: Section III: SFI Definitions. 2015, February 15.) It involves managing, growing, nurturing, and harvesting trees for useful products and ecosystem services and reforesting areas that have been harvested. Certified forests meet certain standards for environmental, social, and economic practices. These standards are intended to protect water quality, biodiversity, wildlife habitat, and species at risk and to provide economic and community benefits, while ensuring a vigorous and healthy future forest.

An important component in forest certification is the tracking of the certified forest material from forest management through manufacturing of the product. That way, when consumers buy a product with a forest product certification claim, they can be sure that it came from responsible sources. This is called **chain of custody** certification. Chain of custody tracks certified forest content, uncertified forest content, and recycled content (as applicable). Information about chain of custody is often communicated through an ecolabel, which provides a visual cue to a consumer that the product comes from a responsibly managed forest. The two most common forest certification labels in the U.S. are Sustainable Forestry Initiative (SFI) and Forest Stewardship Council (FSC).

FOREST FACT

Forests are certified on public lands, private lands, Indigenous and Tribal Lands, university lands, conservation lands, and community lands.

did you know

While forest certification has many benefits, there are also some potential limitations. For example, small landowners may be less likely to participate in the program because it is too expensive for them, and they may not be aware that group certification through some certifying organizations is a possibility for them. Also, whereas forest management, social laws, and environmental claims in the United States and in Canada are highly regulated, that is not the case in all countries, so it may be more difficult to certify forest products from international sources.

Project Learning Tree is an initiative of the Sustainable Forestry Initiative, a non-profit organization which advances forest sustainability through its work across the areas of conservation, community engagement, education and through its certification standards.

GETTING READY

PART A:

- If you are using notebooks, attach a sticky note or other label to each, and label one "Notebook A" and one "Notebook B." Leave room on the label to add price and other information (see Doing the Activity – Part A, Step 2).

PART B:

- For Part B, make copies of the Making a Paper Bag student page. (Students cut apart the student page in Part B, Step 5, but you may choose to cut apart and laminate copies ahead of time.) Gather other materials. For information about the paper-making process, see the activity Make Your Own Paper (in Grades K-2).

DOING THE ACTIVITY

PART A: FOREST CERTIFICATION

1 **PERSONAL CONNECTIONS** Introduce the activity by having students imagine that they need to buy a spiral-bound notebook for school. Ask, "How will you decide which notebook to buy?" Put students in pairs and have each pair list the purchasing factors they would consider. Invite a few pairs to share their most important factors with the group.

2 Have students imagine that when they get to the store, there are only two spiral-bound notebooks—Notebook A and Notebook B—available and they look pretty much the same. Display the example notebooks and ask them to raise their right hand to indicate that they would buy the notebook on the right side of the room, or their left hand to indicate the notebook on the left side. Read the information that follows and allow them to change their choice after each statement if they wish, choosing on the basis of the cumulative data.

- Notebook A costs $3.99 and Notebook B costs $2.99. (Write the price on each label.)

- The paper in Notebook A contains at least 50% paper from sustainably harvested forests and Notebook B's paper was not sustainably harvested. (Write "50% sustainable" on Notebook A.)

- Notebook A's other 50% paper fiber is from recycled content and Notebook B's paper fiber is from unknown sources. (Write "recycled content" on Notebook A.)

- The company that made Notebook A works to support the local community and the one that made Notebook B does not. (Write "supports community" on Notebook A.)

3 Lead a discussion about the notebooks, asking:

- How did your choice change as you got more information about the two notebooks?

- How does your notebook choice affect forests? Communities? What else might your choice affect? (List ideas in a visible location.)

- When you are at the store, you can see the price of an item. How would you know about these other factors?

4 Introduce the term "forest certification" and ask students what they think it might mean. You might ask them whether they've ever received a certificate for taking a class or completing a program and to describe what it means to certify something.

5 Point out that forest certification is a process in which an independent certification body makes sure the forest management organization, the sawmill or paper mill, and the manufacturers meet certain requirements. Once the entire manufacturing chain is certified, they can put a forest certification label on the final product to show consumers that it meets those requirements. Explain that the requirements for forest certification typically cover three categories:

- Environment: positively contributing to the health of the forest and ecosystem, biodiversity, wildlife, water and soils

- Economics: using resources efficiently over time

- Social: taking responsibility for the well-being of people

Ask students to think of examples for each of these categories. (For instance, for environment, they might name protecting wildlife or minimizing air pollution. For economics, they might name recycling materials or not wasting water. For social, they might mention supporting the local community.)

6 **MULTIPLE SOLUTION PATHWAYS** Invite students to imagine that their job is to certify forests. Have teams of two to four students create a list of requirements they would include in their certification system. Challenge them to include requirements under the categories of Environment, Economic, and Social and to put a star next to the five requirements they think are most important. Ask several teams to share their list.

7 Lead a class discussion:

- Which requirements did several of our teams identify?

- Which requirements are most important for the people who live in or near the forest? For consumers? For the business making or selling the product? For the forest?

- Why would landowners or forest managers find value in certification?

- What might be some of the costs or limitations of forest certification?

- What are your thoughts about forest certification?

PART B: CHAIN OF CUSTODY

1 Introduce the concept of "chain of custody," which tracks the flow of paper fiber from certified forests, noncertified forests, and recycled materials. Explain that in legal contexts, chain of custody means recording physical or electronic evidence every time it changes hands or locations. Ask why this might be important. Point out that, similarly, forest certification uses chain of custody procedures to ensure that a product comes from certified sources.

2 Explain that students will be exploring this concept using a paper grocery bag as an example. Ask students: How could we prove that a grocery bag comes from a certified forest? What various steps would we need to track?

3 Divide the group into the same teams as in Part A. Give each team a copy of the Making a Paper Bag student page. Point out that a paper bag is made from a mix of certified paper, noncertified paper, and recycled paper.

4 Direct students to cut apart the steps for manufacturing a paper bag and to sequence them in a way that shows the process from beginning to end. (Note that the sequence will not be in a straight line, as certified, noncertified, and recycled pulp come from different sources before they are mixed together to make the paper.) Have them tape or glue the steps onto a large piece of paper, creating a chain of custody diagram.

5 Have the teams indicate on their chain of custody diagram which of their requirements from Part A go with what steps on their diagram.

6 When the diagrams are complete, ask students to present them to the group and explain their rationale. Discuss:

- At which part of the chain is each category—Environment, Economic, or Social—most prominent?

- Are there any additional certification requirements you would want to add?

- How might the chain of custody be different for other forest products (for example, wood for construction, or a paper notebook)?

- Why is it important to track the chain of custody when certifying a forest product?

- What challenges or problems does the certification process present? How would you resolve them?

TAKE IT OUTSIDE

Conduct a relay race using the Making a Paper Bag student page, challenging teams to get the steps in the right order. Line up teams of students, one behind the other, and place a set of bag-making steps some distance away from the first team member for each team. (To avoid confusion, leave out the noncertified forest and the recycled pulp.) On a signal, the first team member moves to the set, chooses the first step in the paper-making process, and then returns to the back of the line. Continue this way until all the steps have been selected. Have teams check whether team members retrieved the steps in the correct order.

CHAIN OF CUSTODY SEQUENCE KEY

Here is the suggested order for the steps in the Making a Paper Bag student page (the letters correspond to the images in the student page):

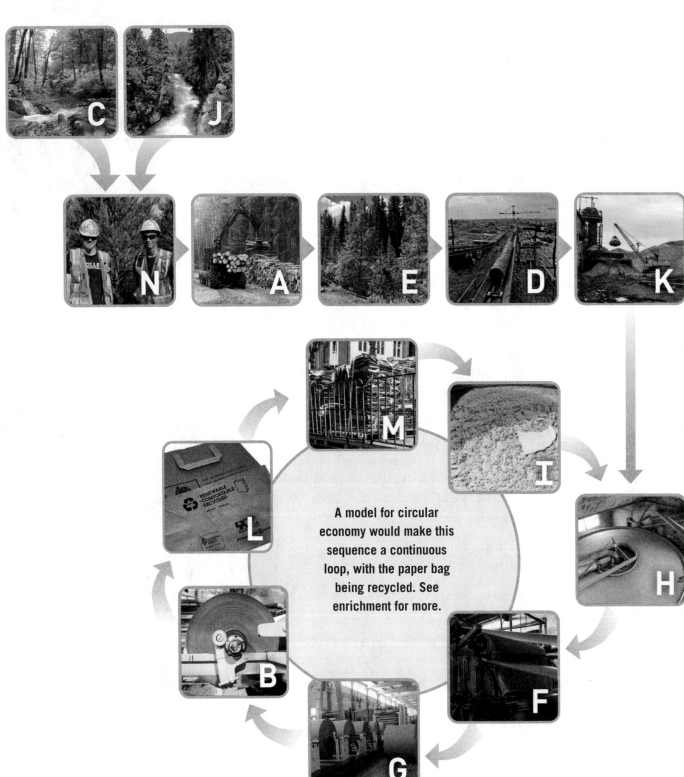

A model for circular economy would make this sequence a continuous loop, with the paper bag being recycled. See enrichment for more.

ACADEMIC STANDARDS

SCIENCE

Practices
- Constructing explanations and designing solutions
- Obtaining, evaluating, and communicating information

Concepts
- Human impacts on Earth systems
- Systems and system models

ENGLISH LANGUAGE ARTS

Practices
- Writing: production and distribution of writing
- Speaking and listening: presentation of knowledge and ideas

MATH

Practices
- Reason abstractly and quantitatively

Concepts
- Ratios and proportional relationships

SOCIAL STUDIES

Practices
- Applying disciplinary concepts

Concepts
- Economics: economic decision-making
- Economics: exchange and markets

ASSESSMENT

Ask students to

- Present chain of custody diagrams to demonstrate their learning about forest product certification and its benefits.
- Write an essay or blog post describing the factors they would consider when buying a forest product in the future. They should support their response with details or examples.

ENRICHMENT

- Invite a guest to speak with the class about certified forest products available in your community. Possibilities include a forest manager; a manager from a lumber yard, do-it-yourself store, or supermarket; a forest product distributor; or a graphic designer or printer. Help students brainstorm a list of questions to ask your guest, such as:
  » What certified products does your company offer?
  » Where do the products come from?
  » Who certifies the products?
  » What certifying factors are most important to you?
  » What are obstacles or other downsides of certification?
- Challenge students to conduct a "scavenger hunt" to look for certification labels at your site or in their homes, including forest product certification and other certification programs such as organic, fair trade, GMO-free, and so on. Ask students to bring in the actual products or to take pictures of the product labels. For one or more of the labels they find, have them research and identify what the label signifies.
- Encourage students to research the chain of custody steps for another forest product and to share their findings with classmates.
- Visit a local forest, sawmill, paper mill, or recycling center that either does or does not participate in forest product certification. Encourage students to ask questions about the benefits and challenges of the certification process.
- Challenge students to research models of **circular economy** and then to revisit the chain of custody sequence for the paper bag to look for ways to create a continuous loop.

NAME _____ DATE_____

Cut apart the following steps for manufacturing a paper bag. Sequence them in a way that shows the process from beginning to end. (Hint: The steps may not form one straight line.)

Trees are harvested and cut into logs.

A

The sack-making machine folds and glues the sheets of paper.

B

A certified forest is managed sustainably so that it meets standards for environmental, social, and economic criteria.

C

Logs are sent to a mill, where they are tumbled to remove their bark.

D

NAME _____ DATE_____

Trees are planted to ensure healthy forests for decades to come. They support biodiversity, wildlife habitat, and recreation and produce fiber to make wood products.

E

The pulp mixture moves through a series of rollers that press and dry it into rolls of paper.

F

At the bag assembling plant, a sack-making machine cuts rolls of paper into sheets.

G

At the paper mill, 70% certified paper pulp, 15% noncertified paper pulp, and 15% recycled paper pulp are mixed together with water.

H

NAME _____ DATE _____

Recycled paper is deinked, cleaned, and cooked to make recycled paper pulp.

I

Healthy forests are a critical part of the web of life. But not all forests are certified by certifying organizations, and their use does not always meet environmental, social, and economic standards.

J

Debarked logs are either put through grinders or cooked in a chemical solution to break down the wood into paper pulp. The process is the same for certified and noncertified forests.

K

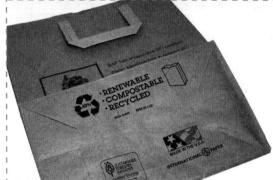

A printing machine prints the store name and forest product certification label on the bag.

L

NAME _____ DATE _____

Recycled paper is gathered at recycling centers and sent to a paper recycling mill.

M

Foresters monitor growing trees to ensure the forest remains healthy and continues to provide a range of benefits, including wildlife habitat, recreation, and future wood products.

N

CAREER CORNER

I LOVE MY GREEN JOB!

PAPER MANUFACTURERS run paper-making machines in a paper mill and inspects the finished products to ensure that they are high quality.

APPENDICES

INDICES

APPENDICES & INDICES

explore your environment

Teaching to Standards

Academic standards ensure that all students acquire the skills and knowledge necessary for college- and career-readiness. They focus on practices and concepts that enable student success in core discipline areas.

PLT helps you meet academic standards by

- Identifying standards connections for each activity.

- Providing lesson plans that are based on rigorous content and the application of knowledge through higher-order thinking skills.

- Emphasizing hands-on, student-centered learning activities.

- Grounding student learning in real-world applications.

- Supporting differentiated instruction to reach diverse students. (For more information about differentiated instruction, see Appendix F: Differentiated Instruction.)

THE STANDARDS

In the United States, each state defines its own education standards and curriculum mandates for schools, so exact curriculum connections vary by jurisdiction. However, many states use national standards as the foundation for their state-specific standards. The activities in this guide are built around these national standards:

STANDARDS CONNECTIONS

To help educators link instruction to standards requirements, each activity in the guide includes an Academic Standards graphic, which lists the disciplinary practices and content areas incorporated in the activity.

For each activity, you can also find detailed connections to NGSS at plt.org/myk8guide, a chart for each activity that identifies the relevant NGSS standards language, specific ways that the activity helps teach toward the standards, and suggestions for deepening NGSS connections.

We invite you to use the information provided to identify curriculum links for your specific subject areas or content areas of interest. For state-specific standards information, contact your PLT State Coordinator at plt.org/yourstate.

NEXT GENERATION SCIENCE STANDARDS (NGSS)+

COMMON CORE STATE STANDARDS— ENGLISH LANGUAGE ARTS (CCSS.ELA)++

COMMON CORE STATE STANDARDS—MATHEMATICS (CCSS.MATH)++

C3 FRAMEWORK FOR SOCIAL STUDIES (C3)+++

In collaboration with state partners, the development of these National Academic standards was primarily championed by the following institutions:

+ The National Research Council, the National Academy of Sciences, Achieve, American Association for the Advancement of Science, and National Science Teaching Association.

++ The National Governors Association and Council of Chief State School Officers.

+++ The National Council for the Social Studies, Center for Civic Education, American Bar Association, National Geographic Society, and more.

Tips for Teaching Outdoors

Many of the activities in this guide involve taking students outside. Learning outdoors has many benefits for students and educators alike. Here are some tips for making these outdoor learning experiences as successful as possible for both you and your students.

WHY TEACH OUTDOORS

The outdoors—whether it's a natural area, a local park, or a parking lot—provides a rich and diverse "laboratory" for learning about the environment. It can foster a sense of wonder, deepen people's connections to their community, and encourage them to engage in environmental stewardship.

Both structured and unstructured time outside can promote academic learning, as well as mental and physical health, by improving learners' attentiveness, self-discipline, and interest in learning. For more about the benefits of learning outdoors, see the activity Get Outside! (in Grades 3–5).

WHAT TO TEACH OUTDOORS

When you are planning what to teach outside, look for this icon ✪, which identifies activities in this guide that are particularly well-suited for outdoor learning. In these activities, students make observations, conduct investigations, or collect data outdoors.

Like all PLT activities, they are designed to be flexible, so don't worry if the only outdoor space you have is a ball field or a city block. You can do the activities in a variety of settings.

In addition, all activities in this guide suggest other ways to get students outside and learning. Look for the Take It Outside! call-out boxes, which offer ideas for extending the activity's learning into the outdoors.

HOW TO BEGIN

If you are new to teaching outside, you may be worried about managing student behavior or about handling some of the logistics. But we encourage you to stick with it, as the benefits can outlast any temporary bumps.

You may find that it helps to think of the outdoors as simply an extension of your teaching space. It doesn't have to be any more complicated than that! Of course, the farther afield you go with students, the more planning and forethought will be required.

We suggest beginning small by staying close to the school building and going outside for a brief exercise. In addition:

- Have a focused task for students, such as making leaf rubbings from a nearby tree or listening to a read-aloud story. For other simple suggestions, see the activity Adopt a Tree (in Grades K–2).

- Prepare students in advance by letting them know that this is a learning experience, not play time. Use positive reinforcement to reward the behavior you want them to exhibit.

- Back inside, discuss with students how it went, what they liked about learning outdoors, and what might make it more successful next time.

- If students have trouble following the rules, consider having another adult take one or two small groups at a time outside to complete the task, while the rest of the students work indoors.

- Be patient and allow students to practice appropriate behavior. Eventually they will get used to investigating the outdoors in an appropriate fashion.

WHAT IS OUTDOOR LEARNING?

There is a subtle difference between outdoor learning and just going outside to learn or play—though both can be valuable.

By **outdoor learning**, we mean that students are interacting in some way with the environment around them to learn more about it. Observing insects that live in a tree is an example of outdoor learning. It differs from doing a math worksheet while sitting under a tree or playing a game of tag, both of which involve being outdoors, but neither of which necessarily involve students in learning about their surroundings.

Many of the Take It Outside! activities we suggest are outdoor learning activities that engage students in exploring their environment. Others are ideas for simply getting outside. Both approaches are supported in this guide, and we invite you to try different ways of teaching outdoors.

PLANNING FOR LONGER EXCURSIONS

When you are ready to lead longer or more involved outdoor learning experiences, we recommend thinking through some of the details in advance to ensure success. For example:

- Review the activity ahead of time, paying particular attention to safety considerations, which are marked with the **SAFETY!** ⚠ icon.

- Check out in advance the outdoor area you plan to use. Note any potential hazards and mark or remove them. Identify boundaries for the activity. Get any necessary permission to use the site.

- Gather all necessary materials and equipment for the activity, including science journals or clipboards for taking notes.

- Set clear rules and learning expectations for students. Safety rules may include:

  » Stay within the boundaries.

  » Stay with your partner.

  » Be aware of your surroundings.

  » Be cautious when lifting boards or rocks to look underneath.

  » Be respectful of all living things, including plants. Do not injure them in any way.

- Set up a meeting signal to get everyone together, such as raising your hand, clapping several times, or using a bird call.

- Be sure students have appropriate clothing and footwear for the weather and for exploring the site.

- Find out whether any of your students are allergic to anything in the outdoors—such as pollen or bee stings—and plan accordingly. Point out any dangerous plants to students at the beginning of the activity, so they know what to avoid.

- Bring along a basic first-aid kit.

- Ask parent volunteers or older students to help with the group.

- Consider assigning different teams of students to different tasks or locations within the study area. This will reduce the group's disturbance of the area and increase students' likelihood of seeing animals.

- Let students pair up and then have the pairs "count off." When you need to make sure all students are present, gather the group and have the first pair begin counting.

ABOUT COLLECTING

In order to model respect for all living things and to minimize the impact on organisms, we recommend limiting any collection of plant materials or animals.

If you decide to have students collect some organisms for closer observation, follow these rules:

- Never collect material from an area unless you have the landowner's permission. You may not collect any material from national or state parks, nature preserves, or land and water reserves.

- Never collect rare or endangered species. Your state Department of Natural Resources or local cooperative extension service can tell you if there are any such species in your area.

- Only take flowers, leaves, seeds, or other plant materials from the ground; do not pick them off living plants. Fall and late spring are great times to collect plant specimens.

- Be gentle when handling organisms. Be aware that some animals might bite or sting to protect themselves.

- Take care when keeping living organisms in a container. Make the animal as comfortable as possible and provide for its basic needs.

- Return all organisms to the spot they were found as soon as the observations are complete.

MORE TIPS

In addition to the tips here, activities marked with this icon ⚫ incorporate suggestions for conducting and managing learning outside.

SOURCES

Angell, Kathy. "Helpful Hints for Leading Outdoor Activities." *A Child's Place in the Environment.* Sacramento, CA: California.

Satterlee, Donna J. *Exploring the Great Outdoors with Your Child.* University of Maryland Eastern Shore, National Association for the Education of Young Children (NAEYC).

Many people think that "the environment" refers only to areas that are separate from humans. However, the environment is really the sum of living and nonliving components that affect people and other organisms. It includes both natural areas *and* dense cityscapes. The environment influences people, and people both depend on and influence the environment.

According to the U.S. Census Bureau, more than 70 percent of the U.S. population lives and works in urban areas of 50,000 or more people, and the percentage is steadily rising.[1] That means that most U.S. students and their families are city dwellers.

HOW PLT CAN HELP

The activities in this guide encourage learners to investigate the world around them, wherever they may be. PLT's mission is to advance environmental literacy so that every student sees the benefits of trees and forests—even in urban settings where they might not be as obvious. Activities that are particularly suited to urban settings are denoted with 🏢.

PLT helps teach about the environment in urban settings through activities that

- **Value urban environments as well as natural ones.**
  Learners can gain an understanding of their connection to the community, the world, and natural systems while exploring the environment right where they are. An urban environment is a vital and rich environment worthy of study and exploration, whether it is a city sidewalk or an urban forest.

- **Demonstrate that we all depend on natural systems to survive.** No matter where you live, everyone needs food, water, air, space, and natural resources, and PLT activities help to show these connections. For example, the activity Water Wonders explores the water cycle, Soil Builders explores how decomposition of dead matter creates healthy soil, and We All Need Trees examines the natural resources we use for building materials and other products.

- **Celebrate diversity.** Just as diversity is an asset in nature—where more variety means a more sustainable system—diversity is also an asset in human communities. Urban environments are not only more densely populated but also often more racially and ethnically diverse than many rural environments. PLT activities encourage learners to share and value diverse perspectives as they explore and examine diverse landscapes. In addition, the activities identify specific opportunities for educators to meet individual learner needs through differentiated instruction techniques.

- **Help students to see nature in the city.** Even if children have never smelled a pine tree or listened to chirping crickets, they can find nature all around them. Sometimes all they need is an invitation to focus on it. Where practical, PLT activities encourage learners to carefully observe their world, taking note of what they see, hear, smell, and feel on city sidewalks or parks. For example, the activity Adopt a Tree can help students focus on a single tree at their school or neighborhood over the course of a year.

- **Get students outside, exploring, and asking questions.** Most children—especially children who live in urban communities—spend more time inside, more time using screens, and less time exposed to natural environments than children in the past. Taking kids outdoors gets them moving and thinking, fosters their love of community, and engenders hope. To support increased time outside, PLT activities include a simple Take It Outside! suggestion that encourages teaching and learning outdoors.

- **Provide urban, suburban, and rural examples whenever possible.** Most PLT activities provide a range of suggestions to deepen a group's exploration of the activity topic and offer urban-focused examples where appropriate. For example, the activity Trees As Habitats provides a variation for urban settings, Tree Cookies offers an urban-based story, Environmental Justice for All includes an urban case study, and Water Wonders suggests exploring the water cycle through an urban lens. Educators are also encouraged to adapt any of the activities for their own settings.

---

1 "New Census Data Show Differences Between Urban and Rural Populations." U.S. Census Bureau, 2016.
Available at https://www.census.gov/newsroom/press-releases/2016/cb16-210.html.

- **Inspire children to learn about the place they live and the community that supports them.** PLT activities help students explore the living and nonliving components of their community—wherever it may be—which helps them better understand how the world works and what sustains them. For example, the activity Did You Notice? invites students to identify short- and long-term changes in their local environment and identify areas for improvement. By learning about where they live, students are empowered to make the world a better place, starting within their own school or community.

Please share your additional ideas for using PLT in urban settings by submitting them to plt@forests.org. We will post resources on our website.

RESOURCES

Urban Environmental Education. Edited by Alex Russ. 2015. Ithaca, NY and Washington, DC: Cornell University Civic Ecology Lab, NAAEE and EECapacity. Available at https://naaee.org/eepro/resources/urban-environmental-education.

PROJECT LEARNING TREE
An initiative of SFI

The term **nonformal education** refers to the wide array of educational activities that occur outside the school-based education system. These types of programs can be more flexible than formal education programs—both in terms of organization and methods—and can often respond more easily to the needs of individuals and specific groups in the community. They help to create learning spaces outside classrooms where learners can flourish.

Organizations offering nonformal education include:

- 4-H clubs
- After-school care programs
- Boys and girls clubs
- Camps
- Community-based groups
- Homeschool co-ops
- Museums
- Parks, reserves, and nature centers
- Scouting and service organizations
- National, state, and local forests
- Zoos and aquariums
- and many more!

Teaching in a non-school setting is often very different from traditional classroom teaching. For example, the venue itself may include both outdoor and indoor spaces. The frequency of sessions and time spent with learners may limit what is possible, as nonformal programs are often one-time experiences or less than one hour long. Learners also may behave differently from how they act in school when they don't know the instructor or when the learning environment is less structured.

Nonformal educators often have little or no formal training in education, but they must be creative in managing learner behavior and group dynamics. While they are typically unbounded by a set curriculum, they often must develop programs that show alignment to academic standards.

HOW PLT CAN HELP

The activities in this guide can be incorporated into nonformal education programs of many lengths and types. They are adaptable to different settings: indoors or outdoors, or in rural, suburban, or urban locations. Also, PLT can be used by anyone: facilitators do not need formal education training to experience success.

The following features of this guide will help educators plan and conduct learning activities for nonformal programs:

- **Nonformal Icon.** Look for the icon that signifies specific PLT activities designed to work well with nonformal settings and audiences. These activities can often be conducted in a one-hour time block, use materials that are readily available, and need little prep time.

- **Fun Comes First.** All PLT activities use hands-on teaching strategies that make learning accessible and exciting through active engagement.

- **Easy to Use.** Each activity provides step-by-step instructions for preparation, facilitation, and assessment. Supporting background information is also included for educators.

- **Outdoor Education.** An outdoor icon signifies activities that use the outdoors as the primary educational setting. These activities actively engage learners in exploring the world around them. Most activities also have simple Take It Outside! suggestions to take learning outdoors.

- **Tips for Teaching Outdoors.** The activities contain many useful tips for managing student behavior both indoors and outdoors. See Appendix B: Tips for Teaching Outdoors for more helpful suggestions.

- **Topic Index.** The activities in this guide introduce a wide variety of environmental topics, from trees and forests to biodiversity, climate change, conservation, waste, water, and much more. Check out the Topic Index to find activities that address particular topics.

- **Connections to Academic Standards.** PLT activities meet a wide range of national, state, and program standards, addressing requirements for science, English language arts, mathematics, social studies, and more. See the Academic Standards callout boxes within each activity for connections to specific academic areas. Also see plt.org/academic-standards for correlations between PLT activities and standardized academic benchmarks.

- **Professional Development.** PLT offers in-person, online, and blended workshops that support nonformal educators in implementing environmental education. Learn more at plt.org/pd.

STEM Skills

Skills in science, technology, engineering, and mathematics (known collectively as STEM) are key to a more sustainable future. According to the United Nations Conference on Trade and Development, STEM skills are crucial to achieving the UN's Sustainable Development Goals, which 195 countries have pledged to meet by 2030. These goals include access to quality education, pathways to responsible consumption and production, and ensuring equitable economic opportunity for all. Teaching and learning STEM skills can pave the way for students to become part of the solution.

STEM is the most common term for these skills, though there is debate about whether they should also include art (STEAM), reading (STREAM), and even the environment (E-STEM). Whatever name is applied, STEM emphasizes an interdisciplinary approach to problem-solving. Activities that are exemplars of this STEM approach are indicated with this icon: ⚙

PLT's STEM skills focus on scientific concepts and build on them by including elements of leadership, inquiry, and problem-based learning methods used in the creative process. These skills provide opportunities for youth to learn creatively, practicing not only 21st century skills such as problem solving, but also skills related to human connection, care, community, and culture.

The activities in this guide provide opportunities for students to practice STEM in authentic ways. Each activity identifies the key STEM skills from the following list that students use as they carry out the learning activities.

TEN STEM SKILLS FOR EVERYONE

PLT promotes 10 essential STEM skills for everyone. At their core, these skills support hands-on learning that encourage youth to ask questions, carry out environmental investigations, and develop new knowledge. To help students identify their strengths, download a STEM skills self-assessment from plt.org/myk8guide.

1. Collaboration
- Cooperating with team members
- Finding points of agreement or consensus
- Taking responsibility for individual contributions

2. Communication
- Exchanging ideas with project partners
- Sharing project results
- Using different media to enhance communication

3. Creativity
- Looking at a problem from different perspectives
- Exploring new ideas
- Learning from failures

4. Data Analysis
- Assessing the accuracy of data
- Presenting data in a useful format
- Identifying patterns in data

5. Investigation
- Posing a question to investigate
- Planning and carrying out the investigation of a question
- Constructing an explanation based on findings

6. Leadership
- Leading projects or supporting a project team
- Developing a project plan and timeline
- Making decisions supported by data

7. Nature-Based Design
- Finding inspiration in and from nature
- Recognizing nature's solutions to problems
- Incorporating ideas from nature into design

8. Organization
- Precisely following instructions, protocols, or blueprints
- Recording data accurately
- Keeping track of lots of different information

9. Problem Solving
- Defining a problem
- Using models to investigate a problem
- Designing solutions to a problem

10. Technology Use
- Identifying appropriate technology for a given application
- Using technology tools effectively
- Troubleshooting technology problems

These capabilities and aptitudes are crucial to growing a future-ready workforce in all disciplines. The U.S. Bureau of Labor Statistics confirms that STEM occupations are experiencing above-average growth rates.

SOURCES

Minnesota State Colleges and University. Understanding Science, Technology, Engineering, and Math (STEM) Skills. Careerwise Education. https://careerwise.minnstate.edu/careers/stemskills.html

Ridwan, A., et al. 2020. Developing 22nd century skills through the integration of STEAM... *Journal of Physics: Conference Series*. 1521 042077. https://iopscience.iop.org/article/10.1088/1742-6596/1521/4/042077/pdf

U.S. Bureau of Labor Statistics. 2014. STEM 101: Intro to tomorrow's jobs. *Occupational Outlook Quarterly*. Spring 2014. https://www.bls.gov/careeroutlook/2014/spring/art01.pdf

How can teachers successfully instruct a group of students with diverse backgrounds and interests, as well as varying skill and readiness levels? Differentiated instruction is an effective way to accomplish the difficult task of meeting many students' individual needs. It means providing different options for students to take in information, process ideas, and express what they learn.

Differentiated Instruction Methods. The activities in this guide provide a range of opportunities for differentiating instruction. Look for the icons highlighting examples of differentiation within the activity steps. These icons ⟩ identify specific differentiated instruction methods used, including:

- **Cooperative Learning:** Combining students into pairs or small groups to work together to achieve a common goal.

- **Hands-on Learning:** Providing students with tangible objects and opportunities to actively engage in practical experiences.

- **Higher-order Thinking:** Challenging students to go beyond basic comprehension to more abstract thinking, such as inferring, predicting, or making connections.

- **Literacy Skills:** Encouraging students to deepen English language arts skills (speaking, reading, and writing) through a variety of instructional methods.

- **Multiple Solution Pathways:** Allowing students to explore and observe diverse approaches to solving a problem.

- **Nonlinguistic Representations:** Helping students learn through modalities other than the printed word (for example, music, role-playing, sketching, or photographing).

- **Personal Connections:** Tapping into students' prior experiences and knowledge and helping them make connections between new concepts and their own lives.

- **Student Voice:** Promoting discourse in the classroom that enables students to expand and deepen their thinking.

Fostering Mistake-Making. Mistakes are a critical component of the learning process as students explore new ideas and test their own developing skills. Differentiated instruction is most effective within a culture of mistake-making, where the focus is more on the process of learning than on getting the correct answer. PLT supports a culture of mistake-making through activities that engage students in examining the world around them, exploring open-ended questions, and finding solutions to challenging problems.

Supporting English Language Learners. PLT activities are effective with English language learners. As students develop their English skills, PLT can help provide them with rich learning experiences and a variety of modalities to help them understand and internalize new concepts. Acquisition of English is a lengthy process that can take anywhere from three to over 10 years, depending on the individual's academic support and program, background, and first language literacy skills. As English language learners acquire the new language, PLT activities help to ensure that they are also building and refining their thinking and investigative skills.

Meeting Needs of All Students. PLT activities are designed for use with a wide range of students to provide learning experiences for all. The activities in this guide can be adjusted for various student populations, including students with physical and cognitive disabilities, as well as the most able students. Contact your PLT State Coordinator (plt.org/yourstate) for support in adapting PLT activities to meet your students' unique needs.

Conceptual Framework

PLT's Conceptual Framework is the foundation for developing all PLT curriculum materials. It is designed to link concepts from different fields to deepen students' understanding of science and the environment. It is organized around five major themes:

- Patterns
- Interrelationships
- Systems
- Structure and Scale
- Stability and Change

As the concept of sustainability is central to environmental education, each theme encompasses the topics of Environment, Economy, and Society—the three main elements of sustainability. Each activity in this guide identifies connections to the Conceptual Framework by number, as shown below.

THEME: PATTERNS

1.0 Ecosystems, organisms, societies, cultures, and economies throughout the world exhibit many observable patterns.

Environmental Patterns

1.1 Living components of the environment interact in predictable ways with nonliving components, such as air, water, and geologic features.

1.2 The arrangement of living and nonliving components within a habitat determines the organisms it can support.

1.3 Patterns of variation from region to region in the Earth's atmosphere, water, soil, climate, and geology create a wide diversity of biological communities.

Economic Patterns

1.4 Humans use environments and resources to meet a variety of physical, social, and cultural needs.

1.5 Alternative approaches to economic issues may have different benefits and costs for different groups, for society as a whole, and for the environment.

1.6 Successful economic solutions are appropriate for the people involved, use resources sustainably, and ensure the preservation and enhancement of environmental quality.

Societal Patterns

1.7 Human societies have many similarities, as well as differences, in their relationships to the landscapes and climates in which they live.

1.8 Humans throughout the world create social, cultural, political, and economic systems and organizations to meet their physical and emotional needs.

1.9 A society's standard of living and individual well-being are dependent on environmental quality; the availability, utilization, and distribution of resources; the government; and the culture of its inhabitants.

1.10 Natural beauty, as experienced in forests and other habitats, enhances the quality of human life by providing artistic and spiritual inspiration, as well as recreational and intellectual opportunities.

THEME: INTERRELATIONSHIPS

2.0 The ecological, economic, and sociocultural systems are interactive and interdependent.

Environmental Interrelationships

2.1 Organisms are interdependent and depend on nonliving components of the environment.

2.2 Altering the environment affects all life forms, including humans, and the interrelationships that link them.

2.3 Organisms adapt to changes in the environment according to the genetic and behavioral capacity of their species.

2.4 Biodiversity results from the interaction of living and nonliving environmental components.

Economic Interrelationships

2.5 All humans make individual and group decisions about the consumption of products, which affects the availability of renewable and nonrenewable natural resources.

2.6 The management of natural resources provides employment opportunities for many people and communities.

2.7 Resource management systems interact and influence environmental quality; the acquisition, extraction, and transportation of natural resources; all life forms; and each other.

2.8 International cooperation in regard to sustainable resource management and environmental protection is beneficial to the well-being of humans and other life forms.

Societal Interrelationships

2.9 Human societies and cultures throughout the world interact with each other and affect the natural systems upon which they depend.

2.10 The quantity and quality of resources and their use—or misuse—by humans affect the standard of living of societies and the well-being of individuals.

2.11 Cultural and societal perspectives influence the attitudes, beliefs, and values that people hold toward resource management and environmental protection.

THEME: SYSTEMS

3.0 Environmental, economic, and social systems are interconnected and interacting.

Environmental Systems

3.1 In biological systems, energy flows and materials continually cycle in predictable and measurable patterns.

3.2 Plant and animal populations exhibit interrelated cycles of growth and decline.

3.3 Harmful byproducts of human and natural systems can enter ecosystems in various ways.

3.4 Ecosystems possess measurable indicators of environmental health.

Economic Systems

3.5 Global and local economies are complex systems involving costs and benefits, labor markets, citizen rights, and resource distribution.

3.6 The application of scientific knowledge and technological systems can have unintended effects on environmental, economic, and societal well-being.

3.7 Sustainable technologies enable human and natural systems to maintain and extend the productivity of vital resources.

Societal Systems

3.8 Most cultures have beliefs, values, and traditions that shape human interactions with the environment and its resources.

3.9 In many societies, citizens have a voice in shaping resource and environmental management policies. Individuals and societies share in the responsibility of sustaining resources and behaving in an environmentally responsible manner.

3.10 In many societies, individuals and groups can work through governmental channels to influence the management of public and private resources.

3.11 Effective decision-making involves a careful study of all sides of the issues, along with the ability to differentiate between honest, factually accurate information and propaganda.

THEME: STRUCTURE AND SCALE

4.0 Components of natural and human-built environments, economies, and societal institutions vary in structure and scale.

Environmental Structure and Scale

4.1 Populations of organisms exhibit variations in size and structure as a result of adaptations to their habitats.

4.2 The structure and scale of ecosystems are influenced by environmental factors such as soil type, climate, availability of water, and human activities.

4.3 When the Earth is studied as an interacting ecological system, every action, regardless of its scale, affects the biosphere in some way.

Economic Structure and Scale

4.4 Economic activities involve short-term and long-term outcomes, and they have positive and negative effects on the environment.

4.5 The structure and scale of an area's natural resources shape the economy on which the society and its culture are based.

4.6 Conservation technologies, when appropriately applied to resource management or environmental protection, can support environmental, economic, and societal sustainability.

4.7 Human-built environments, if planned and constructed to be compatible with the environment in which they will be located, can conserve resources, enhance environmental quality, and promote the well-being of those who live within them.

Societal Structure and Scale

4.8 Cultural perspectives and the actions of individuals and groups affect the management of resources and environmental quality.

4.9 The structure and scale of governments and other organizations in power, as well as their actions, influence the management of resources and affect environmental quality.

4.10 International cooperation on resource management and environmental improvement programs can benefit individuals and communities in many parts of the world.

THEME: STABILITY AND CHANGE

5.0 Structures and systems may be stable, but they change over various periods of time.

Environmental Stability and Change

5.1 Organisms change throughout their lifetimes. Species change over long periods of time.

5.2 Healthy ecosystems are in a state of dynamic equilibrium, with steady inflows and outflows.

5.3 Ecosystems change over time through patterns of growth and succession. They are also affected by other phenomena, such as disease, insects, fire, weather, climate, and human intervention.

Economic Stability and Change

5.4 Economic stability is supported by minor fluctuations in the production of goods and services.

5.5 Consumers influence the marketplace with demands for goods and services. Such demands shift with time and may have positive or negative effects on societal and environmental sustainability.

5.6 Industries often respond to consumer demand for recyclable, recycled, or otherwise environmentally sustainable products.

5.7 New technologies require implementation by a well-informed and highly skilled workforce.

Societal Stability and Change

5.8 Stable governments change and evolve over time. Such changes affect the lives of their citizens, as well as resource management and environmental policies.

5.9 Leisure and recreational pursuits can have positive and negative effects on the sustainability of forests and other resource-producing areas.

5.10 Increased public knowledge of environmental issues and the need for sustainable resource management has resulted in lifestyle and community changes in many cultures.

Storylines ensure connectivity and continuity between individual activities and can serve as the "instructional glue" that bind many areas of knowledge and skills. Here are some suggestions for linking PLT activities into combined units of instruction using a storyline technique. They can serve as a springboard to help you develop education plans and instructional units tailored to the specific needs and interests of your students.

One example unit is described in detail on the facing page, and brief summaries of several suggested units follow.

All suggested units are further detailed online at plt.org/myk8guide.

To demonstrate the value of PLT to teachers and school administrators, all online unit writeups explicitly reference connections to the Next Generation Science Standards (NGSS).

Select units also identify relevant concepts in PLT's *Forest Literacy Framework* (FLF). For more information and resources, visit plt.org/forestliteracy.

SUGGESTED UNITS

The following units of instruction are organized by grade level. All units list activities that support an intentional student learning progression, presented in a recommended sequence. Note that some units reference activities from other grade levels, offering developmentally appropriate elements that support the unit. All suggested units are further detailed online at plt.org/myk8guide.

GRADES K–2

Benefits of Trees*
Storyline: Trees benefit humans in a variety of ways.
FLF Concepts: 2.A.1, 2.B.3

- The Closer You Look
- Adopt a Tree
- Trees as Habitats
- We All Need Trees

Exploring Urban Environments*
Storyline: Urban environments are complex and valuable, just like environments in more natural settings.
FLF Concepts: 1.A.6, 3.A.1
- Backyard Safari
- Adopt a Tree
- Trees as Habitats
- Discover Diversity (in Grades 3–5, see Variation for K–2)

Nature Appreciation
Storyline: Nature provides people with many different benefits.

- Adopt a Tree
- Discover Diversity (in Grades 3–5, see Variation for K–2)
- Backyard Safari
- We All Need Trees
- Get Outside! (in Grades 3–5, see Variation for K–2)

Plant Growth and Life Cycle
Storyline: Plants grow and change throughout their life cycle.
- A Tree's Life
- Bursting Buds
- Tree Cookies (in Grades 3–5, see Variation for K–2)
- Here We Grow Again
- Plant a Tree (in Grades 6–8, see Variation for 3–5)

Structure and Function
Storyline: Trees have different parts that help them grow and thrive.
- Adopt a Tree
- The Closer You Look
- Bursting Buds
- Have Seeds, Will Travel

*Asterisks signify units with *Forest Literacy Framework* (FLF) concept connections.

EXAMPLE UNIT

Cycles of Matter and Energy
GRADES 3–5

Guiding Question
Where do the plants and animals in our neighborhood get the food and energy they need to survive?

Connecting Concepts

- Matter cycles between the air and soil and among plants, animals, and microbes as these organisms live and die. Organisms obtain gases, water, and minerals from the environment and release waste matter (gas, liquid, or solid) back into the environment. (NGSS, LS2.B: Cycles of Matter and Energy Transfer in Ecosystems)

- Food provides animals with the materials they need for body repair and growth and the energy they need to maintain body warmth and for motion. Plants acquire their material for growth chiefly from air and water. (NGSS, LS1.C: Organization for Matter and Energy Flow in Organisms)

- As part of the forest ecosystem, trees have various roles. These roles include supplying oxygen, producing food, providing habitat for wildlife, stabilizing soil, moderating temperature, capturing and storing carbon, and cycling water and nutrients. (PLT FLF, 1.B.6)

- Forest ecosystems include processes such as photosynthesis, energy flow, and the cycling of nutrients, water, carbon, and other matter. (PLT FLF, 1.C.3)

Scope and Sequence
The collection and arrangement of content below supports an intentional student learning progression.

Activity	Description
Web of Life	By conducting research and modeling a food web, students take a close look at an ecosystem and discover ways that plants and animals are connected through the cycling of food energy.
Every Tree for Itself	Students engage in an active simulation to learn what resources trees need to live and grow and how trees must compete for resources.
Tree Cookies	Students examine a tree's growth rings, which show patterns of change in the matter and energy available to the tree.
Fallen Log	Students observe fallen logs or other decomposing pieces of wood and gain a deeper understanding of how matter cycles.

Detailed standards correlations for each activity can be found at plt.org/academic-standards

Storyline
In this unit, students participate in experiences that will help them understand that matter cycles within an ecosystem.

- Begin with the activity Web of Life to introduce the concept that plants and animals are interconnected through food chains and the food web. Plants form the basis because they are able to convert the sun's energy into food.

- The activity Every Tree for Itself reinforces the role of plants in the food web. Be sure to emphasize that plants not only need sunlight and rain to grow, but also carbon dioxide from the air. Use the first Grades 6–8 variation and have students draw a "growth ring" to represent how much their tree grows each year.

- In Tree Cookies, students look at the growth rings of trees, and then in Part B they research events and correlate them to events in the tree's life. After they have completed this work, ask your students what happens to the tree after it dies.

- Conclude with Fallen Log, which focuses on the role of decomposers in food chains.

GRADES 3–5

Adaptation

Storyline: Organisms have complex adaptations that enable them to survive in their habitats.

- Charting Biodiversity
- Birds and Bugs (in Grades K–2, see Variation for 3–5)
- Have Seeds, Will Travel
- Peppermint Beetle (in Grades K–2, see Variation for 3–5)

Cycles of Matter and Energy*

Storyline: Living organisms depend on the matter and energy that cycle through ecosystems to survive.
FLF Concepts: 1.B.6, 1.C.3

- Web of Life
- Every Tree for Itself
- Tree Cookies
- Fallen Log

Ecosystem Services*

Storyline: Trees and other plants are renewable natural resources that benefit humans in a variety of ways.
FLF Concepts: 1.B.6, 2.A.2, 2.B.4, 2.B.7

- Trees for Many Reasons
- We All Need Trees (in Grades K–2, see Variation for 3–5)
- Poet-Tree
- Get Outside!
- Plant a Tree (in Grades 6–8, see Variation for 3–5)

Ecosystems

Storyline: Ecosystems are composed of interrelated systems and living things.

- Discover Diversity
- Field, Forest, and Stream (in Grades 6–8, see Variation for 3–5)
- Web of Life
- Nothing Succeeds Like Succession (in Grades 6–8, see Variation for 3–5)

Forest Products*

Storyline: People depend on forests for many different products and a wide range of benefits.
FLF Concepts: 2.A.10, 2.B.3, 2.B.4, 4.A.2

- Trees for Many Reasons
- Peek at Packaging
- Make Your Own Paper

Habitats

Storyline: Organisms possess a diversity of characteristics that enable them to adapt to a wide range of habitats.

- Discover Diversity
- Every Tree for Itself
- Soil Builders
- Fallen Log
- Web of Life

Patterns of Change

Storyline: Trees and forest ecosystems change over time.

- Did You Notice? (in Grades K–2, see Variation for 3–5)
- Signs of Fall
- Fallen Log
- A Tree's Life (in Grades K–2, see Variation for 3–5)

Photosynthesis

Storyline: The foundation of all life on Earth is the ability of plants to use the sun's energy to make food.

- Tree Cookies
- Every Tree for Itself
- Tree Factory
- Web of Life
- Here We Grow Again (in Grades K–2, see Variation for 3–5)
- Plant a Tree (in Grades K–2, see Variation for 3–5)

*Asterisks signify units with *Forest Literacy Framework* (FLF) concept connections.

Tree Structure

Storyline: A tree is composed of different parts that function together to support the tree.

- The Closer You Look (in Grades K–2)
- Tree Factory
- Nature's Skyscrapers
- Tree ID

Water

Storyline: Water is essential for life on Earth: the water cycle is the process by which water moves through ecosystems and the atmosphere.

- Field, Forest, and Stream (in Grades 6–8, see Variation for 3–5)
- Water Wonders
- Every Drop Counts

GRADES 6–8

Biodiversity

Storyline: Organisms possess a diversity of characteristics that enable them to adapt to a wide range of habitats. Biological diversity is an important element of ecosystem function.

- Field, Forest, and Stream
- Invasive Species
- Life on the Edge
- If You Were the Boss

Careers

Storyline: Green jobs provide opportunities to help ensure that forests are managed sustainably while serving the needs of society and nature.

- Every Tree for Itself (in Grades 3–5, see Variation for 6–8)
- My Green Future
- Nature's Skyscrapers
- Our Federal Forests
- If You Were the Boss

Climate Change*

Storyline: Changes in the Earth's climate impact ecosystems and human communities.

FLF Concepts: 1.D.1, 2.A.3, 3.B.7

- Exploration Energy!
- The Global Climate
- Life on the Edge
- Improve Your Place

Community Planning

Storyline: Community planning helps increase community sustainability and resilience.

- Decisions, Decisions
- Reduce, Reuse, Recycle
- Our Federal Forests
- Forest in the City
- Environmental Justice for All

Energy

Storyline: Energy comes from renewable and nonrenewable sources. Human use of energy has short- and long-term social, economic, environmental, and health-related impacts.

- Global Goods
- Exploration Energy!
- Renewable or Not?
- The Global Climate
- Improve Your Place

Environmental Decision-Making

Storyline: People can improve their relationship with the environment through their collective decisions, as well as individual actions and behavior.

- Decisions, Decisions
- Exploration Energy!
- Life on the Edge
- The Global Climate
- Environmental Justice for All
- Improve Your Place

*Asterisks signify units with *Forest Literacy Framework* (FLF) concept connections.

Forest Management*

Storyline: Humans manage forests to ensure that they remain sustainable and to derive the most benefit from them.

FLF Concepts: 3.B.2, 3.B.4, 3.C.3, 3.D.1

- Forest in the City
- Trees in Trouble
- Invasive Species
- Living with Fire
- If You Were the Boss
- Our Federal Forests
- What's in a Label?

Natural Resources

Storyline: Humans have developed sustainable systems for managing and processing natural resources.

- Global Goods
- Exploration Energy!
- Renewable or Not?
- If You Were the Boss

Sustainability

Storyline: Sustainable use of resources allows us to meet our needs today without compromising the ability of future generations to meet their own needs.

- Decisions, Decisions
- Exploration Energy!
- Peek at Packaging
- Global Goods
- Renewable or Not?
- Reduce, Reuse, Recycle
- What's in a Label?
- If You Were the Boss

*Asterisks signify units with *Forest Literacy Framework* (FLF) concept connections.

PLT's Glossary is available at plt.org/glossary

PLT's online Glossary provides educators with a searchable resource to enhance activities and extend learning. The Glossary defines terms that are highlighted in **bold** in the Background or Doing the Activity sections of this guide. In some cases, these terms have a slightly different or more refined definition in a science or environmental context than in everyday use.

IDEAS FOR USING THE GLOSSARY

To use the Glossary to enhance student learning, try one or more of the following:

- Identify the new or potentially challenging terms used in any given activity.

- Cut and paste terms from the Glossary and use them to create activity-specific vocabulary lists. Or invite students to develop their own list for the activity.

- Have students list terms for the activity in a chart, as in the example below, indicating which words they know and which they don't know. Direct them to either write a definition or guess the meaning of each word. Model how to find terms within the Glossary, and then have students look up their word and compare it with their definition.

Term	What I think it means	Definition from Glossary

- Encourage students to create a nonlinguistic representation (picture, symbol, or emoji) of each term.

- Have students create their own glossary of terms related to PLT activities. This could be a shared online list that students write and refine as a group, or individual glossaries that each student creates for their own use.

- Invite students to use mobile apps to create their own vocabulary worksheets that utilize Glossary terms and associated definitions. Some ideas include word searches, letter jumbles, cryptograms, and crossword puzzles.

- Allow students to practice their new vocabulary with team games, such as charades, categories, or password games.

Share additional ideas for using the Glossary with other educators by submitting them to plt@forests.org

The activities in this guide invite students to explore a range of forest-related careers. Today's youth seek rewarding careers that will enable them to make a difference in the world, such as by creating more sustainable lifestyles and greener economies. Forest careers offer the potential for satisfying work that nurtures forest ecosystems and ensures that forest products are sustainably grown and harvested.

A wide array of forest-related jobs exists, offering ample opportunities for people with diverse backgrounds, skills, interest areas, and personal qualities. The guide presents a sampling of these careers for students to explore.

CAREER-RELATED ACTIVITIES

The activity My Green Future (in Grades 3-5) introduces students to different forest-related careers. Students learn that everyone depends on sustainably managed forests for recreation, essential products, wildlife and biodiversity, and clean water and air. Students are also introduced to the wide variety of people who work in the forest—from foresters to loggers to scientists.

Other activities in the guide also help students make connections to careers. The variation for Every Tree for Itself (in Grades 3–5) invites students to add people with forest-related careers to a forest simulation. In addition, Have Seeds, Will Travel and Get Outside! (in Grades 3–5), and If You Were the Boss and Our Federal Forests (in Grades 6–8) all include an Enrichment suggestion focusing on careers.

CAREER CORNERS

Each student page includes a Career Corner that highlights a forest-related occupation. Brief text describes the career and its connection to the student page content or skills practiced. Use these Career Corners to acquaint your students with the many career possibilities in the forest sector. To make the most of them, try the following:

- Encourage students to identify the skills they used to complete the student page, list which skills they enjoy practicing most, and determine which skills are related to the highlighted career.

- Challenge students to identify other careers that use some or all of the skills they practiced. The careers may or may not be related to forests.

- Provide students with a complete set of Career Corners suitable for their grade range (available at plt.org/myk8guide). Have them sort careers by different parameters, such as setting, skills, experience required, content areas, personal qualities, or other factors.

- Ask students to choose one career to research in more detail. Have them investigate what skills, characteristics, and training would be required to do this job and write a brief report about the career. They should include whether they would be interested in pursuing this career and why or why not.

- Invite guests who work in the forest sector or in other environment-related careers to speak to your students about their jobs and career pathways they took to get there.

- Share additional ideas for using Career Corners by submitting them to plt@forests.org.

GREEN JOBS: EXPLORING FOREST CAREERS

You may also encourage your students to take a fun Green Jobs Personality Quiz (available at plt.org/find-your-green-job-quiz) and a STEM Skills Self-Assessment (available at plt.org/myk8guide), which can help them identify forest careers that suit their particular strengths.

To dig deeper into forest careers, see *PLT's Green Jobs: Exploring Forest Careers*, available at plt.org/greenjobs. This activity guide is geared for educators working with middle- and high-school-aged youth in formal and nonformal settings.

Making a Scientific Argument
APPENDIX K

Many of the PLT activities in this guide challenge students to make scientific arguments with a writing strategy called Claim–Evidence–Reasoning (or CER).

CER starts with any question about a phenomenon or real-world event. Whether it comes from the teacher or students, a good question should resonate with students' innate curiosity about how the world works. CER provides a structure for objectively exploring scientific questions through the following elements:

- **Claim**
  This is the student's answer to the question. It is usually just one sentence long and doesn't include any evidence or explanation.

- **Evidence**
  This is the data that supports the student's claim. It may include a chart or graph and can be quantitative or qualitative, depending on the question. It should only include data that support the student's claim.

- **Reasoning**
  This is supported by the evidence and explains how and why the evidence supports the student's claim. Where appropriate, it should include an explanation of the underlying concept or method that produced the evidence.

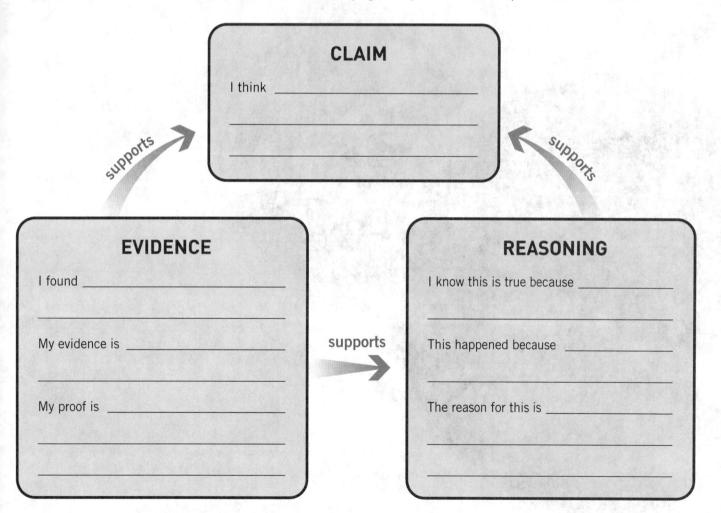

To help give students practice in CER, you may use a standardized form such as the example above. For younger students, focus on just the Claim and Evidence portions. Encourage older students to apply scientific principles to their analysis.

Many of the PLT activities in this guide invite students to plan an investigation to learn about a particular organism, ecosystem, or phenomenon. In doing so, students gain skill in an important scientific practice that enables scientists, engineers, and others to investigate and observe the world.

The activities use two main types of scientific investigation:

- Observational investigations involve describing and quantifying parts of a natural system, or collecting data to compare different populations or conditions.

- Experimental investigations involve designing and carrying out a "fair test," in which variables are manipulated and compared against a control to determine cause-and-effect relationships.

To help students plan their investigations, you may use the following Planning an Investigation student page, which lays out the general steps involved. It may be used for both observational and experimental investigations.

Planning an Investigation

NAME _____ DATE _____

Use this worksheet to help guide your investigation.

Asking Questions

1 What question are you trying to answer?

2 What do you think you will learn?

3 Why do you think so?

Planning and Carrying Out the Investigation

4 How will you investigate your question?

5 What will you observe and measure?

6 If your investigation is an experiment, what will you control (keep the same)? What one thing will you change (variable)?

7 What materials and equipment will you need?

8 How will you record your results?

NAME _____ DATE _____

Analyzing and Interpreting Data

9 What are your results?

10 What do your results show you?

11 How do your results compare with those of other students?

Constructing Explanations

12 What explanation can you give for your results?

13 What evidence supports your explanation?

Communicating Information

14 Who else would be interested in your results? How might you tell them about your investigation?

Assessment Rubric APPENDIX M

Each activity in this guide suggests assessment strategies that enable students to demonstrate what they have learned. A rubric is a scoring tool that you can use to evaluate student work. It typically provides descriptions of work products or behaviors as a means to assess proficiency at different skill levels.

The following assessment rubric template may be used with any of the activities in this guide. Feel free to adjust it for a given activity, to highlight specific content or skills you want students to focus on, or to target it to reflect the aptitude or skill level of your students.

In the four-level scale used here, Level 4 represents a mastery of content and skills that are above the proficiency level. Level 3 represents proficiency, while Level 2 represents progress toward—but not achievement of—proficiency. Level 1 represents beginning steps toward proficiency.

You can download an editable version of the rubric at plt.org/myk8guide

	Level 4 Mastery	Level 3 Proficiency	Level 2 Progressing	Level 1 Emerging
Work Product	• Complete, excellent quality with extra information. • Very creative. • Goes above and beyond requirements.	• Complete and creative. • Good quality. • All basic topics covered.	• Almost complete. • Shows some creativity. • Average quality. • Most topics included.	• Incomplete. • Lacking creativity. • Poor quality. • Not all topics included.
Content	• More than the required content is included and accurate. • More than the required vocabulary is used. • Communicates a complete understanding of concept, including multiple accurate details. • All sources correctly cited.	• Required content is included and accurate. • Required vocabulary is included. • Shares a basic understanding of concept, including 1 or 2 details. • Sources cited but not all correctly.	• Not all content is included, or content contains some inaccuracies. • Some vocabulary included. • Reflects slight understanding of the concept, with only vague details. • Sources cited are incomplete and/or cited incorrectly.	• Incomplete and inaccurate content. • Most of the required content is not included. • Little to no significant vocabulary included. • Does not reflect understanding of the concept, perhaps including conflicting details. • No sources cited.

Assessment rubric template continues on next page.

	Level 4 Mastery	Level 3 Proficiency	Level 2 Progressing	Level 1 Emerging
Collaboration	• Outstanding group collaboration with tasks being shared equally. • All members are prepared and participate. • Group strategies used so that all group members' ideas are shared.	• Group collaboration with tasks being shared somewhat equally. • All members participate. • Group strategies attempted so most group members' ideas are shared.	• Limited group collaboration; tasks not shared equally. • Part of the group participates. • Group strategies attempted, but few students share their ideas.	• Group does not collaborate. • Only one member participates or there is very limited participation. • Group strategies are not attempted.
Presentation	• Good eye contact. • Speech is clear and loud enough for audience to hear. • Ideas are organized and connected with a clear flow of logic. • Gestures are used to emphasize main points. • Can answer questions.	• Eye contact most of the time. • Speech is clear most of the time. • Most ideas are connected and organized but no clear flow of logic. • Can answer most questions.	• Limited eye contact. • Speech is clear some of the time. • Does not connect ideas well. • Can answer a few questions.	• No eye contact, student reads presentation. • Does not speak clearly. • Unrehearsed and disorganized. • Cannot address audience questions.
Critical Thinking	• Critical thinking apparent, with student sharing multiple details. • Student asked for and listened to feedback and made adjustments as needed.	• Critical thinking apparent, with student sharing one or two details. • Student asked for some feedback.	• Some critical thinking apparent, with student offering vague statements. • Student did not ask for feedback.	• Critical thinking not apparent. • Student did not ask for feedback.

INDEX At-a-Glance

PROJECT LEARNING TREE — An initiative of SFI

Use this index to find activities to fit your needs. Squares (■ ■ ■) indicate activities that meet each criterion.

	A TREE'S LIFE	ADOPT A TREE	BACKYARD SAFARI	BIRDS AND BUGS	BURSTING BUDS	DID YOU NOTICE?	HAVE SEEDS, WILL TRAVEL	HERE WE GROW AGAIN	MAKE YOUR OWN PAPER	PEPPERMINT BEETLE	THE CLOSER YOU LOOK	TREES AS HABITATS	WE ALL NEED TREES	CHARTING BIODIVERSITY	DISCOVER DIVERSITY	EVERY DROP COUNTS	EVERY TREE FOR ITSELF	FALLEN LOG	GET OUTSIDE!	MY GREEN FUTURE	PEEK AT PACKAGING	POET-TREE
GRADES	K-2													3-5								
PAGE NUMBER	14	21	29	35	40	44	50	57	63	68	72	76	82	90	97	104	110	116	121	132	136	143
GRADE LEVEL VARIATION*	●	●	●	●	●	●	●	●	●	●			●		▲		★		▲		★	★
SUBJECTS — SCIENCE	■	■	■	■	■	■	■	■			■	■	■	■	■	■	■	■	■	■	■	■
ENGLISH LANGUAGE ARTS	■	■	■			■	■	■	■		■	■	■	■	■		■	■	■	■	■	■
MATH		■		■	■			■	■								■	■				
SOCIAL STUDIES	■					■				■	■		■							■	■	■
ARTS	■		■						■		■				■				■		■	
HEALTH & PE			■																■			
ICONS — TIME: LONG-TERM		■			■			■							■							
NONFORMAL		■	■				■		■	■	■	■	■		■					■	■	■
OUTDOORS	■	■	■	■	■					■	■	■			■							
STEM							■	■				■				■		■				
URBAN			■									■										
STEM SKILLS — COLLABORATION	■			■			■						■	■								
COMMUNICATION	■					■															■	
CREATIVITY	■	■				■				■										■	■	■
DATA ANALYSIS		■		■	■	■		■			■	■						■	■			
INVESTIGATION			■					■	■					■	■	■	■	■	■			
LEADERSHIP													■		■							
NATURE-BASED DESIGN		■		■			■		■	■	■			■		■						■
ORGANIZATION			■	■				■						■	■		■		■			
PROBLEM SOLVING							■			■					■						■	
TECHNOLOGY USE	■		■								■											
DIFFERENTIATED INSTRUCTION — COOPERATIVE LEARNING	■					■	■						■	■	■		■		■			
HANDS-ON LEARNING		■	■	■	■		■	■	■			■					■	■	■		■	
HIGHER-ORDER THINKING				■				■		■	■			■	■		■		■			■
LITERACY SKILLS		■								■				■								■
MULTI SOLUTION PATHWAYS							■											■				
NONLINGUISTIC REP.	■	■		■	■					■		■			■					■	■	
PERSONAL CONNECTIONS	■	■				■				■					■					■	■	■
STUDENT VOICE		■	■			■				■	■		■	■			■			■		

* Symbol indicates available grade level variation (Red Triangle ▲ = Grades K-2, Green Circle ● = Grades 3-5, Blue Star ★ = Grades 6-8)

SIGNS OF FALL	SOIL BUILDERS	TREE COOKIES	TREE FACTORY	TREE ID	TREES FOR MANY REASONS	TREES IN TROUBLE	WATER WONDERS	WEB OF LIFE		DECISIONS, DECISIONS	ENVIRONMENTAL JUSTICE FOR ALL	EXPLORATION ENERGY!	FIELD, FOREST, AND STREAM	FOREST IN THE CITY	GLOBAL GOODS	IF YOU WERE THE BOSS	IMPROVE YOUR PLACE	INVASIVE SPECIES	LIFE ON THE EDGE	LIVING WITH FIRE	NATURE'S SKYSCRAPERS	NOTHING SUCCEEDS LIKE SUCCESSION	OUR FEDERAL FORESTS	PLANT A TREE	REDUCE, REUSE, RECYCLE	RENEWABLE OR NOT?	THE GLOBAL CLIMATE	WHAT'S IN A LABEL?
									GRADES 6-8																			
155	161	171	180	186	193	197	206	216		224	233	247	257	265	272	280	293	299	308	315	325	334	342	350	356	364	375	382
★		▲	▲		★	★				●		●	●				●		●		●	●	●	●	●			
■	■	■	■		■	■	■	■		■	■	■	■	■	■	■	■	■	■		■	■	■		■	■	■	■
■	■	■		■	■	■	■	■		■	■		■		■		■	■	■			■	■		■	■	■	■
		■				■						■	■	■	■	■	■	■	■		■							
	■	■	■			■				■	■		■	■	■	■	■	■	■			■	■		■	■		
■								■		■				■									■					
			■								■																	
	■					■						■				■	■		■			■		■	■			
■		■	■	■			■	■				■						■	■							■		
■				■		■						■				■			■	■			■					
	■						■			■	■	■	■	■	■	■	■	■	■							■	■	
			■			■				■	■			■										■	■			
			■		■			■		■		■		■			■	■		■				■	■			
		■				■				■							■	■					■			■		
			■		■								■			■			■					■				■
■	■			■				■	■			■		■			■		■		■				■		■	
■	■		■			■						■		■			■					■				■	■	
												■				■			■				■					
■	■																					■						
		■		■			■	■								■		■						■				■
						■		■		■						■		■						■		■	■	
								■			■	■							■			■		■				
	■				■					■					■		■					■	■			■	■	
■	■	■	■	■			■	■			■		■		■				■	■	■	■		■	■		
■							■							■		■			■				■			■	■	
		■			■		■						■	■													■	
	■		■								■					■		■	■	■			■				■	■
			■					■		■						■		■	■	■		■					■	
■	■					■		■			■								■					■		■	■	

PROJECT LEARNING TREE
An initiative of SFI

ACTIVITIES

TOPIC	GRADES K-2	GRADES 3-5	GRADES 6-8
COMMUNITY (ECOLOGICAL & HUMAN)	Did You Notice?	Discover Diversity Fallen Log Soil Builders Web of Life	Decisions, Decisions Environmental Justice for All Forest in the City If You Were the Boss Improve Your Place The Global Climate
COMMUNITY PLANNING			Decisions, Decisions Forest in the City Improve Your Place
COMMUNITY SCIENCE	Backyard Safari Bursting Buds The Closer You Look	Charting Biodiversity Discover Diversity Tree ID	Life on the Edge Invasive Species
COMPETITION (BIOLOGICAL)		Every Tree for Itself	Invasive Species Life on the Edge
COMPOSTING		Peek at Packaging Soil Builders	Reduce, Reuse, Recycle
CONSERVATION	Make Your Own Paper	Every Drop Counts	Exploration Energy! Global Goods Invasive Species Life on the Edge Our Federal Forests Renewable or Not? The Global Climate What's in a Label?
CONSUMERISM	We All Need Trees	Peek at Packaging	Global Goods Reduce, Reuse, Recycle What's in a Label?
CULTURAL PERSPECTIVES		Charting Biodiversity Poet-Tree Signs of Fall Trees in Trouble	Environmental Justice for All If You Were the Boss
CYCLES	A Tree's Life Bursting Buds	Fallen Log Signs of Fall Soil Builders Water Wonders Web of Life	Global Goods Living with Fire Nothing Succeeds Like Succession Reduce, Reuse, Recycle Renewable or Not?
DATA COLLECTION & INTERPRETATION	Adopt a Tree Backyard Safari Birds and Bugs Bursting Buds Did You Notice? Have Seeds, Will Travel Here We Grow Again Peppermint Beetle The Closer You Look Trees as Habitats We All Need Trees	Discover Diversity Every Drop Counts Every Tree for Itself Fallen Log Signs of Fall Soil Builders Trees in Trouble Water Wonders	Environmental Justice for All Exploration Energy! Field, Forest, and Stream Forest in the City Global Goods If You Were the Boss Life on the Edge Living with Fire Nature's Skyscrapers Our Federal Forests Plant a Tree Reduce, Reuse, Recycle Renewable or Not? The Global Climate What's in a Label?
DECISION-MAKING	Here We Grow Again	Every Drop Counts Trees for Many Reasons	Decisions, Decisions Environmental Justice for All If You Were the Boss Improve Your Place Plant a Tree Reduce, Reuse, Recycle Renewable or Not? What's in a Label?
DECOMPOSITION		Fallen Log Soil Builders Web of Life	Reduce, Reuse, Recycle
DEFORESTATION		Trees for Many Reasons	Life on the Edge
DESIGNING SOLUTIONS	Backyard Safari Birds and Bugs Have Seeds, Will Travel	Every Drop Counts Every Tree for Itself Peek at Packaging Trees in Trouble	Improve Your Place Our Federal Forests Plant a Tree What's in a Label?

	ACTIVITIES		
TOPIC	GRADES K-2	GRADES 3-5	GRADES 6-8
DISTURBANCE (ECOLOGICAL)		Fallen Log Tree Cookies Trees in Trouble	Living with Fire Nothing Succeeds Like Succession
DIVERSITY	(See Biodiversity.)		
ECONOMICS	Make Your Own Paper We All Need Trees	My Green Future Peek at Packaging Trees for Many Reasons	Exploration Energy! Global Goods If You Were the Boss Reduce, Reuse, Recycle Renewable or Not? What's in a Label?
ECOSYSTEM SERVICES	We All Need Trees	Get Outside! Poet-Tree Trees for Many Reasons	Decisions, Decisions Forest in the City Our Federal Forests Plant a Tree The Global Climate What's in a Label?
ECOSYSTEMS	Adopt a Tree Backyard Safari Trees as Habitats	Discover Diversity Fallen Log Web of Life	Field, Forest, and Stream If You Were the Boss Invasive Species Living with Fire Nothing Succeeds Like Succession
ENDANGERED SPECIES		Web of Life	Life on the Edge
ENERGY	Here We Grow Again	Every Tree for Itself Tree Factory Water Wonders	Exploration Energy! Global Goods Renewable or Not? The Global Climate
ENGINEERING DESIGN	(See Designing Solutions.)		
ENVIRONMENTAL JUSTICE			Environmental Justice for All Improve Your Place Forest in the City
EQUITY & INCLUSION	Adopt a Tree Did You Notice?	Trees in Trouble	Environmental Justice for All Forest in the City If You Were the Boss
EROSION		Water Wonders	Environmental Justice for All Improve Your Place Nothing Succeeds Like Succession
EXPERIMENTS	(See Investigations.)		
EXTINCTION	(See Endangered Species.)		
FIRE	Have Seeds, Will Travel	Every Tree for Itself Tree Cookies	Decisions, Decisions Living with Fire Nothing Succeeds Like Succession
FOOD	We All Need Trees	Peek at Packaging	Environmental Justice for All
FOOD CHAINS & WEBS	A Tree's Life	Fallen Log Soil Builders Web of Life	
FOREST CERTIFICATION		Trees for Many Reasons	Our Federal Forests What's in a Label?
FOREST HEALTH	A Tree's Life	Every Tree for Itself My Green Future Tree Cookies Trees in Trouble	Forest in the City If You Were the Boss Invasive Species Living with Fire What's in a Label?
FOREST MANAGEMENT	We All Need Trees	Every Tree for Itself	If You Were the Boss Living with Fire Our Federal Forests What's in a Label?
FOREST PRODUCTS	Make Your Own Paper We All Need Trees	Peek at Packaging Trees for Many Reasons	Global Goods Our Federal Forests Renewable or Not? What's in a Label?

PROJECT LEARNING TREE
An initiative of SFI

ACTIVITIES

TOPIC	GRADES K-2	GRADES 3-5	GRADES 6-8
FORESTRY PRACTICES	We All Need Trees	Every Tree for Itself My Green Future Trees for Many Reasons	If You Were the Boss Invasive Species Nature's Skyscrapers Our Federal Forests What's in a Label?
GARDENING	Here We Grow Again	Soil Builders	Improve Your Place Plant a Tree
GEOGRAPHY	Adopt a Tree Peppermint Beetle	Discover Diversity Every Drop Counts My Green Future Soil Builders Peek at Packaging Poet-Tree Trees for Many Reasons Trees in Trouble Water Wonders	Exploration Energy! Field, Forest, and Stream Forest in the City Global Goods If You Were the Boss Improve Your Place Invasive Species Life on the Edge Living with Fire Nothing Succeeds Like Succession Plant a Tree Reduce, Reuse, Recycle The Global Climate
GEOLOGY		Soil Builders	Field, Forest, and Stream
GLOBAL CLIMATE CHANGE		Every Tree for Itself Water Wonders	Exploration Energy! Field, Forest, and Stream If You Were the Boss Invasive Species Life on the Edge Nothing Succeeds Like Succession Plant a Tree The Global Climate
GLOBAL CONNECTIONS		Water Wonders	Environmental Justice for All Invasive Species Global Goods Renewable or Not? The Global Climate What's in a Label?
GOVERNMENT			Decisions, Decisions Environmental Justice for All Improve Your Place Our Federal Forests
GREEN BUILDING			Forest in the City What's in a Label?
GREEN ENERGY			Exploration Energy! Reduce, Reuse, Recycle Renewable or Not? The Global Climate
GREEN JOBS	(See Careers.)		
GREENHOUSE EFFECT		Water Wonders	Exploration Energy! Reduce, Reuse, Recycle The Global Climate
GROWTH RINGS, TREE	A Tree's Life	Every Tree for Itself Tree Cookies Trees in Trouble	
HABITATS	Backyard Safari Trees as Habitats	Discover Diversity Every Tree for Itself Fallen Log Soil Builders Web of Life	Field, Forest, and Stream Forest in the City If You Were the Boss Life on the Edge
HEALTH		Get Outside!	Environmental Justice for All Forest in the City
HISTORY	Did You Notice?	Tree Cookies	Invasive Species Life on the Edge Nothing Succeeds Like Succession Our Federal Forests

INDEX Topic

PROJECT
LEARNING
TREE
An initiative of SFI

ACTIVITIES

TOPIC	GRADES K-2	GRADES 3-5	GRADES 6-8
SCOUTING	Adopt a Tree Backyard Safari Birds and Bugs Make Your Own Paper Peppermint Beetle Trees as Habitats	Discover Diversity Every Tree for Itself Fallen Log My Green Future Tree Cookies Tree Factory Tree ID Web of Life	Field, Forest, and Stream Living with Fire Nature's Skyscrapers Renewable or Not?
SEASONAL CHANGE	Adopt a Tree Bursting Buds	Signs of Fall	
SEEDS	A Tree's Life Adopt a Tree Have Seeds, Will Travel Here We Grow Again The Closer You Look	Charting Biodiversity Invasive Species Tree Factory Tree ID	Nature's Skyscrapers
SENSE OF PLACE	Adopt a Tree Backyard Safari Did You Notice? Trees as Habitats	Discover Diversity Signs of Fall Tree ID Trees in Trouble	Environmental Justice for All Field, Forest, and Stream Forest in the City Improve Your Place Invasive Species Living with Fire Nothing Succeeds Like Succession Plant a Tree
SENSES	Adopt a Tree Make Your Own Paper Peppermint Beetle The Closer You Look We All Need Trees	Get Outside! Poet-Tree Tree ID Soil Builders	
SERVICE LEARNING	Adopt a Tree Bursting Buds Trees as Habitats	Signs of Fall Trees in Trouble	Environmental Justice for All Improve Your Place Invasive Species The Global Climate
SILVICULTURE	(See Forestry Practices.)		
SOIL	Here We Grow Again	Discover Diversity Soil Builders Trees in Trouble	Environmental Justice for All Field, Forest, and Stream Plant a Tree
SOLAR ENERGY	(See Green Energy.)		
SOLID WASTE MANAGEMENT	Make Your Own Paper	Peek at Packaging	Environmental Justice for All Global Goods Reduce, Reuse, Recycle
STATISTICS & PROBABILITY			Forest in the City If You Were the Boss Nothing Succeeds Like Succession Our Federal Forests Reduce, Reuse, Recycle Renewable or Not? The Global Climate
STEWARDSHIP	Adopt a Tree	Trees in Trouble	Environmental Justice for All Forest in the City If You Were the Boss Improve Your Place Plant a Tree
STORIES	(See Literature, Environmental.)		
SUCCESSION			Field, Forest, and Stream Living with Fire Nothing Succeeds Like Succession
SUNLIGHT	Here We Grow Again	Every Tree for Itself Signs of Fall Tree Factory Water Wonders	Exploration Energy! Field, Forest, and Stream
SURVEYS	Backyard Safari	Get Outside!	Environmental Justice for All Forest in the City Improve Your Place

PROJECT LEARNING TREE
An initiative of SFI

ACTIVITIES

TOPIC	GRADES K-2	GRADES 3-5	GRADES 6-8
SUSTAINABILITY	We All Need Trees	Every Tree for Itself My Green Future Trees for Many Reasons	Exploration Energy! Global Goods If You Were the Boss Reduce, Reuse, Recycle Renewable or Not? What's in a Label?
TAKING ACTION	(See Service Learning.)		
TECHNOLOGY	Make Your Own Paper	My Green Future	Exploration Energy! Renewable or Not? What's in a Label?
TOXICS			Environmental Justice for All
TRANSPORTATION	Did You Notice?	Peek at Packaging	Exploration Energy! Global Goods
TREE FARM		Every Tree for Itself	Decisions, Decisions Our Federal Forests
TREES	A Tree's Life Adopt a Tree Bursting Buds The Closer You Look Trees as Habitats We All Need Trees	Every Tree for Itself Poet-Tree Signs of Fall Tree Cookies Tree Factory Tree ID Trees in Trouble Trees for Many Reasons	Environmental Justice for All Forest in the City Global Goods Invasive Species Living with Fire Nature's Skyscrapers Plant a Tree What's in a Label?
TREES—CONIFEROUS AND DECIDUOUS		Signs of Fall Tree ID	Nature's Skyscrapers
TREE PARTS	The Closer You Look	Tree Cookies Tree Factory Tree ID	
TREE PLANTING	Adopt a Tree Here We Grow Again The Closer You Look	Soil Builders Trees in Trouble	Plant a Tree
URBAN ENVIRONMENT	Adopt a Tree Backyard Safari Trees as Habitats	Discover Diversity Fallen Log Get Outside! Poet-Tree Soil Builders Trees in Trouble	Decisions, Decisions Environmental Justice for All Forest in the City Nothing Succeeds Like Succession Plant a Tree Reduce, Reuse, Recycle
URBAN FORESTRY		Trees in Trouble	Environmental Justice for All Forest in the City Plant a Tree
VALUES		Trees for Many Reasons	Decisions, Decisions Environmental Justice for All If You Were the Boss
WATER	Here We Grow Again	Every Drop Counts Water Wonders	Environmental Justice for All Field, Forest, and Stream Renewable or Not?
WATERSHEDS		Water Wonders	If You Were the Boss
WILDERNESS			Decisions, Decisions If You Were the Boss Life on the Edge Our Federal Forests
WILDLAND–URBAN INTERFACE			Living with Fire
WILDLIFE MANAGEMENT	Trees as Habitats		If You Were the Boss Living with Fire Our Federal Forests
WOOD	(See Forest Products.)		
ZOOS & AQUARIUMS	Birds and Bugs		Invasive Species Life on the Edge

NOTES

DOWNLOAD RESOURCES FOR THIS GUIDE AT

plt.org/myk8guide

JOIN THE PLT COMMUNITY

Get local resources and support for incorporating environmental education and outdoor learning into your programming. PLT's community consists of mission-driven partners in every U.S. state and several other countries that are supported by a national framework. Our diverse PLT community is passionate, with knowledgeable staff, leadership, and professional development facilitators. This community adapts PLT's offerings to be locally relevant and tailored to specific audiences. Our PLT community provides connections to mentor teachers, community members, and natural resource professionals. It facilitates community collaborations, boots-on-the-ground assistance, and innovation in program delivery to meet the individual needs of formal and nonformal educators. Find PLT in your state at plt.org/yourstate

CREATE A NETWORK WITH PROFESSIONAL DEVELOPMENT

PLT offers educators a variety of self-paced online courses, in-person professional development, and blended professional development opportunities tailored for specific grade levels and education standards, environmental topics, and teaching situations. Educators rate PLT workshops as "one of the best professional development events" they have ever experienced. These professional development events help you learn new teaching skills, deepen your content knowledge, and become comfortable teaching outdoors; receive PLT's instructional materials and supplements tailored to your state's standards; experience PLT activities and get tips for lesson planning specific to your educational setting; get access to a network of professionals and support; and earn continuing education credits. Approximately 15,000 educators attend a PLT professional development event every year. Learn more at plt.org/pd

STAY CONNECTED TO *THE BRANCH*, PLT'S MONTHLY E-NEWSLETTER

A regular trove of ideas to get kids engaged in learning about the environment, with free resources for educators and real experiences from those who use our activities and training. View our latest issue and subscribe for free at plt.org/newsletter

FOLLOW US ON